A GUIDE TO THE CLIMATE APOCALYPSE

OUR JOURNEY FROM THE AGE OF PROSPERITY TO THE ERA OF ENVIRONMENTAL GRIEF

VÍTĚZSLAV KREMLÍK

IDENTITY PUBLICATIONS

A GUIDE TO THE
CLIMATE
APOCALYPSE

For permission requests, write to the publisher at contact@identitypublications.com.

Ordering Information:

Quantity sales. Special discounts are available on quantity purchases by corporations, associations, and others. For details, contact the publisher at the address above.

Orders by U.S. trade bookstores and wholesalers. Please contact Identity Publications: Tel: (805) 259-3724 or visit www.IdentityPublications.com.

ISBN-13: 978-1-945884-53-5 (paperback)

ISBN-13: 978-1-945884-58-0 (hardcover)

ISBN-13: 978-1-945884-54-2 (ebook)

Cover and Interior Formatting Design by Resa Embutin (www.ResaEmbutin.com)

First Edition

Publishing by Identity Publications.

www.IdentityPublications.com

Contact the author at: klimaskeptik@seznam.cz

Reviewers: RNDr. Zbyněk Hrkal, Csc., RNDr. Pavel Kalenda,CSc. and doc. PhDr. Ing. Marek Loužek, PhD.

I would like to thank the following people for valuable comments on the manuscript: Mgr. Luboš Motl, PhD., Prof. ing. Miroslav Kutílek, DrSc., RNDr. Milan Šálek, PhD. and also the reviewers RNDr. Zbyněk Hrkal, CSc., RNDr. Pavel Kalenda, CSc. and doc. PhDr. Ing. Marek Loužek, PhD.

Afterword by Prof. Ing. Václav Klaus, Csc.
Language editing by Dr. Asif Osmani, MD, MBA
Figures edited by VondraCzech.cz

Dedicated to my wife and my daughter.
Live long and prosper.

TABLE OF CONTENTS

DON'T PANIC!

"During the course of the 20th century, mankind's relationship with nature underwent a revolution. At the beginning of the last century, human intervention in nature was regarded as beneficent and a sign of progress of civilization. By its end, such interventions were presumed harmful unless it could be demonstrated they were not."

—Rupert Darwall, *The Age of Global Warming*[1]

In 2019, a 16-year-old Swedish activist, Greta Thunberg, was invited to give a speech at a UN climate change conference. "People are suffering. People are dying. Entire ecosystems are collapsing. We are in the beginning of a mass extinction. And all you can talk about is money and fairy tales of eternal economic growth. How dare you!"[2] The audience seemed to enjoy being criticized by a little girl and rewarded her with applause. But did she really do her homework to get her facts straight?

The average world GDP per capita increased ten times between 1820 and 2010.[3] This economic growth is the reason why poverty has mostly been eradicated, not only in Europe. World poverty rates (including the developing countries) fell from about 85% to about 25% between 1820 and 1990.[4] This is no fairy tale. And all of that was happening in a period of global warming and rising sea level.

Global warming has been occurring, with some interruptions, since the Thirty Years' War. In the 20th century, the planet warmed by about 0.8°C, and the same warming can be expected in the 21st century. Is this increase in temperature really the reason for disruption, hunger, misery, and devastation, as we hear daily in the media?

Between 1975 and 2005, there was a rise in average temperatures with food prices falling by 75% over this period.[5] While 991 million people suffered from malnutrition in developing countries in 1991, it was only 780 million in 2015, despite world population growth over the same period of time. Thus, global warming had no net negative impact on food production. Temporary deterioration occurred only in the era of biofuel boom, when the number of starving people rose y-o-y for several years (from 908 million in 2001 to 927 million in 2006).[6] However, this trend was not caused by climate change; in fact, it was caused by the misguided efforts to fight climate.

So why does the UN depict the world in such bleak colors? "The gap between the poorest and the wealthiest around the world is wide and is growing," UN Secretary-General Ban Ki-moon lamented on the growth of inequality.[7] However, this gap is not growing because some people are doing worse and worse. The opposite is true. This is happening because some have already been liberated from poverty, whereas others have not.

Two hundred years ago, the richest states' average incomes were only four times higher than in the poorest states. But by the end of the 20th century, it was 30-fold higher.[8] This inequality is the difference between a grass hut somewhere in Africa and a skyscraper in New York.

Moreover, the term poverty today means something else than envisaged centuries ago. In the Czech Republic, people are considered "poor" if they have less than 60% of the national median income. These people have no savings and cannot afford a holiday in Hawaii. But they have a TV, refrigerator, computer, telephone, electricity, running water, and all the amenities of modern civilization.[9] Sometimes they are in debt and threatened by execution on their property. In the past, however, such people were at risk of starvation. And the things that are common for today's poor people—a phone, a watch, or shoes—used to be an unthinkable luxury.

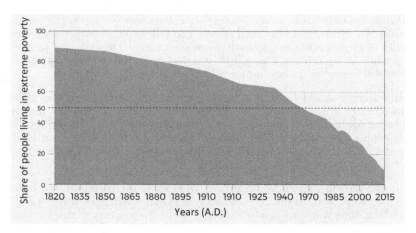

Figure 1—Global poverty rates have been declining since the beginning of the fossil fuel era. Extreme poverty is defined as less than 2 USD per day in present-day prices. Historical estimates take into account inflation and other factors (Source: ourworldindata.org based on Bourguignon and Morrison 2002)[10] [11]

The proposition that higher temperatures threaten the civilization's survival is contrary to the entire experience of human history. Warm periods in history were called "climate optimum" for a good reason. They bring longer growing seasons and richer crops. In a warmer climate, trees also grow better and have wider annual rings. It is from their width that we derive the temperature of ancient times before thermometers were invented. The fact we have emerged from the Little Ice Age (about 1300–1850) over the last 150 years is good news, not a reason for panic. Warm periods and cold periods like LIA are naturally alternating every 1,500 years.[12]

This scientific paradigm of natural climate change was abandoned when the United Nations established the Intergovernmental Panel on Climate Change (IPCC). Governments started funding the "climate crisis" narrative to justify the transfer of more power to authorities. Being fully dependent on government funding, science has fallen victim to the Parkinson's laws of bureaucracy. Researchers hired to assess risk must report something in order to keep their jobs. So, the more researchers we hire, the worse the climate reports look. As a result, our media is dominated by "simulacra," a virtual reality, where a cold spell is labeled as normal weather, but a warm spell is called "climate disruption." And every flood or drought is seen as an unnatural phenomenon. After a brief period of Enlightenment rationality, the ancient superstitions have returned with a vengeance reminiscent of the old days when witches were burned as punishment for causing hailstorms.

The sociologist Barry Glassner, author of *The Culture of Fear*,[13] explains: "By fear-mongering, politicians sell themselves to voters, TV and print news magazines sell themselves to viewers and readers, advocacy groups sell memberships, quacks sell treatments, lawyers sell class-action lawsuits, and corporations sell consumer products."[14]

Nature conservation may have been more rational in the times when we had no specialized enviro authorities that have nothing else to do. The London Clean Air Act was adopted in 1956 (in response to record smog in 1952). The first nature reserve in the world—Yellowstone—was declared in 1872 by US President Grant. The International Convention for the Protection of Whales is from 1946, long before the first Green Party was formed.

But today, manufacturing scary scenarios has become a full-time job for a large army of professionals. In *The First Global Revolution,* the Club of Rome, a UN-advising NGO, writes about the political vacuum after the end of the Cold War: "The scapegoat practice is as old as mankind itself... Bring the divided nation together to face an outside enemy, either a real one or else one invented for the purpose... In searching for a common enemy against whom we can unite, we came up with the idea that pollution, the threat of global warming, water shortages, famine, and the like would fit the bill... All these dangers are caused by human intervention in natural processes, and it is only through changed attitudes and behavior that they can be overcome. The real enemy then is humanity itself."[15]

They say we consume too much energy and resources. People are admonished to feel guilty for not living in hunger and poverty anymore. Even train tickets have a mandatory propaganda slogan on them saying that you should feel bad for your transportation-related greenhouse gas emissions. Strangely, when celebrities like Al Gore or Leonardo di Caprio preach about emission reduction at conferences, they fly there by private jets. Obviously, they do not intend to scale down their own lifestyle. Austerity is for the ordinary people down below their gas-guzzling private planes.

The turning point was the Earth Summit in Rio de Janeiro (1992), when UN member states pledged to finance the fight against carbon. Supporters of the theory of unnatural climate change got rich literally overnight. Now they could flood the market with their publications, and they lost interest in discussions with their underpaid opponents. Scientists who had been researching climate change throughout their whole lives were suddenly accused of denying the existence of climate change. Those who pointed out the lack of evidence were accused of 'manufacturing doubts' as hired mercenaries of the evil Big Oil.[16]

However, the real roadblock on the path to "saving the climate" is neither the skeptics nor Big Oil. The real enemy is pure mathematics. Solar and wind power, despite all promotion advertising, still accounts for just about 2% of the world's energy consumption.[17] The International Energy Agency calculated that meeting the COP21 Paris climate conference pledge would cost the world about USD 16.5 trillion over the following 15 years.[18] But this would delay the supposedly expected 3°C warming—which the alarmists scare us with—by no more than 0.17°C.[19] This policy is a house of cards and its results can be erased from the face of Earth by even the slightest natural climate variability.

The idea that we can control climate by issuing regulations and directives, is an arrogant expression of human pride. The old Greeks called it "hubris." We should instead invest our money somewhere where it would bring some real benefits to real people. "If you can spend a billion dollars and save 600,000 kids from dying and save about two billion people from malnourishment, that's a lot better than spending the same amount to postpone global warming by about two minutes at the end of the century."[20] There is just one sensible thing you can do about climate change. Adapt. Just as our ancestors have been doing throughout our history.

"We need to stop trying to scare the pants off the American public. Doing so has demonstrably backfired. Climate skepticism is on the rise," wrote environmentalists Ted Nordhaus and Michael Schellenberger, Environmental Heroes according to *Time Magazine*.[21] They point out that the apocalyptical awareness campaign on climate change, which culminated around 2006, did not lead to reduction but rather increase in the number of skeptics.

"Greens reacted to these developments not by toning down their rhetoric or reconsidering their agenda in a manner that might be more palatable to their opponents," Nordhaus and Schellenberger continue. "Instead, they made ever more apocalyptic claims about global warming—claims that were increasingly inconsistent, ironically, with the scientific consensus whose mantle greens claimed."[22]

In this book, you will find many examples of how environmentalists exaggerated in order to attract more attention. It reminds of old Aesop's fable about a boy and a wolf. A shepherd was bored on the pasture one day and thought of an idea to get attention. He pretended that there was a wolf and started calling for help. When the scared villagers arrived, he told them that he had managed to drive the wolf away. They were relieved and praised the boy. Since it worked so well, the boy repeated this game several more times, which turned out to be a fatal mistake. People began to suspect that he was simply faking it. And when one day the wolf really came, the boy called for help in vain. Nobody believed him anymore.

I. A BRIEF HISTORY OF CLIMATE

Given that there are skeptics on both sides of the climate change debate, some doubt that we are experiencing a climate crisis. And they are of the view that the weather has always been capricious. Others cannot believe that the power elites could ever tell a lie, that a scientist could be wrong. I hope that both sides will find a few things to ponder in this book.

Readers who know the novel *1984* by George Orwell will have an advantage. It was a story set in a dictatorship with a very sophisticated propaganda. Its central motto is the slogan: "War is peace. Freedom is slavery. Ignorance is power." Through constant repetition, the regime managed to convince people that everything is upside down. In our era, truth is twisted in a similar way. Namely, the motto of our times: "Climate optimum is climate crisis."

In fact, warm periods have been mostly beneficial to humanity. Thanks to the warming at the end of the Ice Age, it was possible to colonize Scandinavia. Six thousand years ago, it was so warm and humid that the Sahara was green and full of rivers and lakes. Rome, Mayans, Mycenae— all these cultures prospered in warm times.

In Orwell's novel, "eternal war" has been waged for decades, sometimes against Eastasia, sometimes against Eurasia. The regime needs to wage a war—any war—to justify a state of emergency. This allows the rulers to keep the population scared and compliant. By the need to contribute to the "war effort," the government comfortably justifies austerity.

Likewise, today we are waging "war" against climate change. We are urged to reduce our consumption. We are to reduce our carbon footprint. As in any war, the climate war is about controlling resources. Energy is the lifeblood of industrial civilization, and whoever controls it keeps others in check. The real power is not in the companies that use energy, but in the hands of the regulators who can permit or forbid its use. Before we know it, Big Brother will remotely (using "smart grids") monitor if you are not wasting energy. They will know what lightbulb you have in the bathroom and what time it was on and off. Privacy and liberty will be gone—in the higher interest of public good, like always.

In Orwell's novel, whenever the regime switches sides in the "eternal war," the Ministry of Truth will rewrite historical records to erase any mention that our present ally used to be our mortal enemy. The falsification of history is expressed by the slogan "Who controls the past, controls the future. Who controls the present controls the past." Just like in the novel, we see in the real world that the climate change narrative is constantly changing. Today, it is vehemently denied that we once fought against cooling. It is said now that only a handful of people feared cooling then. And the charts with the rapid post-war cooling of the northern hemisphere are almost impossible to find anywhere anymore.

But the witnesses are still alive. They remember. In the past, people feared mostly cold weather. For example, the Little Ice Age (14th–19th century) represented the coldest era since mammoth extinction. The Vikings' settlements in Greenland were destroyed by cold weather, as they were unable to adapt. When cooling was the worst, the so-called "general crisis of the seventeenth century" (including the Thirty Years' War) came. War conflicts are more plentiful, on average, when the climate cools down, especially in our Temperate Climate Zone. Actually, it was the harsh climate that might have forced mankind to invent adaptations like the Agrarian Revolution.

Cooling was also a problem for us in the 20th century. In the 1970s, the northern hemisphere was so cold that the US government began to fear the arrival of a new ice age. As a result, special commissions and research programs were created. Also, the Czech climatologist George Kukla was part of this research.

But today, the story is upside down. The cold period of the 1970s is suddenly called "normal," and we are told we should be worried because we are somehow departing from this "normal." The Little Ice Age ceased to be seen as a dreadful period. Now it is touted as some sort of climatic Paradise Lost. Environmental activists keep telling us that—before the Industrial Revolution—the climate was essentially "stable." And that this cooler climate provided the conditions for our civilization to flourish until greenhouse gases destroyed this Eden.

In Orwell's novel, the regime needed an enemy so they could fight against someone. The government blamed all its troubles on the villain Goldstein, who may actually never have existed. In our time, everything bad—especially climate change—is blamed on the fossil fuel industry that emits greenhouse gases. However, if you check the actual data, the coldest phase of the Little Ice Age was the 17th century, when temperatures began rising, long before the Industrial Revolution that supposedly caused the warming. But propaganda cannot accept an idea of natural climate change. If the sun or natural cycles were the main cause of climate change, it would be difficult to "fight" them. Natural phenomena cannot be taxed or thrown into jail.

The war on climate change may turn out to be an "eternal war" just like the one in Orwell's novel. It cannot be won because climate has always been changing. And always will. It is nothing new. Similar climate change can be seen many times in historical records. It happens every one and a half thousand years. The cause is likely to be astronomical, like Halley's comet returning again and again. Climate cooling translates into worsening harvests, which in turn leads to political destabilization. This cycle apparently contributed to the Trojan War, the fall of the Roman Empire, or the demise of Mayan civilization. We could call it a pulse of history.

There is no reason to idealize a cold climate. Environmental dogma, however, strikingly resembles ancient legends. After all, most cultures have a myth about the "golden age." The elders recall that in their youth, the bread used to be crisper and the grass greener. Climate religion also has a myth about expulsion from paradise, this time from an ecological paradise. Once, the climate used to be stable. The wind did not break the trees. It just caressed them gently. There were no storms, just a drizzle. And it rained just enough for the maids to sprinkle their laundry nicely.

Imagine what the average 17th-century peasant would have said to today's propaganda. If a copy of a Greenpeace brochure had fallen through a rift in the time-space continuum, and he had learned from it that his era would once be considered a paradise. If the parish priest had read this to our illiterate farmer, they would have both laughed a lot unless they had been too busy dying of plague or famine.

COLD QUATERNARY

Geologically speaking, we live in one of the coldest periods of history. The previous interglacial was warmer. And for most of the planet's existence, there was no ice on the poles either.

Environmental activists use the slogan "climate change is already happening." It is difficult to understand what this is supposed to mean. The climate has always been changing, constantly. If you want proof, just take a spade and dig in the ground a bit. The whole Earth's crust is actually an archive. At different times, different types of soils were formed, depending on drier or wetter climate. The sediments and rocks that formed during the Mesozoic era reach hundreds of meters of depth.

At the end of the Mesozoic era, in the period called the "Cretaceous," the Bohemian Basin in Central Europe was underwater, mostly covered by the sea. When water disappeared and the seabed began to weather, sandstone rock formations began to form, like the Adrspach or Teplice Rocks, where climbers and tourists flock to now. When the Mesozoic was over, there was no polar ice on Earth. Palm trees grew in the Eocene (56-34 million years ago) in Antarctica, although at that time it was almost the same latitude as it is today. When the Quaternary began, Earth started to alternate between glacial and interglacial states, which translated into sea level changes by up to 100 meters. So much for the idea that the climate used to be "stable" when there was no factory smoke.

Not long ago, mankind believed the world was only a few years older than the first written records. Awareness of climate change was limited to the biblical myth of the Flood. It was not until the 18th century that various people, such as the poet Goethe, noticed boulders scattered throughout the Alps and concluded that they must have been pushed there by the mighty force of ancient glaciers. In 1837, Louis Agassiz went even further. He suggested that long ago Switzerland may have looked just like today's Greenland—covered with ice.

Later, the Ice Age (glacial) was studied even closer. It turned out we can divide the Ice Age into several phases, separated from each other by warmer interglacials. Individual Ice Ages in Europe were named after the locations in the Alps, where the samples were found: Günz, Mindel, Riss, and Würm. In the Ice Age, Central Europe was mostly covered by the tundra, as it is today near the Arctic Circle. Remnants of the vegetation of that time have been preserved on the tops of the Giant Mountains (or Krkonose) in Bohemia. Ice covered the whole Scandinavia, part of Poland, and most of Britain.

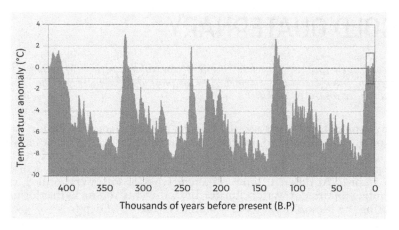

Figure 2—Alternating glacials and interglacials over the past half million years. All previous interglacials were warmer than the current one, which you see on the far right.[23]

At the end of the 19th century, the Swedish chemist Svante Arrhenius thought that greenhouse gas variations could be the cause of alternating glacial and interglacial periods. Half a century later, however, the Serbian university Professor of Mathematics Milutin Milankovic came up with a better explanation. He calculated how the Earth's position to the sun periodically changed, and how it affected the Earth's climate. The most important of the "Milankovic cycles" is about 100,000 years long and explains the alternation of glacial and interglacial times. The Earth's orbit around the sun is changing from more circular to more elliptical. He published his theory in German in 1941 as the *Kanon der Erdbestrahlung und seine Anwendung auf das Eiszeitenproblem* (Principle of Insolation of the Earth and its Application to the Problem of Ice Age).

His theory was only accepted in the "scientific consensus" of the 1970s thanks to the Deep Sea Drilling Project. It turned out that the sea bottom expands over time, confirming the theory of continental drift, which was postulated in 1912 by Alfred Wegener—who did not live long enough to see his work recognized. When Wallace Broecker analyzed this data, it turned out that oxygen isotope fluctuations showed strong cycles of about 100,000, 41,000, and 23,000 years. This is exactly the same as the orbital movements of the planet that Milankovic was once talking about. These are changes where the inclination of the Earth rotation axis (obliquity), the shape of the orbit around the sun (eccentricity) and the direction of the axis (precession) change. These movements lead to climate change on Earth.

Glacials and interglacials have been alternating on Earth for the last million years. But it was not always the case. In the Mesozoic, the climate was much warmer and there were no ice ages at all. Only 35 million years ago it had cooled to such a degree that Antarctica got covered with a glacier.

But most of the geological history of Antarctica was ice-free. Our planet is regularly switching between two states. About 75% of Earth's time is spent in the hot phase (hothouse) and only 25% of the time is in the cold phase (icehouse).[24] There are no ice ages during the tens of millions of years of the "hothouse" phase. At that time, there were no glaciers on Earth, neither in Antarctica nor in Greenland.

So, the present era, although we see it as warm interglacial, is unusually cold compared to most geological history because there are glaciers on Earth, which is an anomaly in the history of the planet. While much is said today about global warming, from a geological point of view we live in one of the coldest times in the history of the planet.

CLIMATE DISRUPTION
IN THE STONE AGE

Contemporary climate change is not exceptional in its extent or speed. But you have to know the history of climate (paleoclimatology) to understand this.

At present, according to some opinions, we are experiencing "Rapid Climate Change" (RCC) at a rate that is supposedly unprecedented in the past 65 million years. *Scientific American* warned: "Climate change is occurring 10 to 100 times faster than in the past, and ecosystems will find it hard to adjust."[25]

This is probably a statistical misunderstanding—comparing long-term averages with short-term precise measurement. According to measurements of tree-ring widths (they grow more in warm years), the temperature change in the 20th century was the same as, for example, the warming between 1600 and 1700 AD and even less than the warming between 900 and 1000 AD.[26]

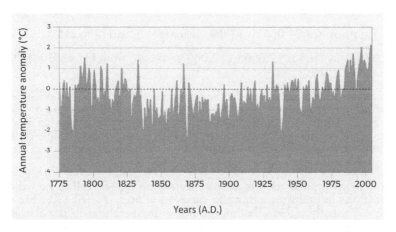

Figure 3—According to the temperature record from Klementinum in Prague, the 20th-century warming was only a return to the formerly higher temperatures. Note that half a degree Celsius of this overall warming is the influence of the Urban Heat Island.[27]

One can verify this on the instrumental temperature record at the Klementinum in Prague over the last two and half centuries. "From 1890 to the present (2005), the average annual temperature has risen by approximately 1.7 degrees Celsius... However, keep in mind that the temperature had dropped by almost the same value (1.5°C) between 1790 and 1890."[28] Temperatures have merely returned to where they used to be during the French Revolution, as confirmed also by measurements from the Alps.[29]

Mankind has experienced much faster and more abrupt climate change at the times when no industry existed. These were changes of natural origin. For most of the Stone Age, there was tundra in Central Europe. But once every few thousand years, rapid cooling occurred, which literally exterminated many prehistoric cultures. There is no evidence of any prehistoric cultures decimated by warming.

On average, every 7,000 years, there occurred Heinrich Events with temperatures dropping a full degree Celsius within just a few decades, causing extensive droughts. This was the time when we truly suffered from "rapid climate change." One cannot even imagine such speed and magnitude of climate change today. For example, the cooling of H1 15,000–18,000 years ago brought such drought that even Lake Victoria in Africa dried up. Prehistoric man would surely be surprised if someone told him that he should be afraid of warm climate. Hard-earned historical experience says the exact opposite. The dating of the demise of individual Paleolithic cultures on the territory of present-day France remarkably coincides with the dates of the cold Heinrich Events.[30]

- Aurignacian (ca 38,000 to 31,000 years ago) from H4 to H3.

- Gravettian (ca 31,000 to 24,000 years ago) from H3 to H2.

- Solutrean (ca 24,000 to 17,000 years ago) from H2 to H1.

- Magdalenian (ca 17,000 to 12,000 years ago) from H1 to H0 (H0 or Younger Dryas)[31]

For example, Magdalenian was the last great culture of the Paleolithic era and bears the name of the locality La Madeleine in Dordogne, France. Its reach extended from Moravia (cave Pekárna in the Moravian Karst) through Germany to France, including the coast of Spain. People of this culture were already able to make things from bones and antlers (harpoons, needles, etc.)

Modern civilization used to central heating no longer realizes how difficult it was in prehistoric times to survive a winter. If a tribe lost fire, its fate was usually sealed. The importance of temperatures in the glacial is also clearly demonstrated by comparing our territory with Scandinavia. People lived in the present-day Czech Republic area about 28,000 years ago—among others, they created the famous voluptuous sculpture of Venus of Dolní Věstonice. However, we do not have similar Paleolithic findings from today's Sweden. Nobody lived there. All of Scandinavia, most of Great Britain and the north of Poland were covered with glaciers.

If global warming had not occurred and the ice had not melted, this part of the world would have remained uninhabitable to this day. The first people came to the south of today's Sweden sometime 12,000 years ago in a warm period called the Allerød. They were reindeer hunters from the Bromme culture who got there from the neighboring Denmark. In North America, the situation was similar. The whole of Canada was covered with glaciers, as was the area around the Great Lakes. Had it not been for global warming, there would be no cities like Toronto, Montreal, Chicago, or Detroit. Only Alaska and the Bering Strait were left without ice—as sea levels were much lower, there was a land bridge that people could use to cross from Asia to America.

DESERTIFICATION OF THE GREEN SAHARA

Warming does not automatically mean desertification, Sahara was green when it was warmer. There were rivers and lakes in the warm period. Sahara actually turned into a desert only when the climate cooled down.

The Sahara has not always been a desert. Half a century ago, Henri Lhote wrote about it in the book *The Search for the Tassili Frescoes: The Story of the Prehistoric Rock-Paintings of the Sahara*. The author described rock paintings (of animals like giraffes) left by local Neolithic dwellers in the era of the Green Sahara. In the first half of the Holocene (Post-Glacial) period, about 8000–3500 years BC, it was warmer and wetter in the northern hemisphere. That era was named the Holocene Climate Optimum (or Altithermal).

As it was hotter, more water was evaporating from the tropical ocean. More water vapor circulated in the climate system leading to higher precipitation. Thus, the idea that warmer weather automatically equals drought and desertification is not true. In the Sahara, lakes and rivers formed due to warming, and their dried-up riverbeds can still be observed by microwave satellite scanning under the millennia of sand deposits. It was only in the fourth millennium BC that the Sahara began to dry up because of climate cooling. Sahara's lakes finally disappeared, and the tribes migrated to Egypt, heralding the establishment of pyramid-building civilization.[32]

Changes in the Sahara climate resulted from precession—an astronomical cycle that alters the plane of Earth's axis—it has not always pointed toward the North Star as it does today. You may have heard about precession from astrologers, because this approximately 20,000-year cycle is divided into 12 periods and defined by respective Zodiac signs (such as the Age of Aquarius and others). Over the following 10,000 years, this cycle is going to gradually warm up the northern hemisphere, not because of human activity but because this hemisphere will be facing the sun more directly. In ten millennia, the Sahara will probably turn green again.

MY NAME IS BOND,
GERALD BOND

Bond Events occur with a frequency of about one and a half thousand years. In recent centuries, we have emerged from the so-called Little Ice Age, the coldest period since the mammoth extinction.

The research of Gerald Bond from the Lamont-Doherty Earth Observatory at Columbia University has shown that every 1,470 ± 500 years the climate cools significantly. These oscillations are named Bond Events after the researcher who discovered them.[33] They have been determining the rhythm of climate change over the last 10,000 years. Bond discovered these oscillations in marine sediments as he examined the varying amounts of floating ice debris in the North Atlantic (1997).[34] When the ice floe gets south, it melts and any sand, dust or gravel it contains falls to the seabed. These deposits can now be examined as a natural archive. As the climate cools, ice floes reach further to the south.

This cycle is most pronounced in the North Atlantic, but we have evidence of its influence in most regions of the northern hemisphere. Such a 1,500-year cycle is a stable feature of terrestrial climate and existed even in the last Ice Age when mammoths still roamed the Earth. In the glacial, these fluctuations were more severe, and we call them Dansgaard-Oeschger Oscillations (DO Events).

However, it should be noted that the timing of these events does not have the precision of a Swiss watch. The same can be said about the timing of individual Ice Ages, after all. In the first half of the Holocene, Bond Events occurred every 1,000 years. Such variation should be expected from natural oscillations. Indeed, even the well-known 11-year sunspot cycle does not always take exactly 11 years, as its length varies from nine to 13 years. Since the invention of writing and birth of the first civilization, mankind has experienced five such Bond Events (Bond Events 4 to 0), with even events bringing more severe cooling than odd events.

- **Beginning of the era of Pyramids (Bond Event 4):** In the fourth millennium BC, this cooling led to the birth of the first civilizations in Sumer and Egypt, when writing was invented. Drying of the Sahara (formerly green) led to migrations, for example to the Nile Valley. Sometimes referred to as the "5.9 kiloyear event."[35] Kilo means thousand in this term.

- **The end of the era of Pyramids (Bond Event 3):** In the third millennium BC, there was a cooling associated with the fall of the Akkadian Empire in Mesopotamia and the migration of Amorites around 2000 BC.[36] In Egypt, this instability marks the "first intermediate period." That meant the end of the Old Empire as well as the era of pyramids.[37] In India, this cold episode is linked to the demise of the Harapp culture,[38] sometimes referred to as the "4.2 kiloyear event," some 4.2 thousand years ago.

- **The beginning of Classical Antiquity (Bond Event 2):** At the end of the second millennium BC, the so-called Minoan Climate Optimum ended. Cooling in the Aegean Sea is evidenced by the loss of thermophilic plankton.[39] Bronze Age civilizations of the Eastern Mediterranean collapsed like dominoes. Mycenaean and Hittite empires fell apart. "Sea People" invaded Egypt. The Israelites escaped "enslavement in Egypt" (Exodus). The Trojan War dates back to this period too. This convoluted complex of events was described, among others, by Eberhard Zangger. Sometimes climatologists refer to it as the "3.2K event" or LBA (Late Bronze Age). This was followed by centuries of Greek Dark Age, after which the classical Greek polis formed.

- **The End of Classical Antiquity (Bond Event 1):** In the middle of the first millennium AD, there was a cooling interrupted by a short period of warming around 500 AD. The first part of this cooling (0–250 AD) coincides with the fall of the Roman Empire.[40] The Roman Climate Optimum ended. The coldest and driest was the 3rd century AD when the Roman Empire went through a severe crisis. This cooling drove the Huns out of the steppes of Central Asia. Their movement was the beginning of the Migration Period. The second part of cooling (about 600–900 AD) coincides with the decline of the Mayan empire, where drought occurred forcing the Mayans to vacate their cities and move elsewhere.[41]

- **Beginning of modern history (Bond Event 0):** In 14th–19th century, cooling set in known as the Little Ice Age. Its coldest phase was the 17th century when solar activity dropped so low that no sunspots were observed (Maunder Minimum). Increased economic tensions resulted in a series of wars (Thirty Years' War) and the so-called Crisis of the 17th Century. The need for adaptation to a colder climate probably led to the English Agrarian Revolution which paved the way for the Industrial Revolution.

Gerald Bond believes that the fluctuations in solar activity are the cause of the Bond Events.[42] Solar activity can be reconstructed because the solar wind protects the Earth from cosmic rays. As solar activity rises, cosmic radiation on Earth decreases, and fewer radioactive isotopes are formed. However, we also need to filter out the internal variability of Earth's own magnetic field, which also affects shielding of Earth from cosmic rays.[43]

Bond's research had its predecessors. In 1973, researchers Denton and Karlén studied how the ice cover varied in Scandinavia and North America.[44] They identified cooling episodes (growth of glaciers) around 3500 BC, 1200 BC, and 1350 AD, and less significant cooling around 2000 BC and 750 BC.

A similarly cyclical nature of climate change was discovered in the 19th century by the Danish geologist Axel Blytt (1876). He noticed that the different layers of peat in Denmark had different colors, and he concluded that there must have been different humidity at different times. This periodization of alternating drier (continental, boreal) and wetter (oceanic, Atlantic) climate is called the "Blytt-Sernander Sequence." Around 3000 BC, the Atlantic climate ends and the Subboreal begins. In the mid-first millennium BC, the Subboreal period ends and the Subatlantic begins. Its end is in the Little Ice Age. Subboreal climate period corresponds to the Bronze Age, the Subatlantic climate period corresponds to the Iron Age.

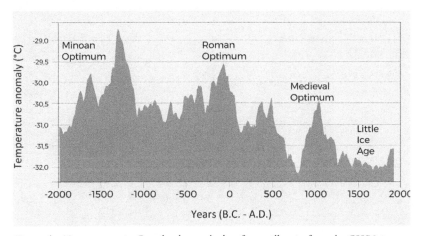

Figure 4—Temperatures in Greenland over the last four millennia from the GISP2 ice core (until mid-19th century). The approximately 1500-year Bond Event cycle of warm and cold periods is apparent.[45]

It seems that Bond Events have had a profound impact on the development of human c ivilization. The first person to realize that civilization highs and lows appear to come in certain rhythm was probably the German philosopher Karl Jaspers. But it had not occurred to him that climate change might be the trigger. In his work, *Vom Ursprung und Ziel der Geschichte* (The Origin and Destination of History)[46], he observed that around the sixth century BC throughout Eurasia—in distant places with no contact with each other—new religions and philosophies emerged suddenly within a few generations, such as Kunfucius, Zoroaster, Lao Tzu, Buddha, Old Testament (monotheism), Socrates, and Greek philosophy. All these spiritual movements offered different alternatives to polytheism. Jaspers called this breakthrough period the "Axial Age" (Achsenzeit).

This theory was later elaborated on and promoted by Karen Armstrong, a historian of religion, in her 2006 book *The Great Transformation*.[47] Climate change may have been the real cause of the "Great Transformation," but neither Jaspers nor Armstrong noticed this correlation. John C. Landon (1999) did not come up with an explanation either.[48] He was merely trying—for reasons hard to understand—to interpret this rhythm of history as an argument against Darwinism. As a result, his thesis on the "Eonic Effect" remained unnoticed.

So far, historians have found little interest in the relationship between climate and history. Researchers like Emanuel Le Roy Ladurie tended to be skeptical about the influence of climate change on historical events. Their interest was limited to weather—local chronicles with records of floods and crop failures, without broader context.

THE END OF VIKINGS
IN GREENLAND

Perhaps the best-known example of adverse effects of climate cooling was the demise of the Viking settlements in Greenland.

These settlements were established in the late 10th century in quite a remarkable way. Greenland was discovered by Erik, who was exiled from Iceland for murder. While he was wandering the seas, he happened to discover a new land. He named it Greenland. In 984, he returned to Iceland and persuaded the locals to come and colonize the new land with him. Erik's son, Leif, became a Christian, and a hundred years later, a Christian bishopric (in Gardar) was established in Greenland.

But a few centuries later, the climate began to get worse. Unlike the Eskimos, the Vikings had trouble adapting to the cold conditions. From archaeological excavations we know that as temperatures cooled, people had less and less food to eat. After 1300 AD, pigs were no longer bred. Cows were slowly replaced with smaller sheep and goats. While in the first generations, fish represented only 15–50% of the diet, in the last generations, seafood represented 50–80% of the diet.[49]

In 1345, the Pope pardoned Greenlanders so that they no longer had to pay church fees in acknowledgement of their very poor status. In 1350, the south-west colony on the coast was abandoned. The last bishop, Alfur, died in 1378, and a replacement never got here. It was not until 1492 that Rome remembered that there used to be a bishopric in Gardar. Pope Alexander VI Borgia (1492–1503) wrote a letter (beginning with the Latin words "Cum Et Accepimus") describing colorfully the effects of climate cooling:

"It has been reported to us that in the diocese of Gardar in Greenland, situated at the confines of the known world, the inhabitants, because of scarcity of bread, wine, and oil, live for the most part on dried fish and milk products. Wherefore because of the difficulty of passing through such immense quantities of ice and likewise because of the poverty of the land, and the scant means of living, ships rarely visit its shores.

We have learned in fact that no vessel has touched there during the past 80 years, and if a voyage be made at all, it must be in the month of August, when the ice has broken up. On this account, during 80 years no bishop or priest has resided personally among those people, and by reason of this, we are informed that many who were formerly Catholics have forgotten the faith of their baptism, and that no memory of the Christian religion is found..."[50]

The Pope supported the plan to send a new bishop to Greenland. But there is no evidence that a bishop ever arrived. The settlements probably no longer existed by then.

LITTLE ICE AGE

The Little Ice Age (14ᵗʰ–19ᵗʰ century) was the coldest period since the mammoth extinction. The need for adaptation to climate deterioration might have been one of the causes of the Agrarian and Industrial Revolution.

It has become fashionable to present an idealized account of the pre-industrial climate. "We had lived in a stable world for 5,000 years, when the climate was not changing—maybe it was changing locally a bit, but in general, it was amazingly stable. And only due to this stability, we were able to build a civilization with enough food for everyone." The climate activists who believe this consider change as something new.

Yet, the people who lived in the cold times prior to "global warming" did not find their climate very hospitable. On the contrary, when it cooled down in the second half of the 16ᵗʰ century, storm activity increased by 85%, and the incidence of severe storms rose by 400%.[51] For example, the flood on All Saints' Day in 1570 killed about 400,000 people in Western Europe. "It is likely that the increased intensity of storms in the Little Ice Age had to do with the source of potential energy in, at that time, the enhanced thermal gradient between the colder ocean surface in the seas about Iceland and the ocean south of 50–55N and the Bay of Biscay," explains Hubert Lamb, founder of the historical climatology in Great Britain.[52]

By contrast, storms should get milder as the climate warms. When the climate is warming, the poles warm faster than the equator because white ice has a higher albedo (light reflecting capability). This reduces the temperature difference between the equator and the poles. This means lower gradients, less windstorms, less atmospheric pressure differences, etc.

Cooling led to the expansion of glaciers. Villages in the Alps, such as Le Bois in the Arva River Valley, had to be abandoned as they were at risk of being crushed by the expanding glacier. In the 17ᵗʰ century, the bishop of Geneva, Charles August de Sales (nephew of St. Francis de Sales), was called by the locals to exorcise the devilish glacier.[53]

Climate deterioration meant shorter growing seasons and thinner crops. Reduced nutrition was also reflected in lower average body height. Research by Richard H. Steckel (2004) indicates that people from the early Middle Ages were almost as tall as today's people.[54] After the 12ᵗʰ century, however, climate cooled down, and in the 18ᵗʰ century, the average North European was about 6 cm shorter than his ancestor of the 12ᵗʰ century.

In agrarian society, the whole economy is linked to weather; so, it is not surprising that real wages in England tracked the changes in temperature.[55] David D. Zhang (2011) writes about the Little Ice Age: "Results show that cooling from 1560–1660 AD caused successive agro-ecological, socioeconomic, and demographic catastrophes, leading to the General Crisis of the Seventeenth Century."[56]

In the Little Ice Age, the rivers along the English Channel used to freeze over regularly, although this part of the world is influenced by the warm Gulf Stream. The cold weather was also reflected in art, and the snow-covered landscape and frozen rivers became a theme of its own. One of the most famous is Breughel's painting "Hunters on the Snow" (1565). Hans Neuberger analyzed 12,000 paintings created between 1400 and 1967 and calculated how dark and cloudy the landscape was.[57] Most of these dark paintings were made between 1600 and 1646, which corresponds to the coldest part of the Little Ice Age.

It is also possible that the English Agrarian Revolution, which was a prelude to the Industrial Revolution, occurred due to deterioration of the climate in the Little Ice Age. People needed to adapt to such climate deterioration. Poor crops forced farmers to look for new ways to increase productivity. They began to rotate crops (Norfolk four-field system) and use fertilizers. Nitrogen was able to enter the soil because clover and pulses were grown in the fields in some years.

The extent of fallow land was reduced, and turnips were planted instead of pastures and used for feeding. At the beginning of the 18th century, Jethro Tull invented the seeding drill and cereal yields rose by a quarter between 1700 and 1800 and by a half between 1800 and 1850. New crops from America, such as potatoes, started spreading. Farmers like Robert Bakewell began breeding sheep, so their weight doubled in a hundred years.[58] Thanks to these innovations, around 1750 the population of England climbed back to the level where it used to be in the Medieval Warm Period: about 5.7 million people. However, population growth continued. One hundred years later, England had 16.6 million people. Thanks to innovations, England not only adapted to climate change but also eliminated recurring famine.

Agrarian revolution slowly transformed into industrial revolution. These were the unintended consequences of a spontaneous process. Thanks to increasing productivity, fewer workers were needed to produce the same amount of food; so, in 1850, only 22% of the population worked in English agriculture. When the wealthy landlords privatized ("enclosed") all the fields, the poor peasants had nothing to live on and became landless.

The unemployed mass of people headed to towns where they became cheap labor for manufactories. Even this primary industry initially served the agricultural sector—processing imported cotton. But soon also mechanization found its way to the manufactories, when James Hargreaves invented the Spinning Jenny in 1765. It was controlled manually until Edmund Cartwright (1785) invented a mechanical spinning machine, first water-powered and later propelled by Watt's steam engine. This was the beginning of the Industrial Revolution—the greatest social change since the invention of agriculture ten millennia ago.

CLIMATE CHANGE CAN FUEL WARS

The idea of global warming causing wars is supported only by fairy tales. Historically, increase in warfare occurred rather in the times of cooling.

Maunder's solar minimum in the 17th century was the coldest phase of the Little Ice Age. Sunspots disappeared from the sun for decades, solar activity dropped, and Earth's climate cooled. When the sun woke up again, the climate began to warm. However, opinions differ as to whether this warming is good news. A study by Peter Schwartz and Doug Randall (2004), commissioned by the US Department of Defense (Pentagon), even warned that global warming could bring about collapse of global security.[59]

The study claims that a fraction of a degree (Celsius) warming is able to bring about global war. But the report itself acknowledges that the climate change scenario described is extremely unlikely. It's not a scientific study; it's just a science fiction story. They call it a "scenario." Here's an example from this text: "In 2025, internal struggle in Saudi Arabia brings Chinese and US naval forces to the Gulf in direct confrontation."[60] Not even the famous Oracle of Delfi was able to provide such detail in her prophecies.

The report was a product of talks between the authors and "leading climatologists." By this term, they mean select proponents of the CAGW (Catastrophic Anthropogenic Global Warming) hypothesis who came to back the report, such as Advisor to German Chancellor, Herr Joachim Schellnhuber or former head of the UN climate panel, Bob Watson. Professional merchants of fear. The usual suspects.

Unfortunately, such fantasies are beginning to leak even into the school curriculum. For example, a Czech NGO called *Man in Distress* (Člověk v tísni) published a brochure *Climate in Distress,*[61] which also contains a chapter "Heat Fueled Wars." It says: "Increase in average temperature by two degrees means reducing rice production by a tenth. Some countries cannot feed their people. There is an increasing number of people in the world who are suffering from hunger." How the authors came to that conclusion, remains a mystery. During the recent global warming period, the number of malnourished people in the world has been declining—see the introductory chapter.

In the article "Global warming could fuel war," the magazine *LiveScience* drew attention to the research by David Zhang of the University of Hong Kong.[62] "Food and water shortages fueled in the future by global warming could spur conflicts and even wars over these essential resources, the authors of a new study warn... The authors reviewed 899 wars fought in China between 1000 and 1911 and found a correlation between the frequency of warfare and records of temperature changes... It was the oscillations of agricultural production brought by long-term climate change that drove China's historical war-peace cycles."[63]

This may sound like a warning against warming. But Zhang's article actually says something else. The wars in China occurred whenever the climate cooled down. "The troughs of population growth and the peaks of various mortality factors in the Northern Hemisphere coincided with a cold climate," says Zhang's study.

The threat of collapse of civilization was also addressed by Professor of Geography Jared Diamond in the book *Collapse*.[64] He provides a list of human cultures of the past that dug their own grave by their irrational behavior: For example, on Easter Island, when they cut down all trees and caused erosion. But what is most interesting about the book is what is missing. You won't find any culture that would be destroyed by warming. For instance, the Anasazi culture in the southwest of today's United States was indeed destroyed by "climate change." But not by warming. Their demise was due to drought induced by cooling.

II. A CENTURY OF RISK

There are two basic types of environmental panic. Fear that there are too many people. And fear that we do not have enough of them. Our grandfathers used to worry about something wiping them out. Nowadays, when we discuss the evils of consumer society over a cup of cappuccino at Starbucks, it is hard to imagine that the world used to look like that. But once upon a time, people in Europe were indeed starving exactly as they do in Somalia today. Bad weather often led to crop failure, which resulted in famine.

But when the cold centuries were finally over and harvests improved, something odd happened. People were not relieved. Instead, they began to worry about rising population. This particularly bothered Reverend Malthus. He was afraid that population might be rising faster than food production. He insisted someone should do something about it. Besides, later, somebody noted that the worst kind of people breed the fastest.: The sick, the dumb, and the lazy. In the past, the population of serfs was regulated by warfare, kindly organized by nobility. Later, population planning programs were designed, but they got slightly out of hand resulting in an industrial-scale genocide, like from a horror B-movie. Eugenics had to be renamed to "fight overpopulation" and "birth control." Racial hygiene institutes had to be renamed, and their staff had to print out new business cards.

Anyway, it turned out to be a false panic. Population growth eventually resolved itself. As the standard of living rose, people stopped breeding like rabbits. Having eight children made no economic sense anymore. And with abortion and contraception, population started to decline again. So, we returned to the fear of extinction once again. An exception here was the skillful biologist Paul Ehrlich, who was able to handle both—he could fear overpopulation and extinction at the same time, for which he received several international awards.

In the age of supermarkets and discount sales, people no longer have to worry about famine, so they had to find something else to chat about—health concerns. So now they are scared that DDT, a nuclear disaster, or the ozone hole might kill us. There have even been reports that cell phones can cause cancer or that you can get poisoned with dihydrogen monoxide. We have become the first hypochondriac civilization.

These false alarms were not without consequences. The DDT ban resulted in the deaths of several million people from malaria. On the other hand, the DDT ban saved the lives of millions of mosquitoes. The hysteria around Chernobyl—where only 50 people died—has hampered the development of nuclear power in many states. And the ozone hole scare? Nobody remembers it anymore. Maybe except the shopkeepers who keep selling sunglasses with UV filters.

Finally, people became upset by the very fact that mankind has eliminated epidemics and famines. The New Puritan movement convinced people that they should feel guilty if their children are not dying of poverty and that we need to reduce our consumption (ecological footprint) in order to delay the depletion of natural resources. Though in the end, it turned out that the whole concept of ecological footprint was just a simple calculation error.

The number of errors we can find in the 20th-century scientific literature is quite impressive. Editors of magazines print sensations to attract more readers. Research is based on statistical data processing, which tends to be... shall we say... far from perfect. A famous quote says that there are three kinds of lies: lies, damned lies, and statistics. Deception may even be unintended; the researcher is simply blind to anything he/she doesn't want to see. Psychology terms it as cognitive bias. Or you could say wishful thinking.

EUGENICS

A hundred years ago, there was a consensus among experts about the need for eugenics. Scientists issued warnings to mankind. However, their expertise was plagued with errors.

Climatology is not the first scientific discipline that just loves issuing warnings to mankind. And certainly, it is not the first immature scientific field that meddles in politics. A hundred years ago, population biology was in a similar situation. It appears that scientists have not learned any lesson from recent history. "If we continue to squander the biological mental heritage as we have been squandering it during the last few decades, it will not be many generations before we cease to be superior to the Mongols. Our ethnological studies must lead us, not to arrogance, but to action—to eugenics." This is what Erwin Bauer, Eugen Fischer, and Fritz Lenz wrote in their alarmist book *Human Heredity* (1931).[65]

They were concerned that population growth was headed in the wrong direction. That there are more and more people who are weak, both physically and mentally, who are unable to take care of themselves and thus end up either among the poor or among the criminals. Eugenics, or racial hygiene, should bring a solution to this. Government should only allow you to have children if you are healthy, strong, and smart. Like when you breed cattle or racing horses.

But it was not quite clear how to identify individuals suitable for breeding. Scientists believed that we inherit all of our talents the same way as we inherit the color of our eyes. But they couldn't exactly measure which gene was causing what. So, they had to resort to wild speculation.

Like C. B. Davenport in the following text about families of naval officers: "One of the most striking characteristics of sea–lust is that it is wholly a male character ... so appeal of the sea develops under the secretion of the germ gland in the boy. It is theoretically possible that some mothers are heterozygous for love of the sea, so that when married to a thalassophilic man half of their children will show sea-lust and half will not."[66] It did not occur to the author that the children might have chosen a naval career simply because they had grown up in such an environment. Instead, the researchers were looking for a mythical gene of thalassophilia.

Genetics was "cool" then, so researchers tried to explain whatever human behavior by inborn attributes. The influence of education, environment, culture, and standard of living was not taken into account. It resembles today's climate alarmism, which blames any climate change or bad weather on greenhouse gases and underestimates the effects of cloud, water vapor, the sun, and other natural factors.

Today, it seems inconceivable that such naive notions were once considered a scientific consensus. "Genetics was corrupted in the 1920s by the confusion of folk knowledge with scientific inference. For whatever reasons, outsiders who recognized it were shunned, and insiders were, as they say, a day late and a dollar short. The fairly obvious lesson to be learned is that where science appears to validate folk beliefs, it needs to be subjected to considerably higher standards of scrutiny than ordinary science,"[67] write the science historians of today.

The problem is that a researcher can confirm almost any theory if he or she chooses only the data that supports this opinion. This is called a confirmation bias. In his book *Hereditary Genius*,[68] Francis Galton noted that many famous personalities were related by family. Therefore, he concluded that talent was present only in a certain set of "quality" families. He overlooked the existence of poor people like Abraham Lincoln, who had worked his way up from scratch. He also did not consider that many wealthy families produced famous personalities only because of their wealth.

Other researchers examined the pedigree of people with intellectual disabilities to prove that "feeblemindedness" is hereditary. Well known and applicable here is the case of the Kallikak family (a pseudonym), described by Henry H. Goddard in 1912. He recounted the story of a soldier from the American War of Independence who had a love affair with a feebleminded waitress. Then he abandoned her and married an honorable Quaker. The first relationship gave rise to generations of feebleminded and lazy criminals of low morals. Whereas, from the second relationship, came generations of venerable citizens. A touching story with a moral lesson. But there is a catch. It is untrue. Decades later, when other researchers interviewed the living witnesses, they discovered that many of the individuals identified by Goddard as feebleminded were, in fact, successful and decent people. And conversely, in the "honest" line of the family, there were actually many troublemakers.[69] The author twisted facts to fit into his theory.

The term "feebleminded" was used arbitrarily as it was not clearly defined. In fact, this vague term can hide many different mental illnesses that have a different genetic cause. Polygenism was not considered, i.e., the possibility that a disease could be caused by interplay of multiple genes. Weakness may not be related to heredity at all. For example, by abusing alcohol during pregnancy, a mother can damage the baby's brain, even if her genes are fine.[70]

Botched attempts to use intelligence testing contributed to the confusion even more. When Goddard tested poor immigrants, traveling by third-class, in 1913, he found that 80% of Hungarians, 83% of Jews, and 79% of Italians were feebleminded. It was not because of any intelligence deficit on their part. It was actually due to intelligence deficit of the tester. The immigrants couldn't speak English so they could barely fill in the test, of course. When the US military applied similar intelligence tests to its troops in 1919, they found that 47% of whites and 86% of blacks were feebleminded. These absurdly high figures indicated that something was wrong with this way of measuring intelligence.[71] Naturally, the soldiers came from multiple social classes and differed in their literacy. They couldn't have known answers to questions they were not taught at school. Some never got a chance to learn to write.

But at that time, eugenic theories represented a scientific consensus. It is like today, when we hear that 97% of scientists support CAGW theory (Catastrophic Anthropogenic Global Warming). Virtually every textbook on heredity written between 1910 and 1930 promoted eugenics.[72] All the founding members of the editorial board of the journal *Genetics* in 1916 were supporters of eugenics.[73] The first biologist who dared to oppose eugenics in the US was only Raymond Pearl in 1927 in the article *The Biology of Superiority.*[74] Until then, we had only heard criticism of eugenics from laymen and journalists like H. L. Mencken. "Pearl acknowledged the social prejudices underlying the research and exposed the flimsy science backing it up. Since Pearl was a respected biologist, his article caused a sensation and was picked up by the major news outlets. Of course, publicly challenging the power structure of the scientific community was not without risk, and Pearl found that his offer of professorship at Harvard was quickly retracted."[75]

In the above article, Pearl rejected the idea that only the "best" members of the society, the affluent people, should have children. Their social standing is not necessarily proof of some talent which their children could inherit from them. Many of them owe their success to a game of chance at the stock exchange, to corruption and acquaintances, or they inherited their property without any effort of their own. Galton's theory of inheritance—that quality parents leave quality children—is simply too simplified.

Even though the understanding of heredity was only modest in those times, and the advice given by the eugenic experts were unsubstantiated, they had the support of philanthropists and celebrities. They honestly believed they were working to improve this world. Economist Maynard Keynes was the director of British Eugenics Society between 1937 and 1944. Eugenics supporters included Winston Churchill and President Woodrow Wilson. Eugenics was commonly taught at universities. In 1928, there were 376 such university courses in the USA.[76] That this was a scientific mainstream at that time is also evident from the fact that in 1921, *Science* magazine published the opening speech of the Second World Eugenics Congress on the front page.[77] Population research required processing a large amount of data, so eugenics became the impulse for development of modern statistics. The founders of statistics are people like Francis Galton, Karl Pearson, and R.A. Fischer. They were the ones who established terms such as correlation, standard deviation, or p-value.

Eugenics was first a theory, then it became a policy, and then legislation. In 1927, the US Supreme Court, in the case Buck v. Bell, decided that citizens could be sterilized against their will.[78] In Sweden, such legislation remained in force long after World War II. In the autumn of 1997, the

Swedish newspaper *Dagens Nyheter* shocked the world public by discovering that between 1935 and 1975, Sweden had a fully legal program of forced sterilization of citizens who were considered problematic.[79] About 60,000 people were sterilized. In Germany, eugenics went even further. The Nazis did not just sterilize the handicapped people; they decided to physically exterminate the weak and ill. Between 1939 and 1941, they executed about a quarter of a million disabled children and psychiatric inmates. The whole operation is called "Action T4" according to the address Tiergartenstrasse 4, where the responsible authority was located. Eugenics, once a philanthropist's dream, turned into a nightmare and has become a taboo ever since.

The fact that the Germans went too far does not mean that there was nothing good in the whole idea of eugenics, of course. Planned parenthood does make sense, as probably no one wants a disabled child. However, in the history of eugenics we can identify a certain pattern that would be repeated many times in the 20th century. A pseudoscientific theory full of errors. Scientists who "warn mankind." Statistical tricks. Scientific consensus. One factor used as a universal explanation of anything. Terrifying unintended consequences.

NATURE RESERVES

The world's largest environmental organization owes its wealth to business tycoons from the home of apartheid. It was established out of eugenic concerns of the Whites that there are too many Blacks in Africa.

Julian Huxley was vice president of the British Eugenics Society in the period 1937–1944 (and president from 1959–1962). In a series of articles for *The Observer* in 1960, he expressed his concern about the booming black populations in Africa.[80] He warned that this demographic development is putting too much pressure on natural resources and wildlife. As early as 1941, Julian Huxley warned: "The lowest strata, allegedly less well-endowed genetically, are reproducing relatively too fast... They must not have too easy access to relief or hospital treatment lest the removal of the last check on natural selection should make it too easy for children to be produced or to survive; long unemployment should be a ground for sterilization."[81]

Similar views—though extreme from today's perspective—were common at the time, shared by celebrities like the writer G.B. Shaw from the Fabian Society.[82] But Julian's brother, Aldous Huxley, had a slightly different view. In the famous dystopian novel *Brave New World*, he imagines a totalitarian society where human beings are produced in a lab according to eugenic criteria.

Needless to say, Julian Huxley's eugenic past is something you do not hear very often about from his followers today. Actually, it is mercifully concealed in many of his biographies. However, it was Mr. Huxley's articles in *The Observer* that inspired the foundation of the world's wealthiest environmental organization, the World Wildlife Fund (the NGO with a Panda in its emblem).

But the controversy does not stop here. WWF owes its wealth to South African apartheid and tobacco corporations. Environmentalists usually like to paint corporations as their archenemy, but the reality is not so simple. In 1970, the South African tobacco tycoon Anton Rupert (manufacturer of the Rothmans cigarettes) came up with the idea of setting up an exclusive club for the wealthy, called "Club 1001." It was an association of large anonymous WWF sponsors who donate more than $10,000.

The list of members was kept secret, although eventually, it leaked to the media. The membership base consisted mainly of businessmen from the country of apartheid, tycoons, shady entrepreneurs, and an assortment of bloody dictators, for example, President Idi Amin of Uganda or President Mobutu of Zaire[83] and especially the members of the South African brotherhood of the whites, the "Broederbond." They were worried that if the black populations kept booming, the whites in South Africa wouldn't be able to keep them under control anymore. However, they understood that after the Holocaust, racial ideology is a taboo. Instead, environmentalist ideology could be used now as a big stick against people.

WWF was so rich that it was able to enlist the world's power elite among its members. The first president of the WWF was Prince Bernhard of the Netherlands, who, a few years earlier, in Bilderberg, Netherlands, also established a controversial tradition where the world's most powerful people would meet and talk behind closed doors. Bernhard fought during the Second World War as an RAF pilot against Nazi aggressors, yet he himself comes from a German family and was a member of the NSDAP and SA during his studies. He only left their ranks when he had to because he wanted to marry a Dutch princess.[84] It is hard to tell how much he was influenced by the eco-fascist ideology. After all, Nazi Germany passed the most ambitious environmentalist legislation in history (Reichsnaturschutzgesetz 1936).

Philip, the Duke of Edinburgh (husband of Queen Elizabeth II and father of Prince Charles), was the first president of the British branch of WWF (1961–1982) and then president of the entire WWF (1981–1996). Philip was open about his belief that population needs to be reduced "If I were reincarnated, I would wish to be returned to Earth as a killer virus to lower human population levels." said the prince, renowned for his wisecracking remarks, the *Deutsche Press Agentur* in 1988.[85]

Under the pretext of nature protection, it was possible to fence off certain "no go" areas where local people are not welcome. These zones were converted to hunting parks, where only members of the wealthy class and foreign tourists were allowed. For example, in the 1980s in Zaire and Uganda, the WWF launched a campaign to expand national parks. The natives, Batwa pygmies, were expelled from places where they had been living for centuries or even millennia.[86] They became homeless.[87]

There were many more such cases. The government of Botswana wants to push Bushmen tribes out of the Kalahari Natural Reserve. The officials say that the wildlife needs a free corridor. Yet, the Bushmen have lived here for thousands of years. Are we supposed to believe now that indigenous peoples who live in close contact with nature do NOT belong to nature? It is a breath-taking arrogance when wealthy middle-class white men from the city—who are unable to tell a sheep from a goat—fly to Africa to teach the naked natives how to live in harmony with nature.

Forced resettlements are monitored by the non-profit organization Survival International. "Game parks all over Africa have been created by expelling people from their ancestral lands or forbidding them to engage in traditional hunting pursuits. Not surprisingly, many Africans living in impoverished rural areas, including in South Africa, have come to equate game reserves with the presence of security forces."[88]

The conservationists have been treating African natives like the conquistadors treated the American Indians. When the Serengeti Nature Park was established in the 1950s, the Maasai tribes were removed from their ancestral lands to the Ngorongoro Crater Reserve. In 1974, the most fertile part of this territory was taken away from them. Conservationists forbid the Maasai from developing agriculture, so there is nothing to support their growing population. One of the Maasai complained to journalists, "The wildlife gets better treatment than people here...We live here on the land, but we cannot plan for ourselves how to use it."[89]

DDT

The ban on DDT was justified by the declining eagle population. But in historical data, no such decline is documented.

Malaria used to be a scourge of many parts of the world, even cold ones like Britain or Siberia. Quinine was used as a treatment for a long time. But only the insecticide DDT really helped to fight against the mosquitoes that spread the disease. Its first mass deployment was in World War II, and its author, Paul Herman Müller, received a Nobel Prize in 1948. Who would have guessed at that time that DDT would be viewed as something evil by future generations!

Even in the 1970s, the US Academy of Sciences Committee praised DDT as a blessing: "To only a few chemicals do man owe as great a debt as to DDT... Indeed, it is estimated that in little more than two decades, DDT has prevented 500 million deaths due to malaria that would otherwise have been inevitable. Abandonment of this valuable insecticide should be undertaken only at such time and in such places as it is evident that the perspective gain to humanity exceeds the consequent losses."[90] It should say 50, not 500, but still, the benefits of DDT were immense.

The crusade to ban DDT was launched in the USA by EDF (Environmental Defense Fund). Its founder, Charles Wurster, wrote: "If environmentalists win on DDT, they will achieve, and probably retain in other environmental issues, a level of authority they have never had before. In a sense, then, much more is at stake than DDT."[91] It was a quest for political power.

When speculation appeared about the adverse effects of DDT, the US Department of Agriculture refused to ban DDT until solid evidence was presented. But there was a way to circumvent the burden of proof. In 1970, pesticide regulation in the US was withdrawn from the Department of Agriculture and entrusted to the newly created Environmental Protection Agency (EPA).

The new director of the EPA did not waste time on trivia like the scientific process. Judge Sweeney concluded that there was insufficient evidence to ban DDT—"DDT is not a carcinogenic hazard to man. DDT is not a mutagenic or teratogenic hazard to man. The uses of DDT under the registrations involved here do not have a deleterious effect on freshwater fish, estuarine organisms, wild birds, or other wildlife."[92] However, despite the findings of the 1972 investigation, the EPA director banned DDT without explanation. The first director of the EPA was William Ruckelshaus, a "green" activist lawyer.

DDT fell into disfavor with environmentalists after 1961, when Rachel Carson published the book *Silent Spring*.[93] One day, she noticed that

39

birds were not singing. Of course, populations in the wild naturally fluctuate (like the legendary lemming population cycles), but Carson did not know that. She was worried that the culprit is DDT, which causes thinning of bird eggshells.

It reads like an elegy, the saddest poem. The thrush bird is dying, and our children would no longer hear the birds singing. Once, the towns in America lived in happy harmony with nature, until the "death cocktails" were brought upon us. Because of the pesticides, the modern plague, people and animals get sick. Her suspicion was reinforced by the research of Charles Wurster, who allegedly found a lot of poisoned thrush birds after spraying DDT.[94] However, according to the annual census, the total thrush population increased even in the era of DDT use.

It turned out that the title of the book *Silent Spring* was a wrong choice. DDT should have the greatest impact not on songbirds but on birds of prey, respectively, the thickness of their eggshells. Birds of prey are at the top of the food chain and eat meat in which DDT has accumulated. The question is, how serious was this health effect? Was it more deadly for the eagle population than parasites, hunters, or the weather? The most famous victim of DDT became the bald eagle, the state symbol of the US, who is said to have been on the verge of extinction due to this pesticide.

For some reason, only the eagle population data since 1963 are presented in the media. In that year, the eagle population in the US was just 487 nesting pairs.[95] It is said to have been an outcome of population decrease due to DDT. However, the Audubon Society had been counting birds since the early 20th century. If you find the data from their Christmas Bird Count, you will be surprised. In the years 1940–1960, when DDT was used, no decrease in eagle population is noticeable—the number of eagles per observer. This remains true even if we leave out the wilderness of Alaska, which might distort the data.[96]

But the fable of the eagle and DDT is still alive and kicking. When the eagle was removed from the endangered species list in 2007, US Secretary of State, Mr. Kempthorne, boasted: "Today I am proud to announce: the eagle has returned. In 1963, the lower 48 states were home to barely 400 nesting pairs of bald eagles. Today, after decades of conservation effort, they are home to some 10,000 nesting pairs, a 25-fold increase in the last 40 years."[97] In fact, this is a statistical mistake. While in 1900, the number of birdwatchers doing the count for the Audubon Society was only 27, in 1960, there were already some 8,000 observers, and in the year 2000, the number of birdwatchers climbed to 52,000. What increased is the number of observers, not eagles. More eyes can see more.

While it is true that the bald eagle was threatened with extinction, it happened long before the invention of DDT. In 1940, an eagle protection law had to be passed because farmers used to shoot them as pest. Already in 1921, 20 years before the boom of DDT use, *Ecology* magazine warned that the bald eagle, the US state symbol, is on the verge of extinction.[98]

Today, eagles have quite a different problem—renewable energy. For example, an actual bird chopping slaughterhouse was built at the Altamont Pass in California, where the plantation of 5,400 wind farms was carried out. According to rough estimates, the windmill blades kill about 2,700 birds a year, of which about 1,000 are birds of prey, and, out of that, 70 are eagles.[99] The penalty for killing one protected eagle is $5,000 or a year in prison. The windmill owners would soon be bankrupted by the penalties, so the US government issued a special "license to kill" for them like the one agent 007 has.[100]

Rachel Carson, who unleashed the panic around DDT, had cancer and died a few years after the publication of her legendary book as an "ecological martyr." Her belief that she was poisoned by pesticides present in the environment may not have been correct. The dramatic increase in cancer incidence in the 20th century is actually a statistical illusion. Today there are more ill individuals per 100,000 people (Age Standardized Ratios) simply because people live longer, and older people make up a larger percentage of the population. Thanks to modern medicine, sick people do not die and continue to be part of the statistics.

Among the main defenders of DDT was Thomas Jukes, a Professor of Biology at Berkeley University, who had previously been involved in the fight against creationism. He wrote about the Audubon Society: "For a member to condone the use of pesticides would be tantamount to the deepest heresy in a religious sect... What motivates those who crusade against the most useful chemical in history?"[101] When green activists printed slander in the *New York Times* (1972) that Jukes was paid by chemical corporations to deny the harmfulness of DDT, he did not hesitate and sued the journalists as well as the Audubon Society and won (the Edwards v. Audubon Case). But the journalists managed to use a hole in the law to avoid payment of compensation to him.[102]

Half a century has passed since the ban on DDT in the USA. Yet even now, DDT has not been proven to have any serious impact on human health. For example, let's look at how Eskenazi et al. (2009)[103] sum up decades of research. Studies suggesting possible health effects were mainly experiments on animals, which were fed large doses of DDT. But people don't eat DDT toasts for breakfast every day. In humans, the health impact of DDT was not confirmed. The US Agency for Toxic Substances and Disease Registry (ASTDR) also agrees—"No effects have been reported in adults given small daily doses of DDT by capsule for 18 months (up to 35 milligrams every day)."[104] Workers in factories where DDT was made were exposed to daily doses of 20 mg.

The demonization of DDT cost the lives of millions of people in Africa. It was impossible to bring malaria to a manageable level without DDT. In 1955, the World Health Organization launched a Global Malaria Eradication Campaign. However, due to the environmental concerns raised by Mrs. Carson's book, DDT was abandoned in Africa before it even started.[105]

In some areas, malaria returned; but, in most cases, it was not because of mosquito resistance to DDT, as is sometimes claimed.[106] The World Health Organization ended its malaria program in 1969. It was not a worldwide ban as with "ozone-depleting gases" later. DDT just fell out of favor because of bad press. And the result? Between 1980 and 2004, the number of malaria deaths in Africa rose from about half a million a year to one and a half million a year. On the other hand, outside Africa, where DDT had already brought malaria to manageable levels, even after 1980, the number of malaria victims continued to decline.[107]

We learned the hard lesson that DDT is still indispensable. The African "Roll Back Malaria" campaign from 1998–2006 was a complete failure.[108] Since the launch of the RMB, the number of malaria victims actually increased instead of declining. The dramatic drop in malaria deaths in Africa by 30% occurred only after 2006 when the World Health Organization admitted that giving up DDT was a mistake. WHO reversed its policy and encouraged the use of DDT to spray inside buildings with dramatic success.

Within just a few years, malaria deaths in Africa dropped by 30%. From about 1,613,000 in 2004 to 1,133,000 in 2010.[109] However, the official RMB materials remain silent on the merits of DDT. The reason for the sudden success of the RMB is—somewhat vaguely—described as "reorganization" of activities and "adjustment" of the mechanisms for the sake of "greater efficiency." Apparently, the failures of the anti-DDT policy are so catastrophic that no one is willing to admit the truth.

So how much did the "precautionary principle" cost us? Robert Gwadz of the National Institutes of Health said in 2007: "The ban on DDT may have killed 20 million children."[110]

POPULATION BOMB

Paul Ehrlich is known for his prophecy that by the year 2000, England would no longer exist due to imminent global famine caused by overpopulation.

"The fight to feed all of humanity is over." In 1968, biologist Paul Ehrlich in his book *The Population Bomb* feared that the world would soon suffer from gigantic famine in the 1970s and 1980s, as there are more people than we can possibly feed.[111] "By the year 2000, the United Kingdom will be simply a small group of impoverished islands, inhabited by some 70 million hungry people... If I were a gambler, I would take even money that England will not exist in the year 2000."[112] Because of famine and hunger riots. For India, he had similar words: "I don't see how India could possibly feed two hundred million more people by 1980," lamented Ehrlich in 1968.

He was wrong. India's population has tripled since then, from 400 million to 1.2 billion people. The population of the planet itself has grown. While at the early 19th century, there were about 1 billion people in the world, in 1960, the Earth had 3 billion people, and today, it is seven billion.

Based on his forecasts, Ehrlich urged politicians to declare a state of emergency. In his book *Ecoscience*,[113] he proposed creating a "planetary regime" that would impose quotas on the use of natural resources and population size.[114] Ehrlich proposed forced sterilization of people. For example, the government should add substances to drinking water that would cause infertility. Or parents would have to ask the authorities for a permit to have a child, like in China.

"Adding a sterilant to drinking water or staple foods is a suggestion that seems to horrify people more than most proposals for involuntary fertility control," Ehrlich writes.[115] And then, he proceeds to discuss the technical measures needed to execute such a plan.

Actually, this whole thing was not Ehrlich's idea. He just copied it from the British clergyman and economist Thomas R. Malthus. In *An Essay on the Principle of Population* (1798),[116] he calculated that population, when unchecked, increases in a geometrical ratio (1-2-4-8-16), whereas subsistence increases only in an arithmetical ratio (1-2-3-4-5). This led him to the conclusion that people tend to breed like rabbits until their numbers get slashed by famine.

The solutions that Thomas Malthus suggested to this problem were rather cruel: "In our towns, we should make the streets narrower, crowd more people into houses, and court the return of the plague. In the country, we should build our villages near stagnant pools, and particularly encourage settlements in all marshy and unwholesome situations."[117]

Fortunately, no one implemented such measures, nor did Malthus's forecasts come true. During the 19th century, the British population grew fourfold, while its gross national product increased fourteenfold.

Malthus did not consider the existence of innovations. Norman Borlaug started the so-called "green revolution" in the 1960s. He was able to breed more fertile and resilient crop varieties that multiplied world food production in just a few years.[118] It was no coincidence that Borlaug was one of the signatories of the Heidelberg protest against UN alarmism in 1992.

It was not the first time that mankind had exceeded the supposed limits of growth. As long as people lived as hunters and gatherers, each individual needed about one square kilometer to make a living. It is possible that their shamans preached of the overpopulation threat as well. They could have convincingly calculated that if more than two people were to live per one square kilometer, they would not be able to feed themselves in such a crowded place. But the invention of agriculture changed the situation.

England still exists and the world is not gripped in global famine. Yet Paul Ehrlich does not recognize that his predictions were too pessimistic. "Perhaps the most serious flaw in *The Bomb* was that it was much too optimistic about the future,"[119] Ehrlich insists today. He claims there appeared many environmental problems since the book was released that he had not foreseen, for example, ozone hole or global warming. Well, but none of these problems have had that decimating effect on the human population that Ehrlich once predicted.

Fear of overpopulation has led many people to make rather radical statements. Jean Jacques Cousteau: "It's terrible to have to say this. World population must be stabilized, and to do that, we must eliminate 350,000 people per day. This is so horrible to contemplate that we shouldn't even say it. But the general situation in which we are involved is lamentable."[120]

CLUB OF ROME

Limits to Growth is a 1972 book published by the Club of Rome that used computer simulations to predict that global oil reserves would dry up by 1992.

In April 1968, Italian industrialist Aurelio Peccei invited a group of intellectuals to the Accademia dei Lincei in Rome to discuss global planning. This is how an association called the Club of Rome was born. They made a sweeping statement of "The Fate of Mankind," but they were basically clueless about how to proceed until they heard of World Dynamics, Jay Forrester's computer simulations at MIT. They were introduced to them in November 1968 at the Rockefeller Conference Center in Bellagio (Villa Serbelloni), Italy, at the OECD Symposium.[121]

The result was a *Bellagio Declaration on Planning* rejecting uncontrolled economic growth and calling for long-term international planning.[122] The Club of Rome then paid Mr. and Mrs. Meadows to use Forrester's "system dynamics" method and then publish the results in a book.

Today, the book *Limits to Growth* is a model example of hasty extrapolation of trends.[123] According to a computer simulation, it appeared that there was only so much oil to last for 20 more years, and it would be depleted by 1992. Even if five times more new deposits were discovered, oil reserves would still be depleted within 50 years (by 2022). They believed that gold deposits would go dry within nine years (by 1981). Even if five times as many deposits were discovered, all the world's gold would still be mined in 29 years (by 2001).

As we know today, none of this has happened. At the current rate of consumption, the known coal deposits are enough to last over a hundred years.[124] Oil, tin, or zinc did not run out either. Economist W.D. Nordhaus described the simulations as absurd "measurement without data."[125] New mineral deposits are being discovered all the time. You never know how much would be discovered and when. Nobody knows what the consumption might be a century later or what the energy use efficiency will be.

Forrester was an engineer, not an economist. Because the technicians tend to scorn social sciences, he probably thought: "I'm going to do economics with equations! And run them through a computer! I'm sure those stupid economists have never thought of that!"[126] But if you don't have the data, even the best computer won't help you. If you feed garbage to the computer, only garbage can come out of it (GIGO, garbage in = garbage out).

In his lecture at Caltech (2006), writer Michael Crichton expressed the view that it was the ufologists who actually paved the way for this fashion of "calculations without data."[127] In the early 1960s, scientists presented the famous Drake's equation from Greenbank. Its authors calculated that there are some 10,000 intelligent civilizations in our galaxy. One can only wonder how they could have calculated it with such precision since we don't even know what percentage of stars have planets. Well, all the input data for the equation was just an estimate, a wild guess. They just made it up.

Not only did they get away with this daydreaming, they even received tens of millions of subsidies for the SETI program, which searches for intelligent radio signals from space. Thus, SETI discovered something even more amazing than alien life. The discovery that grant money can actually be awarded for pure fabrications and pseudoscientific fantasy. All you need is jargon that sort of looks like science.

$$N = R^* \cdot f_p \cdot n_e \cdot f_l \cdot f_i \cdot f_c \cdot L$$

N—number of civilizations in our galaxy with whom we can communicate,

R^*—average number of stars that form in our galaxy per year,

f_p—number of stars with planets,

n_e—number of planets capable of supporting life,

f_l—number of planets where life has evolved,

f_i—number of planets, where intelligent life has evolved,

f_c—number of planets with intelligent life which communicates with other worlds,

L—fraction of the planetary life span during which it is inhabited by a communicating civilization.

We do not know any of these values, of course. Crichton continues: "The Drake equation can have any value from 'billions and billions' to zero. An expression that can mean anything means nothing. Speaking precisely, the Drake equation is literally meaningless, and has nothing to do with science. I take the hard view that science involves the creation of testable hypotheses. The Drake equation cannot be tested."

Crichton also points out that Drake's equation had dangerous consequences: "The fact that the Drake equation was not greeted with screams of outrage—similar to the screams that greet each Creationist's new claim, for example—meant that now there was a crack in the door, a loosening of the definition of what constituted legitimate scientific procedure. And soon enough, pernicious garbage began to squeeze through the cracks."[128]

The success of the *Limits of Growth* encouraged the Club of Rome to expand its activities. As a sequel, they set up a factory—I mean institute—in Austria to begin mass production of such scary scenarios. An inconspicuous title was chosen so that no one would know what this organization was actually doing. It is called IIASA, or "Institute for Applied System analysis." What kind of analysis? What is being analyzed?

A generation later, their "scenario" method was adopted by the newly established UN Intergovernmental Panel on Climate Change (IPCC). One inputs data into a computer model, often somewhat speculative data—because we do not know a lot of things, we just use estimates. When a spooky scenario has been cooked, it is advertised through various "independent" think-tanks to the media. The Special Report on Emissions Scenarios about prospective CO_2 emissions was actually written in the UN climate panel by Mr. Neboisa Nakicenovic, Deputy Director of IIASA.

The Soviet scientist and politician Dzhermen Gvishiani became the first council chairman of IIASA (1972–1987). He was Vice-Chairman of the Soviet State Committee for Science and Technology. As the son-in-law of Prime Minister Kosygin, he belonged to the high society in the USSR. His father was an NKVD officer who deported Chechens to Siberia.

In 1965, Gvishiani was intrigued by Peccei's lecture on economic aid to developing countries given at the Atlantic Community Development Group for Latin America (ADELA), which was Mr. Rockefeller's association of entrepreneurs for investing in the development of Latin America. Gvishiani invited Peccei to Moscow.[129] It was from their meeting that the plan to establish the *Club of Rome* arose.[130] Aurelio Peccei had always been close to the communists. His dissertation was about Lenin's "new economic policy." In the 1930s, he went on a study trip to Moscow and later worked at Fiat offices in the Soviet Union and China.

This may explain the club's reserved attitude toward democracy. The club subscribes to the legacy of Thomas Hobbes, who in the 17th century wrote the book *Leviathan*.[131] He was the first modern philosopher to reject democracy and the idea of economic growth. In *Taking Nature Into Account*, they write: "Fear is especially predominant for Hobbes. Fear largely regulates human behavior. In order to escape fear, men by covenant create the great Leviathan, a semi-absolute state that keeps its subjects in awe and prevents permanent scarcity from developing into outright war."[132]

The authors feared that democracy with its endless debates and meetings was too clunky to address environmental threats in time. In *The First Global Revolution* in 1991, the Club of Rome declares bluntly: "Democracy is not a panacea. It cannot organize everything, and it is unaware of its own limits. These facts must be faced squarely, sacrilegious though this may sound. In its present form, democracy is no longer well suited for the tasks ahead. The complexity and the technical nature of many of today's problems do not always allow elected representatives to make competent decisions at the right time."[133]

EHRLICH'S WAGER

The biologist Paul Ehrlich believed so much in the Limits to Growth that he bet raw materials would soon turn into a scarce commodity. And he lost.

In 1980, Paul Ehrlich, author of *The Population Bomb,* made a bet with the economist Julian Simon that mankind would start running out of raw materials within ten years, as predicted by the Club of Rome. The wager was put on the price of five metals (chrome, copper, nickel, tin, tungsten). Ehrlich lost the bet because, in the meantime, new deposits were being discovered, and the technology became cheaper and cheaper, which meant abundance of raw materials at lower prices—quite the opposite to the forecasted depletion!

In Ehrlich's defense, some argue that if a different ten-year period had been chosen the bet might have gone the other way. In the long run, however, Simon is right. Looking at inflation-adjusted figures for the past 100 years, the price of these commodities varies from generation to generation, but shows no statistically significant trend.[134] Anyone can verify that at the USGS (US Geological Survey) website under the term "inflation-adjusted metal prices." No collapse of industrial civilization is in sight.

In 1995, Simon proposed a new wager to Ehrlich to determine whether people's living standard would improve in ten years. Ehrlich realized that he could not bet on the depletion of raw materials, so he wanted to focus on something else this time. He suggested that in ten years, it will be warmer, that there will be more AIDS victims, that the area of rainforests will decrease, that there will be less arable land available per person, etc.

Simon refused to bet on such indicators because, in his view, they say nothing about human quality of life. Warming can also be beneficial for colder countries. The number of people infected with AIDS may increase, but they may have better medicines and higher quality of life. The area of cultivated land can also be reduced thanks to more efficient farming, which can produce more food from a hectare. In Europe, we cut down the forests centuries ago, and no one seems to miss them.[135]

Simon explained the absurdity of Ehrlich's proposed indicators by the following comparison. "I predict, and this is for real, that the average performances in the next Olympics will be better than those in the last Olympics... What Ehrlich and others say is that they don't want to bet on athletic performances; they want to bet on the conditions of the track, or the weather, or the officials, or any other such indirect measure."

Simon's book *Ultimate Resource* (1981) explains what the Malthusians are wrong about.[136] The Stone Age did not end because we would have run out of stone. It ended because people discovered something better, and fossil fuels are the same story. The ultimate resource is human ingenuity.

People who believe in the limits to growth rely, among other things, on Hubbert's theory of peak oil, i.e., calculations when oil will be depleted. But they probably didn't read Hubbert very carefully.

In his article *Nuclear Energy and Fossil Fuels* (1956), King Hubbert states that when oil has peaked, we can just move on to nuclear energy. Just substitute one raw material with another, a classic substitution, like when we switched from wood to coal. Hubert: "It appears that there exist within minable depths in the United States rocks with uranium contents equivalent to 1,000 barrels or more of oil per metric ton, whose total energy content is probably several hundred times that of all fossil fuels combined... Consequently, the world appears to be on the threshold of an era, which, in terms of energy consumption, will be at least an order of magnitude greater than that made possible by fossil fuels."[137]

The dispute between Ehrlich and Simon was eventually decided by time. Ehrlich survived his opponent (Simon died in 1998) and buried him under a flood of media activity. Though, none of his bold predictions ever came out true—he lost the wager to Simon, and he would also have lost his bet that England would no longer exist by 2000 due to famine. Yet, he still keeps receiving honorary doctorates for his prophetic raving about the apocalypse and is worshiped as a wise sage. He is the recipient of the Blue Planet Prize (1999), the UN Sasakawa Environment Prize (1994), the Frontiers of Knowledge Award (2014), and other awards. He insists that he has never made a mistake. Everything he predicted would indeed happen. In an unspecified future. Someday. Perhaps. Maybe.

CHERNOBYL

In fact, only 50 people died in the "greatest nuclear catastrophe in history.

The Chernobyl nuclear accident of 1986 is often used as the proverbial stick to beat down any supporters of nuclear energy. But for many, even the grim reality is not enough, so they fabricate gruesome details. For example, the video game *STALKER: Shadow of Chernobyl* by the Ukrainian studio GSC Game World describes a gloomy, deserted radioactive zone, full of mysterious physical anomalies, where disfigured mutants live. The fact that there are no such horrors in the area was solved easily by the authors. The story is set in the future after "another" nuclear explosion.

But it is much worse when documentary films resort to this sort of fantasy. In 2003, an Oscar was awarded to the documentary *Chernobyl Heart* about the work of the New York Charity called Chernobyl Children. People in cinemas were weeping when they saw disabled children, allegedly disfigured by radioactivity. One mutant child had its brain overgrowing out of the skull. Then you could see a kidney tumor so large the child couldn't walk.[138] Chills run down your spine as you shiver with horror. However, none of this was caused by Chernobyl. The journalists are just toying with your emotions in their quest for a Pulitzer Prize. In fact, such horrifying cases can be found in every country in the world. There is no evidence this would occur at a higher rate around Chernobyl. The only truly confirmed consequence of the Chernobyl incident was a temporary increase in the incidence of thyroid cancer, which is fortunately well treatable, especially if detected early. It is true that the rate of reported tumors increased globally but only incidence of small tumors. Which indicates it is caused by better scanning techniques, not worsening of health.

In 2006, the UN convened the Chernobyl Forum, which was attended, among others, by the World Health Organization, the International Nuclear Energy Agency, and the Ukrainian Government. The report *Chernobyl's Legacy: Health, Environmental, and Socio-Economic Impacts* concluded that there was no increase in physical deformities or mutations in children or adults.[139]

Physicians have an explanation. "Mutants are not born either because cells damaged prior to mitosis are unable to form gametes or because embryos die in the early stages or are unable to nest in the womb."[140] The embryo either develops into a healthy fetus or does not form at all.

This conclusion is in line with the observation that during the month after the accident, there was an elevated rate of abortions, especially abortions of genetically more vulnerable male fetuses, which is documented by the fact that in former Czechoslovakia in November 1986 (about six months after Chernobyl), for the first and last time in recorded history, more girls were born than boys.[141]

Reuters reported research by Dr. Wertelecki, which indicated that Neural Tube Defects (NTC) are much more frequent in Rivne, Ukraine (22 cases per 10,000 people) than the European average (9 per 10,000).[142] However, NTDs are this high in most poor countries, even far from Chernobyl. For example, in Turkey or India, the incidence is higher than 20 in 10,000, although there was no nuclear explosion.[143]

Anyway, in the world of fundraising, people follow the logic of advertising rather than facts. They know well that one can raise more money when people are crying over pictures of sick babies or puppies. Chernobyl has become a profitable business. People who received the status of "victim of Chernobyl" are entitled to generous welfare benefits, so they tend to exaggerate their problems to be eligible. However, this charity does actually more harm than good. Oxana Garnets of the Chernobyl Commission says: "People getting benefits think they should get more and more. They think everything should be done for them by someone else—it creates a huge sense of fatalism and pessimism, which means they don't get on with their lives."[144]

The people of Chernobyl were much more damaged by the overreaction of the authorities that evacuated the whole region and broke the local community. The previously self-sufficient population has changed into a depressive subculture dependent on donations and frightened by fake news. For example, they heard in the news that Chernobyl was worse than Hiroshima because there was a 400-fold higher fallout. A bomb can only hold a few kilograms of plutonium, while the Chernobyl reactor carried several tons of nuclear waste from many years of operation. Sure, but in Hiroshima, people were not killed by the fallout but by neutron radiation, which was minimal in Chernobyl.

People also often imagine the Chernobyl disaster as an atomic mushroom cloud. But nothing of that sort ever happened. This is evidenced by the fact that except for the faulty 4th block, the Chernobyl power plant remained standing. It produced electricity until 2000.

It is true wind carried the radioactive clouds from Ukraine to Western Europe. There was fear that mutated children would be born all over Europe. When the radioactive cloud arrived over Italy, the Italians were exposed to a dose of 60 mrem. Such radiation occurs commonly in nature, albeit not in such a short time—a person is normally exposed to about 200 mrem per year.[145] This is not very much for the greatest nuclear disaster in history.

The bottom line: the only serious problem was a one-off increase in the number of abortions and increase in the number of thyroid tumors. But there are no mass graves. It is estimated that in Ukraine, Russia, and Belarus, some 4,000 children were affected, but only nine died because in 98% of cases, the disease is easily treatable.[146] Thus, the incidence increased not mortality.

Sometimes you may come across estimates that the effects of radiation "may have contributed" to the death of some 40,000 people. This number can be found in the TORCH report commissioned by the Green Party in the European Parliament. But if you ask for the names of the dead, the answer will be silence because it is only a statistical speculation that can hardly be observed in real data.

The press release of Chernobyl Forum (whose estimate was ten times lower) explains why: "The estimated 4,000 casualties may occur during the lifetime of about 600,000 people under consideration. As about a quarter of them will eventually die from spontaneous cancer not caused by Chernobyl radiation, the radiation-induced increase of about 3% will be difficult to observe."[147] After all, there is no reason to expect severe health problems. The thousands of people who worked on the site clean-up received a total dose of only 100 to 200 mSv. Let us compare it to something we know. AAPM (American Association of Physicists in Medicine) states that X-ray examinations are not dangerous if effective dosage is below 50 mSv per one examination or 100 mSv for consecutive examinations.[148] Besides, there are parts of the world with natural radiation as high as 260 mSv a year. And these places have much lower cancer incidence because the local forms of life have adapted to the radiation ("hormesis").

Writer Michael Crichton recalls when, in 1998, he decided to write a novel about a global disaster. "And in the course of my preparation for this book, I rather casually reviewed what had happened at Chernobyl, because I regard Chernobyl as the largest man-made disaster that I knew about. What I discovered stunned me. Chernobyl was a tragic event but nothing remotely close to the global catastrophe that I was imagining. About 50 people had died in Chernobyl, roughly the number of Americans that die every day in traffic accidents. I don't mean to be gruesome, but it was a setback for me. You can't write a novel about a global disaster in which only 50 people died!"[149]

Sure, everything possible must be done to ensure safety. And after Chernobyl, security did improve, which is a good thing. But this case needs to be seen in perspective. The number of proven victims of the Chernobyl power plant accident is about 50 people. Two of them are power plant workers who were at work when the explosion occurred. The rest are the rescue staff who arrived to contain the disaster and were exposed to radiation. In addition, there are nine children who died of thyroid tumors.

It is true that radioactivity affected the local nature. Elevated radiation levels triggered natural selection in the forests of Chernobyl. Organisms with higher resistance have become more abundant.

After the accident, the whole region was evacuated and turned into a nature reserve, which is rich in wildlife and birds.[150] The ghost towns were engulfed by the forest, and nature not only survived, but it has flourished. Where cars once roared and factories spew smoke, today you can see bears, wolves, or eagles and even the rare Przewalski horse that was introduced here.[151] The idea of a wasteland where only rats, cockroaches, and frightening mutants survived is a myth.

In spite of these facts, the anti-nuclear movement has been blocking the development of energy for decades. The first country to ban nuclear power was Austria in 1978. The Czech branch of Friends of the Earth wants to shut down the Dukovany nuclear plant by 2030 and Temelín by 2045, saying that no more nuclear power plants should be built as a replacement. Not even safer power plants.[152] Germany closed several of its nuclear plants in 2011 and plans to shut down the remaining ones by 2022 because the Germans got spooked by another nuclear incident in Fukushima, Japan.

Or, rather, they got scared by Chernobyl-style media hysteria. Japan was getting 30% of its electricity from the nuclear plants, and although the country was hit by a tsunami and earthquake, not a single power plant exploded. In fact, this is a stunning testament to the safety of modern nuclear technology. Some radioactive water leaked into the ocean but not much. The oceans are already radioactive anyway because a lot of seabed uranium is dissolved in them.[153]

Physicist Kelvin Kemm says: "There was no Fukushima nuclear disaster. The total number of people killed by nuclear radiation at Fukushima was zero. Total injured by radiation was zero. Total private property damaged by radiation… zero. There was no nuclear disaster. What there was, was a major media feeding frenzy fueled by the rather remote possibility that there may have been a major radiation leak."[154] The whole thing is somewhat unfair. Almost nobody was writing about the two and a half thousand tsunami victims because a fictional nuclear disaster sells more newspapers.

Nuclear power plants do not appear more dangerous than mining operations. Let's just look at some examples from the long list of mining disasters from 2009 to 2011.[155] On November 21, 2009, 87 miners died in a mining disaster in Heilongjiang Province, China. On June 27, 2010, a gas explosion killed 73 miners in a coal mine in Amaga, Colombia. On May 8, 2010, a methane explosion in the Raspadaskaja coal mine in Siberia killed 91 people. On March 20, 2011, 45 miners died in a coal mine in Quetta, Pakistan. Which energy is safer? So far, nuclear disasters have killed 50 people worldwide.

Solar and wind energy, of course, have minor death rates, for instance, when a roofer falls off the roof when installing solar panels. But even those death rates are higher than nuclear.[156] Mortality per billion kWh is 100 deaths worldwide for coal (global average), 36 deaths for oil, four deaths for natural gas, 24 for biofuel, 0.44 for solar power, 0.15 for wind power, 1.4 for hydro, and only 0.04 deaths for nuclear.

THE OZONE HOLE

Freons were banned before scientists brought any evidence. The stories of blind sheep were just fake news. In the Czech Republic, the ozone layer is still thicker than it ever was in the tropics.

The ozone layer protects us from ultraviolet radiation. The Montreal Protocol (1987) banned the use of CFCs that damage this layer. Freons—found in refrigerators or sprays—were believed to have caused an ozone hole, a phenomenon that is located on the other side of the world but has increased the sale of UV filter sunglasses in Europe.

A great amount of fake news accompanied the ozone panic. We can illustrate this on the blind sheep hoax from Punta Arenas, Chile. It was claimed the sheep lost eyesight due to UV radiation that penetrated Earth's atmosphere due to depletion of the ozone layer. This rumor was repeated by *ABC Television*, the *New York Times, Newsweek*, and Al Gore's book *Earth in the Balance*. Gore wrote: "In Patagonia, hunters now report finding blind rabbits and fishermen catching blind salmon."[157]

But when scientists came to investigate these claims, they found the disease had nothing to do with ozone. The cause of the blindness was... a local infection of conjunctivitis.[158] Dr. Oliver Schein, an ophthalmologist at Johns Hopkins University in Baltimore, recalls that when his team arrived in Punta Arenas, reporters were fascinated, and everybody wanted an interview.[159]

However, when the research did not confirm any increase in blindness, the journalists lost interest. Good news is no news. "In retrospect, the most interesting part of the story is that every major news outlet chose to believe and print a story about how the Western world was messing with the atmosphere. However, no one chose to report the fact that no shred of evidence could be found to support these stories."[160]

In fact, the ozone hole is no hole at all. On the equator, the ozone layer is almost as thin as in the "ozone hole" in Antarctica. It exists in this thickness all year round, and no one considers it a problem. In addition, the sun's rays penetrate the atmosphere through much thinner optical atmospheric mass at noon on the equator than at the poles. From the poles to the equator, the ozone layer naturally becomes thinner. So, if you travel from Manchester to London, the ozone layer will get thinner over your head by the same percentage as it has weakened in the 40 years of supposed CFC damage.[161]

The main beneficiary of the CFC ban was the chemical company DuPont. Mr. Joseph P. Glas, director of the CFC division of DuPont (part of the Seagram Group), said in 1988 that the CFC ban meant "an opportunity for a billion-pound market out there."[162] DuPont was the first company to announce in 1988 it would stop production of CFCs. It supported the CFC ban against the entire chemical industry.

This company once invented CFCs, but the US patent was valid for 20 years only, so it had already expired. But now, DuPont was able to develop and patent CFC substitutes (especially the HFC-134a gas). When the Montreal Protocol banned CFCs, customers around the world were forced to purchase these substitutes. Thus, DuPont reclaimed its monopoly position in the market.[163] Coincidentally, the Montreal Protocol was signed at the headquarters of the International Civil Aviation Organization (ICAO) at Rue University, just a few hundred meters from Seagram's headquarters on Rue Peel in Montreal. At that time, DuPont was a subsidiary of Seagram.

Freon ban was based solely on precautionary principle. This assessment is confirmed by NASA's monograph *The Case of Ozone Depletion* (2005).[164] We can read there that the father of the ozone panic was a famous ufologist. In March 1971, atmospheric physicist James McDonald spoke at the US Congress against supersonic aircraft that would fly in the stratosphere, in the ozone layer. According to his theory, water vapor escaping from aircraft engines could lead to depletion of the ozone layer.

Due to his controversial interest in UFOs, McDonald was eventually abandoned by the ozone hole activists. But the media panic around ozone, which he helped to unleash, has remained alive. The development of the American equivalent of Concord was halted that same year. Already in 1978, the use of Freons in sprays in the US was banned out of precaution.

When the British geophysicist Joe Farman of Cambridge found an ozone hole over Antarctica in 1985, scientists were taken aback.[165] The theories of the time did not predict any localized "hole" in the ozone layer at the South Pole and had no explanation for it. The NASA monograph says about Farman: "Through his own research, he discovered that ozone loss varied with season, a fact suggesting meteorology rather than chemistry might explain the loss. However, in his paper, Farman specifically pointed to CFCs as the cause, while proposing that the meteorological conditions were a contributing factor."[166]

In 1986, NASA sent an expedition to Antarctica in a hurry, led by Susan Solomon. She decided to turn it into a media spectacle rather than research. Before publishing the study, she organized a theatrical press conference, broadcast via satellite directly from Antarctica (October 20, 1986). Although the expedition did not yet have complete data, Solomon told the press that she thought CFCs might be the cause of the ozone hole, not meteorological conditions. Many scientists rejected her hasty conclusions, and a special issue of the *Geophysical Research Letters* was dedicated to this criticism in November 1986.[167]

Environmentalist James Lovelock, author of the Gaia theory and inventor of a CFC measurement apparatus, compares that shoddy science to the Climategate scandal: "I have seen this happen before, of course. We should have been warned by the CFC/ozone affair because the corruption of science in that was so bad that something like 80% of the measurements being made during that time were either faked, or incompetently done. Fudging the data in any way whatsoever is quite literally a sin against the holy ghost of science."[168]

Because of these controversies, Robert Watson himself, head of the AAOE (Antarctic Airborne Ozone Experiment), personally traveled to Antarctica. An international commission headed by Watson (International Ozone Trends Panel) was also set up. Researchers measured the dependence between Freon concentration and ozone concentration but did not actually address the dependence on meteorological factors such as cold temperature. In September 1987, Watson flew with his results to Montreal, where politicians discussed a global ban on Freons.[169] But he didn't make it in time. By the time scientists arrived, the protocol had already been signed.

Policymakers did not wait for scientific evidence. Lambright: "Indeed, the regulatory policy process, galvanized by the ozone–hole issue, was now moving faster than that of the science." In the ozone cause, Watson proved useful, so that later the American Clinton and Al Gore administration selected him as the chairman of another commission—as the second chairman of the UN climate panel (IPCC). It was during Watson's reign that the IPCC decided to rely on the famous "hockey stick graph."

ECOLOGICAL FOOTPRINT

The ecological footprint was supposed to be an indicator of how ecologically we live. In fact, this model does not even assess pollution or extinction of endangered species; it has little to do with ecology at all.

If every human being on Earth had the same consumption as the average US citizen, we would need five planets.[170] Therefore, we should live more modestly, consuming fewer resources. Environmentalists even celebrate an Earth Overshoot Day. From that day onwards, for the rest of the year, humanity is reportedly living on ecological debt.

The Czech Republic has the 15th largest environmental footprint in the world. The United Arab Emirates, rich in oil, has the largest footprint in the world. The footprint is basically an indicator of quality of life! Starving children in Somalia have a much smaller ecological footprint than a British tycoon who owns a castle and a yacht. And North Korea, with its decaying economy and failing electricity grid, is an absolute ecological champion.

But this concept has several weaknesses. The authors failed to notice that developed countries, though having high consumption, also have advanced agricultural technology. So, if the whole planet lived like Americans, we would consume less farmland, not more. Between 1961 and 2005, globally, the area of cultivated land increased by 27%. But yields per hectare increased by 135%.[171]

Nathan Fiala (2008) writes: "In 2006, American production levels were 40% higher than the world average... If current trends continue... the world average yield could one day reach the 2006 American yield... This could mean that, rather than needing five Earths to sustain consumption if everyone consumed like Americans, one earth may be enough."[172]

The ecological footprint should have been an indicator of how much your life is burdening the planet. In the traditional church, you had to repent to earn forgiveness for your sins. Environmentalists came up with an innovation—they measure the sinfulness of man in hectares. They calculate how many hectares of land is consumed for everything a person uses—from food to waste, energy production, and built-up area. In the early 1990s, this concept was developed by Professor William Rees from Canada and his student Mathis Wackermagel, who today operates the GFN (Global Footprint Network).[173] Unfortunately, ecological footprint is calculated in a way that makes little sense.

Already, the study by Van den Bergh et al. (1999) pointed out that the ecological footprint fails to assess chemical pollution or even soil degradation.[174] Nor does it assess the extinction of endangered species. And what if you happen to use nitrogen fertilizers that leak into the sea through waterways and create dead zones devoid of oxygen? It doesn't matter to your footprint either. With such technologically intense farming, your ecological footprint will be even lower because less land is needed to grow crops.

Another weird anomaly is that land use for highway construction scores no different from land use for sheep grazing. In fact, the ecological footprint has little to do with ecology. Rather, it helps production planners track resources. In the conclusion of the *Ecological Footprint Atlas 2010*, these problems were acknowledged by the authors themselves.[175]

Over 50% of the ecological footprint is carbon dioxide, although it is not a toxic gas. You will get a bad score for coal mining because it is a non-renewable resource. But depletion of other raw materials, such as iron ore, nickel, and sandstone, is not punished in any way, although they are also non-renewable resources.

Meat consumption is also counted as something that increases carbon footprint. That is why in August 2019, the United Nations published a report (*Climate Change and Land*) with recommendation that the global stock of cattle should be decreased by a third in order to fight climate change.[176] Similarly, in 2018, Greenpeace demanded that meat consumption be halved.[177] The plan is to put extra tax on meat just like on alcohol and cigarettes so that only rich people could afford it.[178] In Copenhagen, Denmark, green politicians already proposed to ban meat in municipal schools.[179]

However, we need to look also at carbon sinks and not only carbon sources. Cows do emit methane (farts, burps), which is a potent greenhouse gas. But it is a short-lived greenhouse gas, and it decomposes into CO_2 within ten years. This CO_2 is then absorbed by plants as part of photosynthesis and the amount of carbon at the start and end of this loop is exactly the same. Nothing is added to the atmosphere.

A comparison of the ecological footprint of individual states is also devoid of any sense. If a country specializes in electronics, for example, but imports food products, it will have a larger ecological footprint (consumption) than its own biocapacity (production). Therefore, it has an ecological "debt." So, everyone who imports food is living on ecological debt. The authors' ideal is apparently food self-sufficiency, like when Robinson Crusoe lived on a deserted island.

The following absurdity could be read on the website of the Center for the Environment of the Charles University, Prague: "The available biological capacity in the Czech Republic is overshot in the categories of pastures (1.2 times) and sea fishing (29 times). Here the aggregate demand of the Czech population for meat and fish is saturated through a debt to the global biocapacity."[180]

Are they saying that by eating seafood in a restaurant in Prague, I am actually increasing an imaginary ecological debt of the Czech Republic? But if I eat a Czech carp from a local market, I don't? The alleged environmental debt of a country is, in fact, no debt at all. It is just division of labor. I paid the fishermen for the seafood, their catch. I didn't steal or borrow it. I have no debt. The fisherman will use my money to buy shoes, as he lacks the skills to make shoes. But since he can't produce his own shoes, Wackermagel would probably say that his legs are "not sustainable." The shoemaker, on the other hand, can make shoes, but has no garden to grow his own carrots. So, according to the dumb ecological footprint concept, he lives in carrot debt?

Anyway, mankind as a whole does not import anything. We don't import beef from Mars or bloodwine from the Klingon Star Empire, for example. So how can the ecological footprint of mankind exceed the planet's biocapacity? The reason is the consumption of fossil fuels. More than half of the ecological footprint is the CO_2 gas, which is surprisingly measured in hectares.

There is an explanation to this. The authors recalculate how many hectares of trees we would have to plant if we wanted to "suck" all greenhouse gases out of the air. But coal deposits formed from many generations of forests that once grew in the same place at different times. If we wanted to resurrect all the trees that had ever lived in history, we wouldn't have enough space for all the zombies on Earth. That is why the authors believe that we need five planets.

Normal people have a bit different idea of what ecology is supposed to do. I remember the legendary Erin Brockovich, who, after a fierce court battle, convicted a factory in Hinkley that had been leaking poisonous chromium from its tanks into the surroundings.[181] The factory left behind a poisonous trail of death and illness. But times have changed, apparently. Today, the same company could boast of its ecological footprint and pretend to be a "green business" because poisons do not score negative points in the ecological footprint concept.

SCIENCE IN CRISIS

Scientific journals do not publish only breakthrough research but also lots of junk science. Editors publish bad things when they are fashionable in order to increase readership. Surprisingly, most scientific articles are read by no one.

The English term "peer-review" refers to a system where an article to be published in a scientific journal is first checked by experts for correctness. But this system does not always guarantee quality and sometimes actually plays a role of censorship. Who do you think are the reviewers in peer-reviewed journals on alternative medicine? Fellow esoteric crackpots. Go and read *The Journal of Parapsychology*.[182]

According to a survey presented in *Nature*, 90% of surveyed researchers agreed that we are experiencing a crisis of science.[183] More than 70% of researchers experienced not being able to replicate an experiment of another scientist, and more than half of them even failed to replicate their own research successfully, indicating that these experiments were flawed and should not have been published in the first place.

Peer-review problems are best documented in medicine. It is an area of science where political correctness has not silenced freedom of speech yet. John P.A. Ioannidis explains "why most published research findings are false."[184] Research findings are claimed reliable even when based on just a handful of cases. In order to publish neatly sounding conclusions, the authors avoid problematic issues.

No wonder that so often a "discovery" is first celebrated with fanfare and later debunked by newer research. "Imagine, though, that five different research teams test an interesting theory that's making the rounds, and four of the groups correctly prove the idea false, while the one less cautious group incorrectly "proves" it true through some combination of error, fluke, and clever selection of data. Guess whose findings your doctor ends up reading about in the journal, and you end up hearing about on the evening news?"[185]

In 2012, F. Fang's study calculated that in medicine since 1975, the percentage of articles retracted due to fraud has risen ten times.[186] As many as 67.4% of the retractions were removed because the authors violated the scientists' code of ethics. In 43.4% of cases, the reason for retraction was fraud or suspected fraud.[187] Scientists apparently behave as badly as lawyers, politicians, or people in other fields. There are so many studies retracted due to serious errors that there is even a specialized website monitoring them—Retraction Watch.[188]

According to an analysis by R.G. Steen (2011), about 30% of retracted articles are not marked as retracted or erroneous and are still considered valid by readers.[189] Fang et al. believe that scientists are being pressured to fraud by the tough competition for research funding. In addition, disproportionately high rewards are given to scientists who publish in magazines with a large impact factor. Some individuals cannot resist the temptation and attempt to "improve" their results to make them look more impressive than they really are.

It is no different in climatology. Australian researcher Jo Nova in her *Climate Money* report, says that the US government invested around $32 billion into climate research between 1989 and 2009.[190] If you give out more grants, you get more studies but also more errors or fraud.

Whereas criticism is considered socially acceptable in medicine, in climate science, it is characterized by the Union of Concerned Scientists as attacks by "enemies of science paid by the fossil industry." In fact, the trust in science is undermined exactly by organizations like The Union of Concerned Scientists. It is not really an association of scientists—they just dress like scientists to fool people. It's a non-profit organization like Greenpeace. Anyone who has a credit card can become a member. Meteorologist Anthony Watts successfully registered his dog Kenji as a member.[191]

Why is so much bad science published? In the old days, when a scientist wanted to share a discovery with colleagues, he used to send them a very long letter. But only as soon as he was sure he has something to say. Today, scientists write articles because they must. Even if they have nothing to say because if they don't have enough publications, they could lose their job. Publish or perish. Under this funding system, Einstein would probably lose his job before he could say "relativity."

Meho (2007) states: "Indeed, as many as 50% of papers are never read by anyone other than their authors, referees, and journal editors."[192] How can such a journal survive? They do not pay the authors for their texts; on the contrary, authors have to pay to the journal to get printed. Simkin and Roychowdhury (2003) estimate that only 45% of peer-reviewed articles are cited in the first five years. And only 20% of people citing an article have actually read it. They usually just take over a citation from someone else without verifying the source. We know this thanks to citation analysis of typos found in the citations of highly circulated articles.[193]

This is why Randy Schekman, the Nobel Prize winner for biology, decided to say goodbye to prestigious journals. He will publish his work on the Internet. "We all know what distorting incentives have done to finance and banking. The incentives my colleagues face are not huge bonuses but the professional rewards that accompany publication in prestigious journals... These journals aggressively curate their brands in ways more conducive to selling subscriptions than to stimulating the most important research... A paper can become highly cited because it is good science—or because it is eye-catching, provocative, or wrong. Luxury-journal editors know this, so they accept papers that will make waves because they explore sexy subjects or make challenging claims."[194]

III. SCIENCE-BASED POLICY

There are plenty of ways to attain power. For example, there is that proven strategy of scaring people into submission. You tell them a story about an imminent disaster. Then you offer them a helping hand—only you and you alone can save them. If there is no crisis, do not be lazy and make one. Here are some examples from the movies. Invasion of space aliens against whom all humanity will unite (preferably under the leadership of the heroic US president, played by Harrison Ford). Or mankind will start working together when the planet is threatened with an asteroid. If you, as a beginner, don't have enough confidence to organize a collision with an asteroid, try something smaller first. For example, you can leak the news that a flu epidemic is here, and people need your vaccine.

The pioneer of this "alarmism" was the Club of Rome. Thanks to a network of contacts and influential friends, they managed to plant their Trojan horse into the heart of the United Nations. Their man, oil tycoon Maurice Strong, founded the United Nations Environment Program as a body responsible for fabrication of environmental alarms, seated in the heart of Africa, far away from the prying eyes of UN officials in New York.

This office—let us call it the "Disaster Fabrication Bureau"—was searching for scientists with creative talent to tell scary scenarios. Then they hired them for work in UN committees. The climate committee at the Disaster Fabrication Bureau was chaired by such luminaries as the Indian railroad engineer Pachauri, who happened to be also an energy tycoon like Strong.

This marriage of science and politics proved remarkably productive. It also finally brought a solution to the old problem what to do when some law of physics or nature is unclear. Well, you just vote about it at a meeting! Like the laws in parliament. One and one equal three? No problem. The warming is probably all caused by people. Sure, warming must not exceed two point three degrees Celsius? Hands up. Who needs scientific calculations and measurements if all you need is just convene a meeting and make a deal... I mean a consensus.

Lack of scientific peer-reviewed studies in some areas was also resolved. Instead, newspaper articles or brochures of eco-activists will be used as sources of knowledge. There is no shortage of such texts. Unfortunately, the use of such unorthodox sources led to a series of scandals such as Climategate or Glaciergate. Scientists got the estimate of Himalaya glaciers melt wrong by three centuries because they relied on a hoax perpetuated by activists.

However, the scandals were successfully swept under the rug. The perpetrators themselves set up a committee of inquiry to investigate them, consisting of trusted and independent personalities—like their brother-in-law or schoolmate and so on. This "impartial" investigation "exonerated" them. Like, you know, in the "inquiry committees" in Congress, where they never convict anyone because they are in the same boat.

Sociologists call this blend of science and politics "post-normal science." Policymakers hire experts to advise them in risk assessment of serious social problems. But no one wants advisers who don't have the answers. So, the experts try to please their masters. And rather than admitting ignorance, they substitute missing data with speculation. Like a butcher adding sawdust to sausages instead of meat.

THE WIZARD OF BACA GRANDE

The founder of the UN Environmental Program was a man of many professions: An oil tycoon, philanthropist, founder of an apocalyptic sect, and a visionary dreaming of utopian dictatorship.

Maurice Strong begins his autobiography *"Where on Earth Are We Going?"* with a vision of the upcoming apocalypse. It is narrated as a science fiction story set in the year 2031. An enlightened dictator, Rolf Schmidt from Germany, is leading mankind to rise from the ashes of a climate apocalypse.[195] "He's no Adolf Hitler, but he nevertheless borrowed from Hitler the tactic of winning his office democratically and then granting himself emergency powers, giving him virtually total authority. Unlike Hitler, however, he has, in his few months in office, demonstrated a remarkable combination of benevolence, fairness, and toughness."[196]

The founder of the UN Environmental Program, Maurice Strong, was probably one of the most influential members of the Club of Rome. This wealthy industrialist (president of the Power Corporation) was a friend of the Canadian Prime Minister, and the Canadian government eventually entrusted him with the management of the External Aid Office (CIDA). He proved so successful that in 1972, he was chosen to chair the first UN environmental conference in Stockholm.

To ensure publicity for the conference, he hired Barbara Ward, a World Bank economist, to write the book *Only One Earth.*[197] Even then scientists were hired by politicians. This is the book that coined the phrase "sustainable development."

As a result of the Stockholm Conference, the United Nations Environmental Program (UNEP) came into being that would later create the climate panel (IPCC) as one of its working sub-committees. The highlight of Strong's career was the Earth Summit in Rio de Janeiro (1992), where the UN Framework Convention on Climate Change (UNFCC) was adopted. The negotiations were chaired by Strong. Getting heads of so many countries to sign the convention required a lot of behind-the-scenes negotiations, plotting, and informal contacts, which were skills that Strong understood so well.

Strong was always frowned upon for having too much power, although nobody ever elected him anywhere, although the Prime Minister of Canada once asked him to run for election. But Strong soon withdrew his candidacy. He realized that as a backstage lobbyist, he has much greater influence. Strong was forced to master these behind-the-scenes skills out of necessity. When he first applied for a position in the Canadian External Aid Office (CIDA), they turned him down because he had no education. So, he set out to get rich in the oil business—then he would be able to "buy" his influence. When you have cash, and lots of it too, people somehow stop asking about your credentials.

"But out of frustration came a decision. In the depths of my disappointment, I had the second of the two epiphanies that shaped the course of my life. I knew what I wanted. But as long as I lacked the minimum educational qualifications, a direct route to my aspirations was closed—I'd never get in by banging on the front door... There was only one thing to do—find a back door in. That would be a successful business career... Perhaps as a businessman, I could earn the credentials I needed to catch the attention of those who could help me achieve my real aspirations.... I already understood that power is augmented by influence derived from extensive and diverse networks."[198]

In 1948, he was just a poor boy working at a far northern trading post of the Hudson's Bay Company, among the Inuit. When a Canadian oil tycoon, James Richardson, was passing by to prospect the area, he was impressed by the boy's hobby, a collection of rock samples. So, he gave him a job. Maurice worked hard, and soon, he was promoted. Between 1961 and 1966, he went from becoming a vice president to president of the Power Corporation of Canada. The point is that Strong didn't have any education, and his worldview was based on folk doomsday superstitions. Before the Stockholm Conference, in an interview with David Frost for the BBC (1972), he said: "I am convinced that the prophets of doom have got to be taken seriously. In other words, doomsday is a possibility. I am equally convinced that doomsday is not inevitable."[199]

Strong was probably much closer to spirituality rather than science. At the end of the 1970s, he founded a New Age spiritual community at Baca Ranch in the San Luis Valley near Crestone, Colorado. The website of Crestone refers to it as the "Shambala of the Rocky Mountains," and this "spiritual community" was also promoted by the *New York Times.*[200] Celebrities from all over the world come here to pray, including the Dalai Lama and Prince Charles.

The legend has it that Strong's wife, Hanne, when reading *The Last of the Mohicans,* suddenly had a feeling as if she had been an Indian from Colorado in her previous life. So, in 1978, she came here and had a sense of déjà vu. One day an 80-year-old man with wild hair knocked at her door. It was Glenn Anderson, also known as "The Prophet," a weirdo living in the mountains here. "So, you've finally come," he said.[201]

He had a prophetic vision that a woman would come and save all the faiths of the world from the impending global catastrophe. He pointed into the distance as a true prophet and said that if she built a ranch in the San Luis Valley, this place would become the spiritual center of the planet in the future. So, she did as he told her. She went to the place the prophet had designated and spent three days fasting and meditating.

Maurice Strong had a revelation in Baca too. When the TV host Bill Moyers arrived to speak at the conference in Aspen, they went for a walk together, when suddenly a burning bush appeared to them, like the one Moses saw when God spoke to him. They said it was their greatest spiritual experience ever.[202] Since then, Strong has probably seen himself as a new incarnation of Moses because, together with the former Soviet leader Gorbachev, they wrote the New Ten Commandments (called the Earth Charter) and deposited them in the Ark of Hope (paraphrase of the Ark of the Covenant in the Bible).

In a 1990 interview with Canadian magazine WEST, Strong said he would like to write a novel on the following plot: "What if a small group of these world leaders were to conclude that the principal risk to Earth comes from the actions of the rich countries? And if the world is to survive, those rich countries would have to sign an agreement reducing their impact on the environment. Will they do it?... The group's conclusion is "no." The rich countries won't do it. They won't change. So, in order to save the planet, the group decides: Isn't the only hope for the planet that the industrialized civilizations collapse? Isn't it our responsibility to bring that about?"[203]

The journalist was spellbound to hear this. From the mouth of a chairman of the World Economic Forum in Davos, plans like that may sound a bit disturbing. Even more today, when the German Minister of Economy is concerned that Germany is at risk of "deindustrialization" due to the unintended side-effects of the transition to renewable energy.[204] As if Strong's plans were coming true.

Strong's career plummeted infamously in 2005. He was the right hand of the UN Secretary-General, Mr. Kofi Annan, until the corruption "oil for food" scandal broke his neck. Saddam Hussein's Iraq was under international sanctions, as the blockade only allowed trading oil for food. But Iraq found a way to get cash anyway. The country only awarded oil contracts to foreigners willing to share their profits with Saddam. High UN officials also participated in the scheme.

To avoid investigations, Strong fled to China, where his comrades greeted him like a lost son. His cousin, communist journalist Anna Louise Strong, was a close friend of the Chinese dictator Mao Zedong. She even had a state funeral.[205] Strong became an honorary professor at Beijing University and a government advisor on ecology and energy issues. Perhaps they took his advice to heart. Soon, China opened its first climate exchange in Tianjin (2008) and got involved with the sale of climate indulgences.[206] He, in turn, spoke praise of the Chinese dictatorship, as if it was a role model for the whole world.

BIRTH OF THE IPCC

The UN chose the climatologist Bolin as the first chairman of the IPCC, a man known for his interest in greenhouse gases. The committee's job description was drafted accordingly.

In *The Age of Global Warming*, Rupert Darwall writes: "Global warming's entrance into politics can be dated with precision—1988; the year of the Toronto conference on climate change, Margaret Thatcher's address to the Royal Society, NASA scientist James Hansen's appearance at a congressional committee, and the establishment of the Intergovernmental Panel on Climate Change (IPCC)." The path to this "annus mirabilis" was paved by the signing of the Montreal Protocol (1987) to ban the ozone-depleting CFCs (1987). This created an impression that eliminating greenhouse gases might be no more difficult than this. But there is a difference—freons are easy to substitute with something else; fossil fuels are not.

When considering who could chair the greenhouse gas investigation committee at the UN, it was not easy to find a suitable person. Moreover, there was no consensus among scientists on the harmfulness of greenhouse gases. The most renowned climatologist in the United States, Roger Revelle, refused to demonize the greenhouse effect. Hubert Lamb, a pioneer of British historical climatology, wasn't suitable for this role either. For him, the biggest threat was the next ice age, not warming. Robert Jastrow, Research Director at Goddard Institute, NASA, actually fought against the ecological radicals (and founded the Marshall Institute). So, UNEP (United Nations Environmental Program) ultimately chose the loyal political climatologist Bert Bolin whom they had been using for similar clerical roles for years.

He got onboard politics as an advisor to Swedish Prime Minister Olaf Palme, who hosted the first UN eco-conference in Stockholm in 1972.[207] Bolin worked for the UN for years. In 1985, he chaired a meeting in Villach, Austria, where it was decided to establish the IPCC. Even then, scientists were smart about what one should write if one wants money: "Governments and funding agencies should increase research support efforts on crucial unsolved problems related to greenhouse gases and climate change."[208]

Bolin also participated in the preparation of the Brundtland Report "Our Common Future" on the state of the environment, commissioned by the UNEP in 1987.[209] It was also rich in apocalyptic visions—like most texts this UNEP agency has ever published.

Bolin designed the way the UN Climate Panel works. He decided to focus on human influences. Each anthropogenic gas is detailed on dozens of pages, while only about four pages are dedicated to the influence of the sun on the climate.[210] Even the 200-year long Suess cycle of solar activity is missing in the text. Since the IPCC is not looking for natural causes of warming, it is impossible for them to find any. What a surprise!

FORGING THE CONSENSUS

The conclusions of the UN climate panel are not decided by scientific mea-surement but by endless meetings. He who falls asleep the last has the last word.

Every six years, the IPCC publishes a 1,000-page report on the state of the climate, which virtually nobody reads except for a couple of experts. Policymakers are given a 20-page "Summary for Policymakers." Journal-ists usually read only the one-page press release. Thus, the whole complex climate system is ultimately reduced to a simple slogan.

Moreover, the slogan is not written by scientists but is negotiated by representatives of the UN governments behind closed doors. This meet-ing, where the Summary for Policymakers is written, lasts a few days. The talks often end long past midnight, so the ones who manage to stay awake are those who have the last word.

Climate negotiators are not allowed to leave until they reach an agree-ment, kind of like the conclave that elects the Pope. The cardinals are locked in complete isolation for a few days in the Sistine Chapel in the Vatican and cannot go home until they agree on the choice of a new pope. When they reach an agreement, it is announced by white smoke from the chapel´s chimney.

It is a great pity that these hours of squabble at the IPCC meetings are not broadcast on television.[211] Fortunately, thanks to the questionnaire that the IPCC staff had to fill for the InterAcademy Council investigation of IPCC scandals, we can at least read eyewitness testimonies in print.[212]

- "IPCC plenary meetings where reports are approved are an organized chaos. The hour-by-hour tensions are extraordinary, and the process is dominated by countries that can send big delegations (so that members can spell each other). It is always sad to see paragraphs being debated while delegates from coun-tries whose interests are central try (vainly sometimes) to stay awake in the middle of the night. Authors sometimes want to drop heavy books just to wake up the house."[213]

- "Every IPCC plenary that I have attended has been among the most physically and mentally challenging moments of my life."[214]

- "In my experience, the summary for policymakers tends to be more of a political process than one of scientific précis."[215]

- "As a Coordinating Lead Author, I have observed the behavior of delegations from individual countries, which certainly reflects a completely different mindset than my own as a scientist. The political intrigues that appear to be well known on the international scene pop up again and again."[216]

- "It was a bitter process for AR4, especially for WGII... At the end, when time was up, and everybody was tired, something was changed and passed in a hurry and carelessly."[217]

- "Precious time was wasted in unnecessary comments at the last plenary and resulted in a rush to finish the report."[218]

The purpose of the meetings is to discuss how much the attendees believe in different scenarios. There are many scenarios that could explain the recent warming. But the IPCC considers only one of them—the possibility that people are the culprit. They ask whether or not human sin can be ruled out as the cause. They debate how strong their faith is. This is reminiscent of the ancient religious councils that discussed the wording of the credo, a declaration of faith.

VERY LIKELY

The UN believes that humanity is "very likely" responsible for most of the global warming. But this statement is not supported by any calculations. It's just a nice-sounding phrase approved at a meeting.

From the UN climate panel reports, journalists read only a press statement that "it is extremely likely that human influence has been the dominant cause of the observed warming since the mid-20th century." But few people know what this claim is based on and how it has changed over the years.

In the first report (1990), the IPCC was still cautious: "The size of this warming is broadly consistent with the predictions of climate models, but it is also of the same magnitude as natural climate variability. Thus, the observed increase could be largely due to this natural variability."[219] However, the second report (1995) already used stronger language. "The balance of evidence suggests a *discernible* human influence on global warming."[220]

Later, however, it turned out that this sentence was inserted into the text by politicians. At their request, the climatologist Benjamin D. Santer removed all skeptical wording from the IPCC's Second Report and replaced it with a radical political slogan. The hundreds of scientists who wrote the report were not asked for permission.

Fred Seitz, former chairman of the American Academy of Sciences, informed about this scandal: "In my more than 60 years as a member of the American scientific community, including my service as president of both the National Academy of Sciences and the American Physical Society, I have never witnessed a more disturbing corruption of the peer-review process than the events that led to this IPCC report."[221]

The original text of the Second Report said: "None of the studies cited above have shown clear evidence that we can attribute the observed [climate] changes to the specific cause of increases in greenhouse gases... No study to date has positively attributed all or part [of the climate change observed to date] to anthropogenic [man-made] causes."

Even after Santer's scandal, the situation did not improve. On the contrary, radicalization progressed further, and the Fifth Report of the UN Climate Panel (2013) came out with the following statement: "It is extremely likely that human influence has been the dominant cause of the observed warming since the mid-20th century." The media circulated the claim widely, and, as an example, *USA Today* used this headline: "95% odds that humans are to blame for warming."[222]

But no one knows how the UN reached that conclusion. Why 95%? Why not 92.5? Although the IPCC is supposedly the highest scientific authority, there are no equations or calculations to support that claim. The IPCC documents do not provide any procedure on how to calculate this probability.[223] They merely refer to a study by Patt and Schrag (2003),[224] which is a psychological treatise about how different stylistic expressions give a different impression to the reader. Indeed, IPCC directives care more about media image than scientific rigor. Like some sort of advertising agency.

Nobody knows why the wording of the probability statement changes. The working draft of the Third Report (2001) stated that human activities "contributed substantially" to the observed warming. But the final government-approved version said that "most of the warming is attributable to human activities." But when *New Scientist* asked Tim Higham, the representative of the United Nations Environmental Program (UNEP) about the scientific basis for these changes in the text, Higham just shrugged: "There was no new science since October, but the scientists wanted to present a clear and strong message to policymakers."[225]

How does one craft such a message? It is not the result of scientific experiments or calculations; it is rather an "expert judgment," a subjective feeling of an expert on a question that science is not able to measure precisely. And as we know, when you ask two experts, you usually get two different opinions. Or three, if one of them changes his mind. Therefore, it is very important who speaks first at such a meeting, because in the face of uncertainty, people tend to accept the first opinion they hear. The IPCC guidelines warn: "Be aware of a tendency for a group to converge on an expressed view and become overconfident in it."[226]

The very fact that the IPCC borrows terminology from the probability theory is controversial in itself, as it gives an unjustified impression of being an exact science. As early as 1837, Siméon-Denis Poisson distinguished between statistical frequency (what is "chance") and subjective judgment ("raison de croire"). Statistical frequency can be expressed in numbers. For instance, when you roll the dice in a casino, you can predict how many times out of a thousand throws you will get a six. On the other hand, subjective judgment in an individual case is expressed by the words "maybe" or "likely." Such a feeling may often be supported by nothing at all. For example, "I bet my horse will certainly win the race this time... even though he has lost all previous ones."

Climate scientists cannot repeatedly flood the planet with greenhouse gases and watch how many times out of a thousand this would worsen the climate. So, they rely on their models (which cannot prove anything) and subjective judgment. However, they express it with numbers "as if" it was a calculation of statistical frequency. If it is not fraud, it is certainly misleading at the very least.

THOU SHALT NOT EXCEED X DEGREES

We are told that scientists discovered the maximum safe limit of warming: Two degrees Celsius. In fact, it is just a random number pulled by politicians out of a hat.

This limit was agreed on by the Council of the European Union in June 1996 as a common position of the EU states before the international negotiations on the Kyoto Protocol.[227] Although it is a political decision, politicians like to pretend it is science. Even the G8 summit of economic powers declared: "We recognize the scientific view that increase in global average temperature above pre-industrial levels ought not to exceed 2°C."[228]

But why two degrees? What will happen when we cross that two-degree limit? Is it some sort of a turning point? Will an unstoppable reaction be triggered? Will the climate fall into a loop, and will Earth end up as hot as Venus? This limit was proposed to the Council of the European Union by scientific advisers to the German Chancellor, the Climate Advisory Board (WGBU, founded in 1992) led by Hans Joachim Schellnhuber.

Today, Schellnhuber admits without shame: "Two degrees is not a magical limit -- it's clearly a political goal." Yet, he likes to claim the authorship of the two degrees concept. He even explains how he came to that figure: "Average global temperatures in the last 130,000 years were no more than two degrees higher than before the beginning of the Industrial Revolution. To be on the safe side, we came up with a rule of thumb stating that it would be better not to depart from this field of experience in human evolution. Otherwise, we would be treading on terra incognita."[229]

When the last ice age ended, there was warming to the extent that homo sapiens had "never experienced" since arriving in Europe. And yet, it did benefit us. The warming made agriculture and civilization possible. Homo sapiens has already demonstrated clearly that it can cope with temperatures from Scandinavia (annual average temperature of zero) to the equator (annual average temperature of 30°C). Why believe that mankind would become extinct because of a temperature change of a fraction of a degree Celsius? The average annual temperature in northern Italy is five degrees Celsius higher than in the Czech Republic. Yet it is possible for humans to survive in Italy, and people even travel to spend their holidays there.

But some believe that even 2°C is too much. In 2018, the Intergovernmental Panel on Climate Change published "An IPCC special report on the impacts of global warming of 1.5°C," recommending that global

CO_2 emissions should peak by 2030. But this doesn`t mean "we have 12 years to save the planet." Activist slogans like "there will be no XY on a dead planet" even suggested that if warming exceeds 1.5°C the planet will die. A surprising notion since life on this planet has survived much worse things, including meteorites and ice ages.

The activists are misled by confusing economic numbers. Such as: "Economic nightmare: By 2100, climate change could tank US GDP by 10.5%."[230] But this damage is cumulative—annually, it is almost invisible. Economists estimate that in the 21st century, global warming will slow down economic growth by some 0.5—1% a year. So, the average global economic growth may not be 3% (global long-term average) but only 2% annually. Global economy will flourish anyway. It is expected that "income per capita in the poorest economies will more than quadruple by 2060, and that China and India will experience more than a seven-fold increase," according to OECD estimates.[231] India is believed to have already lost 30% of GDP due to global warming. Again, this frightening number only means that for decades its growth has been 1% weaker annually than it might have been.[232] In spite of that, World Bank reports that Indian poverty levels dropped from 38.9% population in 2004 to 21.2% population in 2011.[233]

GLACIERGATE

The most famous scandal of the IPCC is the Glaciergate affair. It turned out that their prediction of Himalayan glacier melting was wrong by 300 years because the scientists quoted from a non-scientific source without bothering to verify.

At the beginning of 2010, a series of errors was uncovered in the IPCC, undermining the credibility of the UN climate panel. The most famous was the "Glaciergate" affair (named after Nixon's 1970s Watergate scandal).

In its Fourth Assessment Report (2007), the IPCC claimed that the Himalayan glaciers would "likely" shrink from 500,000 to just 100,000 km2 by 2035 if warming continued as it has been so far. In the end, it turned out that they were mistaken by centuries. The date should have been 2350, not 2035.

The error was caused by unprofessional work of the IPCC scientists. They lazily quoted the wrong date from a brochure published by an eco-activist group, the World Wildlife Fund. These WWF activists, in turn, quoted this thing from a newspaper article in *New Scientist* without verification.[234] It was an interview of the journalist Fred Pearce with an Indian glaciologist Syed Hasnain.[235] Hasnain apparently misquoted the findings of an older study by the Russian scientist Kotljakov, who had calculated the melting date as 2350.[236] The erroneous *New Scientist* article was published in 1999, and for ten years (!) this "wild duck" was flying all over the world, cited by many. And none of the thousands of scientists on this planet noticed until the problem was raised by Graham Cogley, a glaciologist.

Dr. Murari Lal, who wrote that chapter in the IPCC, admits now it was a shame: "We knew the WWF report with the 2035 date was 'grey literature.'" Grey literature are sources that did not undergo expert review prior to publication. So why did they include the unverified assertion in the text? For political reasons. "We thought that if we can highlight it, it will impact policy-makers and politicians and encourage them to take some concrete action. It had importance for the region, so we thought we should put it in."[237]

The first to notice that the Himalayas were not melting at the pace advertised by the IPCC was the Indian geologist V.K. Raina.[238] He pointed this out in a report to the Indian government in November 2009. However, the head of the IPCC, Pachauri, opposed this criticism with unkind words. Claiming that Raina's study is "voodoo science" and mocking him, "With the greatest of respect, this guy retired years ago, and I find it totally baffling that he comes out and throws out everything that has been established years ago."[239]

As a reason why he does not take Raina seriously, Pachauri gave the following explanation: "IPCC studies only peer-review science. Let someone publish the data in a decent credible publication. I am sure IPCC would then accept it. Otherwise, we can just throw it into a dustbin." Pachauri was not telling the truth. The IPCC uses non-peer-reviewed "grey literature" frequently.

The circumstances of the whole cause are a bit odd. Mr. Syed Hasnain, the author of this hoax, got a cushy job at Pachauri's company TERI a year after the IPCC Fourth Assessment Report was published. He was put in charge of the glacier research in the Himalayas. TERI received a number of grants and subsidies for this research, including grants from the European "High Noon" grant program and grants from the American Carnegie Foundation.[240] In short, Pachauri's TERI got a lot of money for researching the Himalayas thanks to Hasnain's hoax and then generously rewarded him. One hand washes the other.

The glaciers in the Himalayas have been waxing and waning all the time throughout history, partly due to numerous climate cycles. 4,500 years ago and 7,000 years ago, they melted to the same extent as the late 20th century.[241] The current melting episode began in the mid-19th century when the concentration of greenhouse gases in the atmosphere was low. People may have contributed to the late phase of this melting too, but the main cause of the post 1850s melting was most likely of natural origin.

AFRICAGATE

According to alarmists, global warming will bring droughts to Africa. Yet, in the recent warming period, Sahel actually turned green.

The "Africagate" affair, discovered in 2010, was another example where the UN scientists misinformed the public. In its 2007 report, the UN climate panel said: "By 2020, in some countries, yields from rain-fed agriculture could be reduced by up to 50%."

An average person would probably think twice before scaring poor Africans with statements like that. But—as the British writer and political scientist Richard North (eureferendum.com) revealed[242]—the IPCC based this bold statement on a single source only. They quoted it without fact-checking from Canadian eco-activist group International Institute for Sustainable Development (IISD), specifically from a study written for IISD by Ali Agoumi, a Moroccan carbon offset salesman. He took his data not from scientific literature but from reports by UN bureaucrats. Yet only one of these UN reports, the one from Morocco, was talking about the possibility of lower crop yields. Other reports indicated the opposite![243]

In Germany, a renowned climate scientist attempted to silence the press so they would not write about this Africagate scandal. Climatologist Stefan Rahmstorf of the Potsdam Institute for Climate Change (PIK) threatened the newspaper *Frankfurter Rundschau,* which had published Irene Meichsner's article about Africagate. The newspaper's chief editor wanted to avoid conflict and withdrew the article. Rahmstorf then publicly boasted that Ms. Meichsner acknowledged personally that publishing the article was a mistake on her part. But something unprecedented happened. The journalist stood up to the influential climatologist and this slander. She brought him to court in Cologne, and she won. The climatologist had to pay the journalist symbolic damages of €511.58 plus interest and two-thirds of court expenses.[244]

At other times, the UN claimed that "the Sahel region of West Africa is 'ground zero' for vulnerable communities struggling to adapt to climate change."[245] Rainfall in the Sahel in the 20th century is said to have dropped. And the media make it appear as if it happened as a result of warming. "The Sahara Desert has grown significantly over the past century, and climate change is largely to blame... Analyzing data collected since 1923, a research team... found the desert... had expanded by about 10% over the period covered by this data,"[246] the journalists claimed. The architect Magnus Larsoon even came up with a grand plan to build a great wall around the Sahara Desert, 6,000 kilometers long, to prevent the desert from spreading further.

But *New Scientist* (2002) noticed some inconsistencies: "In August, the UN Environment Programme told the World Summit in Johannesburg that over 45% of Africa is in the grip of desertification, with Sahel the worst affected." However, recent research shows the exact opposite. "Vegetation is ousting sand across a swathe of land stretching from Mauritania on the shores of the Atlantic to Eritrea 6,000 kilometers away on the Red Sea coast... Burkina Faso, one of the West African countries devastated by drought and advancing deserts 20 years ago, is growing so much greener that families who fled to wetter coastal regions are starting to come home."[247]

The truth is that rainfall in this region did decrease, but it happened in the post-WWII cooling (!) period. When the climate began to warm up, precipitation started rising.[248] When tropical ocean warms up, hot water evaporates like when you boil water in a kettle. The air is then more humid. A comparison of 1982 and 2002 satellite images confirms that in Africa, a wide band of countries, including Chad and Sudan, had turned green due to warming. National Geographic also writes about it: "The transition may be occurring because hotter air has more capacity to hold moisture, which in turn creates more rain," explains Martin Clausen of the Max Planck Institute for Meteorology in Hamburg, Germany.[249]

AMAZONGATE

Could the Amazon rainforest disappear due to warming? As far as we know, the last time it disappeared was in the ice age. However, glacial climate was cold and dry.

The Fourth Assessment Report of the UN Climate Panel (2007) argued that "up to 40% of the Amazonian forests could react drastically to even a slight reduction in precipitation." But Richard North—who had previously discovered the Africagate scandal—found that this bold statement was based just on an unverified non-scientific source.[250] The UN climate panel took this quote without any fact-checking from the World Wildlife Fund eco-activists. The source they provided for this claim, the study by Mr. Nepstad, discusses how rainforest is endangered—but endangered by logging and cutting, not climate change.

The real source of the claim, about 40%, is the website of Mr. Nepstad's organization IPAM (Instituto de Pesquiza Ambiental da Amazonia)—from an article for children. The article "Fire in the Amazon" contains funny pictures of trees with eyes and sunglasses, which is not quite common in peer-reviewed scientific literature.[251] The scandal was nicknamed Amazongate.

Dan Nepstad may be trying to scare us in order to promote his business. He is the architect of REDD (Reducing Emissions from Deforestation and Degradation). Companies plant trees and receive credits as a reward. They can then sell the credits. Companies that have large CO_2 emissions buy these credits as "indulgences" for their climatic "sins." In fact, it's a zero-sum game. The forest is cut down, the wood is sold, and then the trees are planted back where they were in the first place. In their 2012 report called *Outsourcing Hot Air*,[252] Greenpeace pointed out that this will not reduce net CO_2 emissions overall.

But the social impact is not good. In order to cut trees and capitalize on climate indulgences, companies first force native tribes out of the forest so that they become homeless. Arnold Schwarzenegger, then Governor of California, also promoted this controversial program. In 2006, he helped to pass the AB32 Global Warming Act, and California launched its own stock market to sell indulgences. At the end of his term, Schwarzenegger decided that indulgences would also be given for planting trees in Mexico.

It may sound nice at first glance, but the reality is much worse. The impoverished natives of the Mexican state of Chiapas begged the Californian governor to stop supporting the project: "REDD+ is a new version of old colonial practices that pursue the appropriation of earth and territory via expropriation, direct violent evictions, or their perpetual rent to the possessing indigenous communities... Peasant farmers' production systems are criminalized, accusing them of causing climate change."[253]

The Amazon is still the humid jungle full of dangerous insects as it used to be. This is confirmed by the UN climate panel's own data.[254] If we look at the hundred-year records of the water level in the Rio Negro, there is no 100-year trend of drying out.[255] In the 1970s, precipitation increased sharply, and since then, it has been gradually falling to the previous level. Of course, in the newspapers, we are shown only the "worrying decline" charts since the 1970s, but it's just a return to normal.

The Amazon forest can indeed disappear and turn into a savannah... when it is colder. Not when it's warmer. Although there has been some controversy about this theory lately, the Amazon jungle seems not to be as "ancient" as activists imagine; it has existed in this form for only a few thousand years.

In the Ice Age, there was a dry savannah in these places and only scattered isolated islands of the forest (so-called refugia), which explains the local biodiversity—the abundant occurrence of endemic animal species that do not occur anywhere else.[256] It was only global warming at the end of the glacial that apparently led to the creation of a coherent rainforest. It was the same story with rainforests in Africa, which, by the way, proves that life is better in warmer climate.

FIFTY SHADES OF
GREY LITERATURE

UN climatologists have long claimed that they use only pure scientific sources. Later, it turned out that one-third of their sources are not scientific at all. They are "grey literature."

The Glaciergate, Amazongate, and Africagate scandals happened because scientists quoted unverified claims from non-scientific sources called "grey literature." Unlike peer-reviewed scientific studies, grey literature did not pass expert checking prior to publication. Grey literature covers sources like unpublished scientific texts prior to peer-review, draft PhD thesis in progress, and also bureaucratic reports of various authorities or even magazine and newspaper articles.

Rajendra Pachauri, chairman of the UN climate panel, once assured the public: "This is based on peer-reviewed literature. That's the manner in which the IPCC functions. We don't pick up a newspaper article and based on that come up with our findings."[257]

But it turned out that the reality was much different. First, it was claimed that errors like Glaciergate and Africagate or Amazongate were just three tiny exceptions that someone overlooked. Donna Laframboise of Noconsensus.org decided to deal with these excuses once and for all. In 2010, with the help of volunteers, she performed an audit (called a Citizen Audit) and calculated that unverified claims (grey literature) account for a third of the IPCC resources.[258] For example, an article from a rock climbing magazine, etc. Grey literature is a problem as it may be the source of half-truths. IPCC frequently quoted eco-activist brochures, which selectively give only arguments in support of their cause.

Most grey literature (57%) was in the third part of the IPCC report (Working Group 3), which deals with economic measures to combat climate change (mitigation). The second part (WG2) on the impacts of warming was better (34%). However, if you expect the IPCC to learn from mistakes and to prohibit the use of grey non-scientific literature in the future, think again!

In the summer of 2011, after some thought, the IPCC decided to continue using unverified sources.[259] IPCC vice president, Thelma Krug, explains: "There is a lot of information available in [the grey literature of] developing countries that would balance IPCC literature." Requiring only reliable peer-reviewed literature would be discrimination of underdeveloped countries, where quality research is hard to find.

UNITED NATIONS IN THE SPOTLIGHT

When it was necessary to investigate a series of scandalous errors by the UN climate panel, a smart approach was taken. One UN committee investigated another UN committee. No one was punished, and even friendly suggestions that mistakes should be avoided were ignored.

Affairs like the Glaciergate were a disgrace to the UN climate panel. And the approach of IPCC chairman Pachauri, who first ridiculed critics and then played dead, did not help the situation either. The IPCC made so many serious mistakes in its Fourth Assessment Report (2007) that investigation seemed necessary. Former IPCC chairman Robert Watson himself said: "The mistakes all appear to have gone in the direction of making it seem like climate change is more serious by overstating the impact. That is worrying. The IPCC needs to look into this trend of errors and ask why it happened."[260]

This tendency to exaggerate the negative impacts of climate change stems from the belief of many scientists that the public needs to pay more attention. IPCC vice-chairman John Houghton explains: "If we want a good environmental policy in the future, we'll have to have a disaster. It's like safety on public transport. The only way humans act is when there's been an accident."[261]

IPCC investigations followed the principle that dirty laundry should be washed at home. UN Secretary-General commissioned another UN commission to investigate, meaning that the United Nations Organization actually investigated "impartially" itself. Like a dog chasing its own tail. Or like a dentist drilling his own teeth. If you look at who was appointed to the InterAcademy Council's investigation commission, it is the "Who Is Who" in the campaign against climate change.[262] If you want to get a picture of how impartial such a committee can be, imagine Josef Stalin investigating the crimes of communism. Among others, the following people sat in the committee chaired by Robert Dijkgraaf:

- Goverdhan Mehta: Former director of the Indian Institute of Science in Bangalore. This institute was established as the foundation of the industrial giant Tata. The same company set up Pachauri's TERI foundation for research on climate and energy. They are siblings.

- Mario Molina: One of the leading authors of the IPCC Fourth Assessment Report was asked to investigate the quality of his own work. But how would he interrogate himself? In front of a mirror? He is director of the Union of Concerned Scientists, which advocates the carbon hypothesis. He signed a letter to the US Congress protesting against attempts to investigate the Climategate scandal.

- Sir Peter Williams: vice president of the Royal Society in the United Kingdom. A few days after the Climategate affair, the Royal Society's bosses issued an incorrect political statement claiming that the rise in sea level is accelerating (albeit it is just a periodic fluctuation in speed). Williams's superior, Lord Rees, president of the Royal Society, fantasized in an interview: "The human race has only a 50/50 chance of surviving another century." Rees helped the University of East Anglia (UEA) to choose people who would investigate the Climategate scandal at UEA. His predecessor, Lord May, described climate skeptics as crackpots. This radical was a member of the InterAcademy Council from 2005 to 2009.

- Syukuro Manabe: Pioneer of computer 3D climate models of the atmosphere. He is called the "father of greenhouse gases." What if the climate models are proven faulty? A bit difficult task if they wanted him to bury his own life work as an impartial arbitrator.

- Louise O. Fresco: She is on the Board of Directors of Rabobank, which deals with carbon trading on the CLIMEX electronic stock exchange. If she does not defend the interests of carbon business enough, the value of their stock will fall, and her colleagues will not be pleased.

- Ernst-Ludwig Winnacker: The first head of the European Research Council, which is a group of people appointed by the European Commission to decide what the scientists should investigate and what they should avoid. I doubt that the president of the European Commission would entrust this function to someone who does not bow to the EU climate religion.

What is remarkable is the mechanism that ensures that no person with an independent opinion can get into the InterAcademy Council. The IAC comprises a total of 15 people who are an "extract" from the InterAcademy Panel using a special mining method. The 15 people are nominated by the IAC and IAP chairmen (co-chairs) from the IAP members. And from this "filtered" selection, the successors are chosen by... the leaving 15 IAC individuals. In addition, ten out of 15 must always be re-elected members of the outgoing committee. Therefore, no one can get inside unless they have the same worldview as the original founding team. Continuity guaranteed.

Therefore, it was not a real investigation. Investigators in the InterAcademy Council did not try to find and punish the culprits. They only made non-binding recommendations to improve the work of the IPCC in the future. For example, the IPCC should finally have a directive against conflict of interest. But even these mild reform proposals were eventually ignored. This is how UN climate panel chief Pachauri replied to Oliver Morton of *The Economist* upon being asked when the new conflict of interest rule would come into effect: "It's applicable right away. Of course, if you look at conflict of interest with respect to authors who are there in the Fifth Assessment Report, we've already selected them, and therefore, it wouldn't be fair to impose anything that sort of applies retrospectively."[263] Well, so maybe next time?

The IAC recommendation that the head of the IPCC should serve only one term was also ignored. Pachauri served for the second time and remained in office despite the scandals. Czech meteorologist L. Metelka, representative of the Czech Republic at the IPCC, wrote: "Whether Pachauri stays or leaves as IPCC head will give a clear signal to the professional and general public about the direction in which the IPCC wants to go... If he should stay in office even after the October plenary session, it would be a clear indication to me that problems can be swept under the rug at the IPCC and that being in conflict of interest is considered a non-problem here." The IPCC even ignored the InterAcademy Council's recommendation to ban grey literature.[264]

The InterAcademy Council's investigation had only one purpose—creating a press release that the scandals have been "investigated" and people "exonerated" so they could swipe the scandal under the rug. Actually, the InterAcademy Council had served alarmists even earlier. In 2001, 16 academies of science supported the conclusions of the Third Assessment Report of the UN Climate Panel (it was the one with the hockey chart).

The statement "The Science of Climate Change" was published as an editorial in *Science* on May 18, 2001.[265] The statement said: "We recognize the IPCC as the world's most reliable source of information on climate change and its causes, and we endorse its method of achieving this consensus." Bruce Alberts, the first co-chairman of IAC, says that the idea to create IAC as a tool for politicization of science "arose initially from the UN Secretary-General."[266] I doubt Kofi Annan would have been so devious. But his top adviser at the time was the usual suspect, Maurice Strong.

ALL THE KING'S MEN

IPCC staff is often selected according to political criteria. These considerations may have more weight than expertise. And like everywhere else, your career depends on knowing the right people.

Despite numerous mistakes, the media is full of praise for the UN climate panel. Especially because they quote the self-praise that the representatives of this institution sing to themselves. For example, the chairman of the IPCC, Rajendra Pachauri, said: "These are people who have been chosen on the basis of their track record, on their record of publications, on the research that they have done... They are people who are at the top of their profession."[267]

On another occasion, he said: "What I want to emphasize is the fact that this is a very objective, open, transparent process whereby we get the best scientists from all over the world to work on each of these assessments. I also want to ensure I mention that the review process ensures scientific integrity, objectivity, openness, and transparency."[268] Wow! Such modesty!

However, in reality, things are a bit different. Even the scientists who worked in the IPCC complain about the working conditions.[269] "There are far too many politically correct appointments so that developing country scientists are appointed who have insufficient scientific competence to do anything useful... This is reasonable if it is regarded as a learning experience, but in my chapter in AR4 we had half of the LAs who were not competent." (p. 138).

"The whole process, all steps above, are flawed by an excessive concern for geographical balance. All decisions are political before being scientific." (p. 554).

"Not much attention is paid to building good teams, and half of the authors are there for simply representing different parts of the world." (p. 296).

The United Nations Organization stressed that the UN Climate Panel consists of 2,500 experts from all around the world. But when you think about it, this number is not high—it is surprisingly small. IPCC assessment reports have about 2,500 pages of text. So, with 2,500 people (including reviewers), that means only one author per page.

In 2005, Professor William Gray, a pioneer of predicting hurricanes in the Atlantic, spoke at a hearing in the US Senate. "Despite my 50 years of meteorology experience and my many years of involvement in seasonal hurricane and climate prediction, I have never been asked for input on any of the International Panels on Climate Change (IPCC) reports. They know my views and do not wish to have to deal with them."[270]

Scientists for the IPCC are proposed by governments of UN member states. The Ministry of Environment is usually in charge of the nominations. It is well known that these ministries are usually dominated by radical environmentalists, for whom climate skepticism is an insult. From such ideologically nominated people is selected the leadership of the IPCC, the "bureau," consisting of the chairman, vice-chairmen, and heads of individual working groups—a total of about 30 people. They are selected behind closed doors. Why

are some people selected and others aren't? Nobody knows. In a questionnaire for the InterAcademy Council, researchers described their experience as follows:

- "By experience, I know quite important scientists who are never part of the IPCC because they are not known or not friends of focal points."[271]

- "The selection process of picking the LAs from the nominations is not at all transparent. How the nominations are made by governments is also a somewhat mysterious activity."[272]

- "After being a Lead Author or Coordinating Lead Author several times, I still have no idea how I was selected. This is unacceptable."[273]

- "This is completely mysterious to me... An issue of concern is how and why Michael Mann ended up as a lead author for the TAR, when he had just received his PhD in 1998. In the selection for lead authors, it is critical that publications by a lead author play a minor role in the particular chapter that the author is leading. Otherwise, the assessment will be biased by the lead author's own strong opinions related to his/her own papers."[274]

Political activists sit in many key positions instead of scientists. Donna Laframboise, in her long-titled book *The Delinquent Teenager Who Was Mistaken for the World's Top Climate Expert*,[275] gives a shocking picture of the types of people who are behind the IPCC reports. Climate activists from Greenpeace often write chapters on the impact of warming.

For example, William Hare was a Greenpeace spokesperson after 1992 and later also Greenpeace Director for Climate Policy. This activist was hired by the IPCC for the Fourth Assessment Report (2007) to be a lead author and reviewer. In addition, he was one of the 40 people who wrote the Summary for Policymakers. If the IPCC wants to ensure that IPCC reports are in line with Greenpeace's policy line, why won't they just let Greenpeace write the whole IPCC report? It would save a lot of time.

Richard Klein is another case. He completed his PhD in 2003, but he had been a Lead Author in the IPCC already since 1994. He was probably the youngest lead author of the IPCC ever. His qualification was that he worked for Greenpeace.

In 2011, the IPCC demonstrated that it did not learn anything from the series of Climategate scandals. When they published the Special Report on Renewable Energy Sources and Climate Change Mitigation (SRRN), they hired Sven Teske of Greenpeace to do the job. He was commissioned to "impartially" review his own brochure *Energy (R)evolution,* which he had previously written for Greenpeace. He highly recommended himself—certainly impartially—and so the IPCC gave prominent support to his extreme scenario and listed it at the top of its press release.[276]

Quote: "Close to 80% of the world's energy supply could be met by renewables by the mid-century if backed by the right enabling public policies." The author just forgot to mention the devastating costs! There is no cost-benefit comparison (CBA) in the analysis. The IPCC behaves as a kind of advertising agency that helps green business sell its products.

As if that wasn't enough, Greenpeace cooperated on Teske's report, *Energy (R)evolution,* with the European Renewable Energy Council, which defines itself as an umbrella organization for the renewables lobby. Sometimes it is hard to tell where the IPCC ends and where the marketing department of these companies begins.

The foreword to the Greenpeace study was written by the IPCC chairman Pachauri, who himself runs energy businesses (TERI, Glori Oil, Chicago Climate Exchange) and whose companies profit from climate subsidies. Imagine that a Medicine Safety Authority that approves new drugs and medicaments worked in this way. Would you feel safe?

PACHAURIGATE

Most scientific errors in the UN climate panel occurred when it was chaired by Rajendra Pachauri from India. The author of an erotic novel finally resigned because of a sex scandal.

The British *Guardian* newspaper used to call the UN climate panel chairman the world's leading climatologist.[277] Pachauri was called a top UN climatologist by *The Associated Press* too.[278] But, in fact, Mr. Pachauri is a railway engineer by education. He graduated from the Indian Railways Institute of Mechanical and Electrical Engineering in Jamalpur. He worked for railways and later completed his economics education in America.

The cradle of Pachauri's power is the Indian industrial giant Tata Group, which has a wide range of interests ranging from automobiles to power engineering. This giant also owns TERI (Tata Energy Research Institute), which deals with energy and climate research. Pachauri built TERI from scratch. When TERI was launching in 1982, it consisted of just two rooms, a hallway, and a bathroom. Today, TERI is a giant who has six centers in India and another six abroad.

For example, Pachauri's TERI developed technology to extract oil residues from hard-to-reach sites. Based on this technology, Pachauri founded the company Glori Oil in 2005 in Houston, along with Jack Babcock of the oil company Amoco. Two years later, Kleiner Perkins Caufield & Byers (KPCB) also supported the project financially. Probably because the green politician Al Gore (Global Investment Management) joined the KPCB by that time,[279] the same Gore who received the 2007 Nobel Peace Prize, along with Pachauri, for fighting global warming.

Interestingly, in 2013 TERI was declared the best climate research center in the world. This "independent" appraisal was made by a friend of Pachauri's. It was carried out by the International Center for Climate Governance based in Venice. By coincidence, ICCG Director Mr. Carlo Carraro had been elected vice president of the IPCC Third Working Group in 2008.[280]

ICCG assessed the quality of TERI according to specific indicators— such as the number of TERI staff hired for the prestigious UN climate panel. Since Pachauri was the head of the IPCC, he could easily hire his own TERI staff to work in his own IPCC. And he did. Although such nepotism is usually frowned upon, Pachauri was actually praised for this by one of his subordinates.[281]

Pachauri was a pretty busy man.[282] According to the TERI website, he was a member, advisor, or chairman of about 18 other organizations at the same time. For example, Asian Development Bank adviser, Bangalore International Center vice president, Darjeeling Himalayan Railway Heritage Foundation chairman, Asian Energy Institute president, a member of King Abdullah International Advisory Committee of Saudi Arabia (KAPSARC), and many others. Where did he find the time? On the Yale Climate and Energy Institute's website, you can find a list of his present and past functions, and it is over 70 items long. Perhaps Pachauri collects functions just like other people collect stamps.

Pachauri was exonerated from the accusations of conflict of interest in a way that is quite common in politics. He hired an "independent examination" from the ranks of his loyal friends. He asked KPMG, a company that deals, among other things, with trading in climate offsets. It was just at that time that Yvo de Boer, formerly the head of the UNFCCC (United Nations Framework Convention on Climate Change), joined KPMG. He moved to KPMG after the Copenhagen climate conference turned out to be such a disappointment.

Loyal media said that an "independent audit" exonerated Mr. Pachauri, but in the very text of the report, it clearly says it was not an "audit," and KPMG waives any responsibility for the correctness and completeness of the text.[283] Why did KPMG examine the accounts for only a year and a half (April 2008– December 2009)? After all, Pachauri had been the head of the IPCC Fourth Report before 2007. KPMG writes in its report that they only read the papers that Pachauri himself provided, and they did not check their veracity in any way.

KPMG only wrote down what Pachauri dictated. An investigation like that is the dream of every suspect. In the end, Pachauri resigned from the IPCC, but due to a completely different scandal. In 2015, one of the TERI workers accused Mr. Pachauri of sexual harassment at the workplace. No surprise for such a passionate man. After all, while he was flying from one climate conference to another, he found time to write a smutty sex novel, *Return to Almora,* about a horny climatologist.[284]

IV. CLIMATE CHANGE IMPACTS

For the first time in history, we have almost full literacy, yet many people cannot distinguish fact from fiction. It is astonishing how many people believe in hoaxes and fake news. And what is worse, not only Facebook but also top scientific journals and media like CNN and BBC are plagued with misinformation. People want to believe whatever confirms their worldview, and they welcome such news with open arms rather than critical skepticism. In such intellectual drought, untrue claims spread like wildfire. This is also made worse by the tendency of journalists to give preference to bad news, which attracts more readers. Thanks to all these factors, we live now in a mass delusion of virtual apocalypse.

Increased greenhouse gas concentrations are said to have caused a surge in natural disasters. This is called carbon pollution. But calling carbon "pollution" is an odd notion since carbon is the fundamental building block of life on Earth. I wonder what will be declared pollution next. Perhaps water? In the Jurassic era of dinosaurs, CO_2 was at much higher levels than today, yet life flourished. Linking extreme weather to warming is also questionable. When severe droughts or floods occurred in the 1970s, climatologists blamed it on cooling. Today, they say the exact opposite. It is difficult to take them seriously after this.

American politician Al Gore once said that weather reports are looking more and more like a walk through the Book of Revelations. It is the Bible's prophecy about the end of the world. There is a colorful description of how the rivers will turn into blood, fire will rain from the sky, the dead will rise from their graves, and so on. According to environmental activists, these prophecies are already beginning to come true. We have only a few years to save the world. The signs that the end is nigh are all around us.

Ever since the biblical times, doomsday prophecies have involved a worldwide flood, a deluge. The Bible says it rained for 40 days and 40 nights, and the world was flooded so much that only Noah and his zoo were saved. Today, the situation is repeating again, and the oceans are rising faster, and the islands disappear underwater one after another. Deluge number two.

But if you look at the data over a longer period, you can see that such things have always been happening. In the Medieval Climate Optimum, the oceans were 20 cm higher than they are today, and in the Neolithic, they were even higher. Coral islands keep up with the surface as corals continue to grow. What is extraordinary about our floods is that we have naively built up flood plains over the last hundred years—thanks to the growth of cities. However, nobody remembers the old floods, because few people live healthy enough to live two hundred years.

The notion that life on Earth is dying and that mankind is on the brink of extinction is problematic too. Polar bears are said to drown because of ice melting under them. But when ecologists travel there to sell them life jackets, it turns out there are so many bears that the ecologists must run away. The penguins were supposed to be another mascot of global warming. But it turned out the opposite is true. Antarctic penguins are periodically threatened by cooling because they cannot reach their seafood through thick ice. Usually, when a species is described as extinct, it will either be found again soon or its demise is due to hunters—not climate. When the animals look around timidly in the pasture, they are not scared of climate change but rather afraid of something that is going to eat or shoot them.

Hurricane Sandy was nicknamed as a superhurricane by the media, yet its strength was average. And in fact, the only outstanding thing about it was that it happened to hit a well-known city, New York, which, however, was not the first time it happened. As the poles are warming faster than the tropics, the temperature difference and thus the pressure difference is decreasing—the wind flow must clearly be weaker and not stronger, as we are led to believe.

Over the past hundred years, the number of people who lost life due to natural disasters has fallen by more than 90%, partly because meteorologists are able to warn you now about an incoming hurricane, and you have time to hide. The same is true of forest fires—their number has dropped dramatically over a hundred years, also by more than 90%. Thanks to the work of foresters who remove dead dry trees and grass from the forest.

But misinformation in the media is nothing new. In 1932, journalist Walter Durranty received the Pulitzer Prize for denying the existence of famine in Ukraine. He just blindly reprinted the deceptive official propaganda of Stalin's totalitarian regime. It is also quite common that newspapers print an obituary of someone who is not dead at all. There are so many of such fake news that they have their own Wikipedia page. It happened even to Mark Twain, who allegedly responded like this: "The report of my death has been grossly exaggerated."

CARBON POLLUTION

Some environmentalists fail to notice the difference between toxic poisons and carbon, which is the basic element of life on Earth. Those are all just "emissions" to them.

In 2009, the US Environmental Agency (EPA) used the term "carbon pollution" for carbon dioxide emissions. And they decided to regulate these emissions under the Clean Air Act.[285] The opposition protested because this law was created half a century ago for a different purpose, to protect human health from toxic substances. And carbon dioxide certainly is not a poison of any kind.

According to measurements by R.A. Berner (2001), there was about five times more carbon dioxide in the atmosphere in the era of dinosaurs than today.[286] Vegetation did not perish due to "carbon pollution." On the contrary, forests of Araucaria trees flourished up to 100 meters tall. Actually, it was the ice age that represented a true ecological catastrophe. As the ocean cooled, it absorbed more CO_2 so that atmospheric CO_2 concentration dropped to dangerously low levels in the glacial period, and vegetation suffered from malnutrition. Experiments show that at 150 ppm (parts per million), the growth of some plants is reduced by up to 92%, and they are unable to reproduce.[287]

Nature adapted to the glacial conditions in two ways. Firstly, C4 plants evolved that are able to survive even at low CO_2 concentrations where other vegetation dies. Secondly, Homo Sapiens evolved and discovered how to make fire. After some time, humans discovered they could burn coal and return carbon, once buried underground, back into the life cycle of the planet. Who knows, perhaps that is the very purpose why God or nature created human beings. Thou shalt mine the coal and put the carbon back into thine atmosphere where it once was. Because if carbon did not return to the atmosphere in time (via volcanic activity or mining etc.), life—which is based on water and carbon—would cease to exist on this planet.

Dr. Craig Idso says: "The Industrial Revolution has been a tremendous boon to humanity, as it has lifted large numbers of our kind from poverty to prosperity. It has also helped the rest of the biosphere—and thereby us once again—via the powerful *aerial fertilization effect* of the carbon dioxide that has gone into the atmosphere as a consequence of the burning of fossil fuels."[288] Craig D. Idso runs the Carbon Research Center (CO_2science.org), and he dedicated his entire professional life to CO_2 research.

Experiments have shown that C3 plants, which account for about 95% of vegetation (e.g., rice, potatoes, wheat), have higher yields at higher

CO_2 concentrations.[289] FACE experiments clearly measured that when atmospheric CO_2 concentrations increased to 475–600 ppm, the rate of plant photosynthesis went up by an average of 40%.[290] Only C4 plants, which account for about 5% of vegetation, are not sensitive to CO_2. But these are mostly various species of grasses and weeds that won't be missed dearly if they are outcompeted by C3 plants.

And as a bonus, there is another advantage. At higher concentrations of CO_2, plants need fewer stomata in their leaves to breathe. And when they have fewer stomata, they lose less water by evapotranspiration, which makes them more resistant to heat and drought.

The positive benefits of global warming can already be observed today. Satellites show that since the early 1980s, there has been "greening of the planet." In North America, the growing season was extended by 12 ±5 days and in Eurasia by 18 ±4 days.[291] If it keeps warming at the current rate, the 21st century will bring a temperature increase of about 0.5 to 1°C. Economic analyses concur that such moderate warming will have a positive impact on world agriculture and human health in the 21st century, especially in the temperate climate zone where it has been too cold so far.[292]

For example, warming is good for the quality of wine, which is very temperature sensitive. Warming by 1°C means an increase in wine quality by 13 points on a 100-point scale. For example, for Rhine wine, it has been an increase of 21.5 points or for red Burgundy wine by 12.7 points so far. Thanks to global warming, wine can also be grown in England again. England had plenty of vineyards in the Medieval Climate Optimum, as evidenced by old street names. Then the climate cooled in the Little Age, and England had virtually no vineyards left before World War II. Thanks to warming, today, there are over 400 commercial vineyards.[293] They are back.

All we need is common sense to understand this problem. If warm climate was something bad, why would the warm periods in history be called a "climate optimum"? Why would gardeners put plants in greenhouses if warmth was harmful to them? How come they have two harvests a year in the tropics? And why do trees have stronger annual rings in warmer years? Doesn't that actually mean they are doing better and growing more when it is hotter? Don't the tropics have the greatest biodiversity?

For these reasons, many environmentalists are skeptical about the notion that carbon is "pollution" for nature. Conservationists such as David Bellamy (author of BBC science programs), Bjørn Lomborg (author of *The Skeptical Environmentalist*), Jim Steele (founder of Sierra Nevada Field Campus, SFSU), or Patrick Moore (one of the founders of Greenpeace) reject such views.

Norman Borlaug received the Nobel Prize in 1970 for his "Green Revolution." He cultivated more fertile cereal varieties, thus preventing famines in Third World countries with booming populations. He opposes radical environmentalists who take efforts to block genetically modified crops (GMO). And he also decried the global warming policies, especially biofuels, i.e., burning of food crops as fuel. "I do believe we are in a period where, no question, the temperatures are going up. But is this part of another one of those (natural) cycles that have brought on glaciers and caused melting of glaciers!"[294]

EXTREME WEATHER

Weather extremes are always said to be getting "worse," no matter if it be warming or cooling. Bad weather is blamed conveniently on anything that just happens to be occurring at the moment.

Global warming, caused by "carbon pollution," is said to cause "climate disruption."[295] This term was made popular by President Obama's advisor John Holdren. However, the planet has seen a lot of warmer periods. So, when warming is caused by forces of nature, it is just weather; but if people should cause the same temperature rise, suddenly it becomes a disruption?

In 2013, the World Meteorological Organization published the report *2001–2010: A Decade of Climate Extremes*. It suggests that bad weather is somehow caused by elevated temperatures. But in previous decades, scientists claimed the exact opposite. As the climate was cooling after World War II, no one felt that weather would be getting milder. At that time, it was thought that the weather extremes were getting worse due to cooling.

In 1975, in the midst of the cooling era, Carl Christian Wallen of the World Meteorological Organization in Geneva explained: "The principal weather change likely to accompany the cooling trend is increased variability—alternating extremes of temperature and precipitation in any given area—which would almost certainly lower average crop yields."[296]

In 1970, on the anniversary of Lenin's 100th birthday, the first Earth Day was celebrated in the US, a kind of ecological May Day. Kenneth E.F. Watt of the University of California at Davis said at the celebrations: "If present trends continue, the world will be... 11 degrees colder by the year 2000. This is about twice what it would take to put us in an ice age."[297] But there was no enthusiastic applause. Instead of rejoicing that we are rescued from the threat of global warming, people were afraid of crop failures. The newspapers noted the extremes of weather around the world and discussed them in the context of climatic cooling.

In April 1974, *Newsweek* magazine published Peter Gwynne's article *The Cooling World*: "If the climatic change is as profound as some pessimists fear, the resulting famines could be catastrophic... Last April, in the most devastating outbreak of tornadoes ever recorded, 148 twisters killed more than 300 people and caused half a billion dollars' worth of damage in 13 US states..."[298] Then the article scolds politicians for not doing enough to warm the climate, such as warming the Arctic by pouring black soot on ice to change the albedo. "The longer the planners delay, the more difficult will they find it to cope with climatic change once the results become a grim reality." The same language is used to demand the exact opposite action now.

In the past, scientists used to believe that weather gets more extreme when the climate cools down. Today, they say the opposite. But one thing doesn't change—alarmists sound the alarm in any weather and any climate whatsoever. "We cannot simply afford to gamble against this possibility by ignoring it. We cannot risk inaction. Those scientists who say we are entering a period of climatic instability are acting irresponsibly. The indications that our climate can soon change for the worse are too strong to be reasonably ignored."[299] This is a quote from Lowell Ponte's book *The Cooling* (1976). But before any decisive action could be taken, the cooling suddenly stopped. It was a false alarm.

Today, the UN Climate Panel (IPCC) is trying to give the impression that weather becomes more extreme when the climate is warming. However, they do so by "cherry-picking" by the selective use of data. The IPCC evaluates increase in "weather extremes" such as drought only based on instrument measurements over the recent decades, and, based on a handful of decades of data, they jump to conclusions.[300]

Older proxy data, derived from sediments and other indirect indicators, is ignored. Because otherwise, the IPCC would be forced to admit that in ancient times the weather used to be much worse than today. Why don't they mention that in the African Sahel, for example, drought episodes were much worse during the Little Ice Age?[301] Before we warn India of impending droughts, we should check historical data first because Indian monsoons (rainfall) are weak in cold periods (like the Little Ice Age) and strong in warm ones (like the Medieval Warm Period).[302] Of course, even in a relatively humid period, a dry year will occasionally occur. This was confirmed in the research by the Czech team of Y. Markonis, according to which the warmer 20th century had more precipitation than the previous colder centuries.[303]

FLOODS

Floods are a type of natural disaster that—not surprisingly—harms people who built their homes in flood plains. As people do not remember events from a century ago, they often say that they have never seen anything like it.

In the past, rivers used to flow far beyond the city walls. But in the last two centuries, the cities have grown so that the rivers are now surrounded by the densest urban areas. Nevertheless, we can hear people say that global warming is responsible for flooding of the homes in flood plains. Every flood is hyped by the journalists as "the greatest in history" because they do not remember what floods were like in the past.

When Australia was hit by floods in 2011, the media presented it as a "flood of biblical proportions." But according to historical records, the 2011 flood in Brisbane (4.48 m) was far less severe than the 1893 flood there.[304] The biggest flood ever to hit Brisbane was in 1841 (8.4 m). The popular press cliché "the biggest flood in decades" means nothing. Because compared to the whole history, a decade is just a blink of an eye.

In the heart of Europe, in the Czech Republic, the second half of the 20th century brought unusual absence of floods in Prague on the Vltava River. This period has the least recorded floods in centuries. When the floods came back again after 2000, people thought something unusual was happening. Our memory is apparently short. In the period 1851–1900, there were 47 floods in Prague. Between 1901 and 1950, there were 26 floods, and finally, between 1951 and 2000, only 14 floods.[305] The same decline in floods was observed elsewhere in Central Europe.[306]

Around 2000, the frequency of floods rose again to the original level. But is it extraordinary? Hardly. For instance, in the 16th century, according to the stone mark called "Bearded Man" on the medieval Charles Bridge, floods occurred every few years, such as 1566, 1568, 1570, 1582, 1587, and 1598.[307]

The post-2000 pluvial (rainy period) was not unexpected. In 1997, the magazine *Vesmír* published an article by Zdeněk Vašků *Our Little Pluvials,* which showed that the period of stronger floods returns every 200 years.[308] Which corresponds to Suess's solar cycle and glacier fluctuations in the Alps.[309]

V. Contemporary little pluvial

IV. 1763–1804

III. 1560–1600

II. 1310–1350

I. 1078–1118

The question is whether the floods are causing more damage today than in the previous pluvial 200 years ago. Possibly. During the period of instrument measurements, the highest floods occurred in the years 1940, 1890, 1872, 1862, and 1845 on the Vltava River, but the 2002 flood was the largest of them,[310] which doesn't mean it must have been caused by climate change.

We can probably blame it on the changing land use in the 20th century. With urban sprawl, regulation of rivers, drying up of marshes, merging of small fields into large latifundia, and sprawl of paved surfaces, nature's water retention capacity logically decreases.[311] Over the last 150 years, millions of people have moved to cities, and flood plains became a place of housing construction. So, when the storm comes today, the rainfall sweeps through the landscape fast, causing flood and the water runs quickly away. Drought follows. However, this may not be related to the increase in the average global temperature at all.

DELUGE

Ocean levels used to fluctuate long before man threw the first shovel of coal under the first steam boiler. But despite rising sea levels, Pacific Coral Islands are not sinking. Corals are live beings, and, as such, they are able to grow.

Ocean levels have always fluctuated. At the time of the Holocene climate optimum 5000 years ago, it was warmer than today, and sea levels were higher. Even in the Sumerian era, about 3000 BC, the Persian Gulf reached higher levels and further inland than today. Sumerian cities like Ur, Uruk, Lagash, and Kish used to be right on the coastline, whereas the territory of the present-day Basra in Iraq was underwater.[312]

Even today, levels are changing; but the media usually exaggerates. *Climate Home News*: "Dying oceans rising faster than predicted, UN warns in a stark report."[313] *Science Daily*: "Collapse of Antarctic ice sheet would likely put Washington, D.C. largely underwater."[314] In Costner's post-apocalyptic film *Waterworld* (1995), all continents were underwater because of global warming. Only the tip of Mt. Everest remained dry (which is now 8848 meters above sea level). In fact, oceans would need to rise eight kilometers to turn Mt. Everest into an island. James Hansen, director of NASA's Goddard Institute, is only a little less extreme. He expects sea levels to rise 4–5 meters by 2090.[315] He believes that we can reach a "tipping point" after which the climate will suddenly collapse practically overnight with no warning.

US meteorologist Anthony Watts argues that a simple calculator is enough to debunk this fantasy. We know sea levels have been rising over the last 200 years at a rate of three millimeters per year, so increasing sea levels by four meters would take 1,333 years.[316] A document called the *Copenhagen Diagnosis* (2009) claimed that sea level growth has accelerated. But this transient variation in speed occurs every 60 years according to the 60-year climate cycle, the Pacific Decadal Oscillation.[317] In the period 1945–1975, the sea level rise was slower; in 1975–1998, it was faster, and then it decelerated again.

The UN climate panel is actually right on this issue. According to their estimate, by 2100, sea levels can rise by about 18 to 59 cm. The lower end of the range seems to be the most plausible. The oceans will only return to the level where they used to be in the Middle Ages around the year 1200.[318]

The rise in sea levels is a threat to islands and coastal cities. But the media tends to exaggerate. A few years ago, newspapers wrote about the evacuation of a sinking island in the Pacific: "The authorities in Tuvalu have publicly conceded defeat to the sea rising around them. Appeals have gone out to the governments of New Zealand and Australia to help in full-scale evacuation of Tuvalu's population. After an apparent rebuff from Australia, the first group of evacuees is due to leave for New Zealand next year."[319] But nothing like that ever happened, Tuvalu is still inhabited.

According to satellites, sea levels are rising, but coral islands like Tuvalu or the Maldives are still increasing in their landmass. Professor Paul Kench explains that atolls stand on corals, which are living and growing organisms. Dead coral shells are blown away by winds to the coast, and, thanks to these sediments, the islands grow.[320] The capital of Tuvalu is on Funafuti Atoll, parts of which have increased by 28.2% (Isle of Funaman), 13.3% (Falefat), and 10.1% (Paava). The author of the Tuvalu evacuation hoax was the green economist Andrew Simms of the New Economics Foundation, who proposes that we should stop economic growth. He publishes the Happy Planet Index.

The president of Maldives was also scared by reports of alleged sinking of his home island. If the climate keeps warming, the islands will drown, he worried. And the government meetings will need to take place underwater. In order to demonstrate this risk, President Nasheed held a government meeting at the bottom of the sea in 2009 in diving masks. In front of TV cameras, the ministers in scuba gear signed a declaration against global warming.[321]

When Axel Nils Mörner, a former director of the International Commission on Sea Level Change (INQUA), heard of this sensation, he wrote an angry letter to the president. He explained to him what the scientific expeditions had measured in the Maldives. Today's coral islands have not always been here, as environmental activists think. They only formed some 5,000 years ago. Some 4,000 years ago, the sea levels were 0.5-1 m higher than today, and the islands still remained above water.[322] Sea levels on the Maldives coast have been stable for about 200 years, then suddenly dropped by 20 cm around 1970 and have remained stable ever since.[323] No flooding seems to be in the offing.

Mörner begged the president: "Let us, for Heaven's sake, lift the terrible psychological burden that you and your predecessor have placed upon the shoulders of all Moldavians, who are now living in the imagined threat that flooding will soon drive them from their homes, a wholly false notion that is nothing but an armchair fiction artificially constructed by mere computer modeling constantly proven wrong by meticulous real-world observations."[324]

Venice is another example of a city that is said to be endangered by warming-induced drowning. But the sinking of Venice is mainly due to tectonics, not the oceans. The city is sitting on the Adriatic continental slab that slowly slides under the Apennine continental slab (Alps) and therefore, is being pushed lower and lower. The city is also tilting to one side, which can absolutely not be explained by rising sea level.[325] Climate warming, on the other hand, will help Venice—because it is expected that frequency of storms will decrease, with fewer floods coming (Aqua Alta).[326] According to Dr. Alberto Troccoli of CSIRO, the storms could decrease by as much as 30% by 2100.

CASUALTIES

Heat is unpleasant when you don't have air conditioning. On the other hand, in a cooling climate, we would be freezing to death. Since winters have a higher mortality rate than summers, global warming brings a net decrease in mortality.

According to the Center for Research on Epidemiology of Disasters (CRED), the number of victims of natural disasters fell by more than 90% in the 20th century despite population growth and climate warming. We are safer because we have better technology and warning systems, such as satellites and powerful forecasting systems.

In the 1920s, an average of 485,000 people perished globally every year due to weather extremes, especially due to floods and drought. In the 1930s, it was 446,000 deaths a year. In the 1980s, it was only 66,000 victims per year, and in the 1990s, only 33,000 deaths per year.[327]

As global temperature rises, freezing days decrease, and hotter days increase. Thus, winter mortality decreases, and summer mortality increases. But journalists only write about the negatives. *The Guardian*: "UK heatwave may have caused hundreds of deaths."[328] BBC: "French heat toll almost 15,000."[329]

Heatwaves have little effect on total mortality compared to other years. The victims are mostly people with poor health, who would die soon anyway. So, it is not a net increase in mortality; it is only "displaced" mortality.[330] If we discount people who would have died within 30 days anyway, the number of summer heat victims will fall by 75%.[331] They are mostly very old people. The heatwave in France in 2003 led to the death of some 15,000 people, but 80% (about 12,000) were people over 75 years.[332] Despite global warming, people live longer than they lived in the cold centuries. So, we cannot really call it an extinction of the human race.

In the past, heatwaves had worse impacts than today. Summers used to be a season of epidemics in Europe. London's worst cholera epidemics occurred in the summers of 1832, 1849, 1854, and 1866.[333] Even today's temperature extremes are not as unique as they might seem. Australia experienced the worst heatwave in the Marble Bar area at the turn of 1923–1924. Temperatures remained above 37.8°C for 160 days. The highest ever temperature on the planet was recorded on July 10, 1913, in Death Valley, USA, where it was an incredible 56.7°C.

Since the invention of fire, we know that people can protect themselves from temperature fluctuations. Kyselý and Plavcová (2012) investigated deaths from heatwaves in the Czech Republic (1986–2009) and found decreasing mortality trends despite rising temperature trends.[334] People are less vulnerable to heat today because they are richer and can afford things like air-conditioning. A rich country can also afford to invest in urban planning so that cities are greener and not overheated in hot summers. "The results suggest that climate change may have relatively little influence on heat-related deaths since changes in other factors that affect vulnerability of the population are dominant instead of temperature trends." People get accustomed to the warmer climate over time. In the southern United States, the summer heat mortality rate is lower than in the north.[335]

People can tolerate heat better than winter, as fewer people die in August and September,[336] whereas twice as many deaths (excess deaths) occur in winter than in summer.[337] There are even more heart attacks in winter—for example, in California, 33% more people die of heart disease in winter than in the rest of the year.[338]

In their 2001 study, Martens and Huynen asked: "Will global climate change reduce thermal stress in the Netherlands?"[339] They calculated that an increase in CO_2 to 550 ppm would result in 67% decrease in extreme winter temperatures, which should reduce winter mortality in the Netherlands by 1,100 people a year.[340] Climate warming slightly increases summer mortality, but at the same time, winter mortality decreases sharply.[341] The net result is an overall decline in mortality associated with temperature extremes.

POLAR BEARS

A polar bear is so threatened by global warming that its population... is growing. Despite this, polar bears replaced pandas as a symbol of endangered species. It has become a symbol of all animals endangered by climate change reporting.

Polar bears are very popular with journalists. *The Guardian*: "The polar bear who died of climate change."[342] *Telegraph*: "Starving polar bears turn to cannibalism."[343] In fact, we should rather pity the poor brown bears that ended up in the Arctic in a warm interglacial and got stuck there, having to adapt to the harsh conditions of the Ice Age.[344] If the heat-loving brown bear was able to survive and adapt in the freezing wasteland of the Arctic and evolve into a polar bear, why couldn't it work the other way around?

"The Arctic seems to be warming up. Reports from fishermen, seal hunters, and explorers... all point to a radical change in the climatic conditions and hitherto unheard-of high temperatures... Where formerly great masses of ice were found, there are now often moraines, accumulations of earth and stones... With the disappearance of white fish and seal has come other life in these waters." Familiar language, isn't it? Reports like this are used to prove that polar bears suffer due to carbon dioxide. But the text above is an observation of the Norwegian scientific expedition of 1922.[345]

In the 20 years from 1915 to 1935, the Arctic warmed by 1.5°C, and the polar bears survived with no harm. At that time, CO_2 concentrations were low in the atmosphere, so the cause of the warming must have been something else.[346] Then, in the 1940s, the Arctic warming stopped, and cooling began. Bears survived again. But you will not find this information in the UN climate panel reports. They only show graphs of Arctic ice melting after 1960.[347]

There is no evidence of any decline in polar bear population. Since the 1950s, the number of polar bears has increased thanks to the regulation of hunting. The Polar Bear Expert Group (PBSG) of the International Union for Conservation of Nature declared in 2009: "The total number of polar bears is still thought to be between 20,000 and 25,000." Just like ten years earlier. "The PBSG recognizes that where habitats are stable, polar bears are a renewable resource, and reaffirmed its support of the right of aboriginal groups to harvest polar bears within sustainable limits."

In addition, the number of polar bears is underestimated. PBGS chief Dag Vongraven admitted: "It is important to realize that this range has never been an estimate of total abundance in scientific sense, but simply a qualified guess given to satisfy public demand." In regions with no data (Russia, Arctic, East Greenland), the population is recorded as zero.[348]

The Fish and Wildlife Service stated: "The polar bear was not facing sudden and catastrophic threats [and] was still a widespread species that had not been restricted to a critically small range or critically low numbers."[349] Eskimos who have been hunting bears since forever and live with them in symbiosis say it openly: "Just about every day you see something on TV about bears," says the Eskimo hunter Chucky Gruben. "So much of it is bullshit!"[350]

The fact that the polar bear has become a symbol of global warming is largely due to a study by Charles Monnet. He claimed that polar bears drown because, due to global warming, they have to swim further to find a solid piece of ice to climb on. One might argue that if polar bears really had a problem with melting ice, it would be better to equip them with inflatable lifeboats. It would certainly be cheaper than the hundreds of billions invested in futile efforts to control weather.

Many years later, the origin of the "polar bear extinction" hoax was discovered. In 2004, Mr. Charles Monnet flew over the Arctic by plane and saw a few white spots in the dark sea. Well, probably drowned bears, he thought. And he wrote an article about it.[351] In fact, these polar bears drowned in a storm, not due to exhaustion. In 2011, Monnet was investigated because of this shaky study.

When the investigator asked him why he claimed that only 25% of the bears survived, Monnet shrugged shoulders, "Oh, well, that's just a mindless thing. That's in the discussion. Um, that is not a statistic... We didn't have sufficient sample size... And we put caveats throughout that section, saying that, uh, it's possible."[352]

Whereas the controversial Monnet study became famous, critical views in this field of science are not very welcome. A clear example is Mitchell Taylor. He has published over 50 scientific articles on polar bears in his life and is co-author of the report on the status of endangered species in Canada (COSEWIC).

When the International Polar Bear Research Group (PBSG) was to meet in 2009, Taylor received a letter saying they did not want him there.[353] "It was the position you've taken on global warming that brought opposition." They wrote that Taylor's views are "extremely unhelpful" for combating climate change, especially before the upcoming Copenhagen climate conference. In addition, Taylor had signed the Manhattan Declaration that the main cause of today's climate change is nature, not man. This is said to be "inconsistent with the position taken by the PBSG." That is how consensus is formed. The consensus that appeals to environmentalists! They invite only people who can be trusted, trusted not to have any opinion of their own.

Another example that it is researchers, not bears, who are endangered, is Susan Crockford, a polar paleontologist, whose blog *PolarBearScience* has become a scourge of alarmists. When giving lectures at elementary schools, she was "astonished to learn that every single teacher believed that only a few hundred to a few thousand polar bears were left." And she considered it her duty to debunk these myths. Alarmists retaliated first by banning her from representing the university at such speaking events. Then they published a pamphlet about her in the *Bioscience* journal (2018).[354] The text accused her blog of being frequently quoted by the proverbial "deniers." The following year, she lost her job as an adjunct professor at the University of Victoria after 15 years of teaching there![355]

OCEAN ACIDIFICATION

Ocean acidification is sometimes nicknamed the "evil twin" of global warming. There were concerns that acidification is detrimental to sea life. On the other hand, sea life is also affected by increase in water temperature. And this warming is actually good for life.

Even if it turns out that the greenhouse effect is beneficial to vegetation, we must still stop emissions, or else life in the seas would be extinct. The *Guardian*, in the article *Carbon Emissions Creating Acidic Oceans Not Seen Since the Dinosaurs,* says: "Chemical change placing 'unprecedented' pressure on marine life and could cause widespread extinctions, warn scientists."[356] Coral bleaching is said to occur due to acidification of seawater because when under distress, the polyps get rid of symbiotic algae that give them their color

Turley et al. (2006) show the acidification of the ocean as a sort of hockey stick graph—millions of years of stability followed by a sudden jump.[357] But the hockey stick blade is not real measured data; it is a pessimistic forecast of the future. This is a favorite trick played by the alarmists, stitching together different data, comparing apples and oranges.

In fact, the oceans are not "acidic." In order to become acidic, their pH would need to drop below 7. The oceans were not acidic even when the dinosaurs were obliterated by an asteroid—at that time, the pH was about 7.4. Corals evolved over half a billion years ago in the Cambrian period when the concentration of CO_2 in the atmosphere was up to 25 times that of today.[358] So it is unclear why acidification should all of a sudden endanger life.

Even a slight variation is hyped as some sort of disaster. Scientists warn: "Surface ocean pH is estimated to have dropped from near 8.25 to near 8.14 between 1751 and 2004." [359]That's a drop of just 0.1 in 250 years. Compare this to the pH of something we know well from our lives. Coca-Cola has a pH of about 2.5. Tap water has a pH in the range 6.5 to 8.5. The acidity of the aquarium water must also be monitored. Aquarium fish can withstand pH variation in the range 5.5 to 9. Try changing their pH by one-tenth. Do you think they'll notice?

The alarmists argue that the pace of change is too fast, so corals can't adapt in time. But corals are used to much larger fluctuations in a much shorter time. Measurements from California, in the famous Monterey marine aquarium, show a year-on-year pH fluctuation of 0.3 to 0.5 over just 13 years. In the area of the Great Barrier Reef, Australia, pH fluctuates in a 60-year climate cycle between 7.95 and 8.15.[360]

Alarmists actually know that. That is why they don't show the pH graphs to the public at all. Searching for this data in scientific studies is like finding a needle in a haystack. Instead, they show us the development of calcification, where it appears that it becomes more difficult for organisms to form their calcium shells. "Such a severe and sudden decline in calcification is unprecedented in, at least, the past 400 years,"[361] they warn us.

But one thing is rather suspicious. They keep showing us the one and only graph by Glenn De'ath et al. (2009). However, other studies show the exact opposite. The original data show that calcification has been improving since the 17th century, and only the last two years (2004–2005) show deterioration. The jump in the graph is caused by change(s) in the measurement method. This is cheating with statistics. The whole chart is based on data from dozens of coral reefs, but in that critical year, they only have data from the two reefs they selected.[362] Moreover, the authors have smoothed and averaged the graph over the past 50 years to the point that it appears that the alleged decline in calcification has been going on for decades, whereas, in fact, it happened only in 2004. Welcome to the amazing world of statistics!

How can conditions for marine organisms improve despite acidification of the oceans? The negative effect of acidification is counterbalanced by warming. Warmer water is good for corals.[363] McNeil states: "Previous studies have neglected the effects of ocean warming in predicting future coral reef calcification rates... Our analysis suggests that the annual average coral reef calcification rate will increase with future ocean warming and eventually exceed pre-industrial rates by about 35% by 2100."[364]

HURRICANES

Hurricanes have fewer and fewer casualties. But the alarmists inexplicably conclude that hurricanes are getting worse because of global warming.

Chris Landsea works as a Science and Operations Officer at the US National Hurricane Center. In 2005, he protested that IPCC executives misinformed journalists, claiming that hurricanes are getting worse, despite the fact that the IPCC's own reports acknowledge the hurricanes are not getting worse.

"I was disappointed when the IPCC leadership dismissed my concerns, when I brought up the misrepresentation of climate science while invoking the authority of the IPCC. Specifically, the IPCC leadership said that Dr. Trenberth was speaking as an individual even though he was introduced in the press conference as an IPCC lead author... I was told that that the media was exaggerating or misrepresenting his words, even though the audio from the press conference and interview tells a different story."[365] Landsea resigned from the IPCC in protest.

In fact, the number of tropical cyclones has declined globally over the past 100 years, as recognized by the UN climate panel.[366] However, the situation differs in different parts of the world. Somewhere, the number of cyclones has increased. Elsewhere, it has decreased.[367] The increase of future hurricane strength, based on model calculations, is expected to be modest, around 3% in 100 years. On the other hand, their frequency should decrease.

Most often, we hear about hurricanes that hit the coast of the United States. As Roger Pielke pointed out, in the early 21st century, the United States was experiencing the longest quiet period without strong hurricanes since Abraham Lincoln was president.[368] Hurricane Sandy in 2012, despite the media frenzy, was only a weak hurricane, and when it hit the District of New Jersey and New York, it was less than category one at that time, so it should not be even called a hurricane. The only thing interesting about Sandy was that it happened to hit a well-known city.[369]

By comparison, in 1900, Hurricane Gàlveston killed about 10,000 people, whereas Hurricane Sandy killed less than 100. This did not prevent journalists from calling Sandy a Superstorm or even Frankenstorm. They declared it to be an unnatural phenomenon that proves how the climate system is beginning to disintegrate due to human sins.

In 2012, ex-Hurricane Sandy caused damage of about $50 billion, less than Katrina of 2005.[370] Katrina was one of the main themes of the documentary film *An Inconvenient Truth* (2006). The author suggested that without global warming, the hurricane would have been weaker and caused less damage. But he did not say how much weaker. 1%? That would have no impact on the damage. When comparing the damage caused by hurricanes in the 20th century, remember that the dollar in 1900 had a different purchasing power than in 2000. Moreover, we have more people now, and the population density has increased. This is why, in statistics, you need to "normalize" the insured damage data to correct these confounding factors.[371] If the insured damage is higher today, it is not because the hurricanes are worse, but because population is higher, and the residential areas are denser. The most devastating hurricane of the century hit Miami in 1926,[372] at a time when greenhouse gas concentrations were low.

PENGUINS

Historically, penguins in Antarctica have always been threatened by cooling rather than warming. They died out several times at the South Pole—each time because of cold. Today's penguins are more threatened by hunters than the weather.

When illustrators want to draw a picture of an animal endangered by global warming, they will show you either a polar bear or a penguin, sadly standing on a melting ice floe, waiting to drown.

Reports of penguin population decline should be taken with caution. In 2012, Peter Fretwell conducted a new census of emperor penguins and told the journalists of BBC News: "It surprised us that we approximately doubled the population estimate." In 1992, they counted just 135,000–175,000 penguins. But now, a satellite survey counted about 595,000 emperor penguins. In addition, seven previously undiscovered colonies were found that somehow eluded former researchers.[373] Every census, a different result. The problem is that penguins are dark, and the rocks on which they sit are also dark, so they are rather difficult to see.

If penguins could speak, they would tell you that they have never been afraid of warming, but rather of cooling. For example, the Adélie Penguin inhabited the Ross Sea 45,000–27,000 years ago. Then it disappeared because the sea froze due to cooling. It could not return back until 8,000 years ago, when the Ice Age ended. Then this penguin species disappeared twice again, 5,000–4,000 years ago and 2,000–1,100 years ago.[374] Every time, its demise was due to the inability to withstand the dramatic... cooling! Most of today's penguin colonies—which the ecological enthusiasts wrongly consider to be an ancient part of pristine Antarctica—have only been formed in the last 2,000 years.[375]

One look at the map is enough to understand that penguins are threatened not by warming but by the proximity of human settlements. Endangered penguin species do not live in Antarctica but in New Zealand or South Africa.

Today, however, we live in an absurd era when a species can be declared as "near threatened" even though the population is rising. For example, the Adélie Penguin was thought to be of "least concern" for years, but suddenly in 2012, it was reclassified as "near threatened."

With the following explanation: "This species has been uplisted to Near Threatened because it is expected to undergo moderately rapid population decline over the next three generations owing to the effects of projected climate change. It should be noted, however, that there are considerable uncertainties over future climatic changes and how they will impact the species" (Red Book of Endangered Species, IUCN). In short, the reason for the new classification was merely a speculation, not data. A couple of years later, it was rightly reclassified as Least Concern again.

For most of the past 13,000 years, Antarctica was as warm or warmer than it is today.[376] And 130,000 years ago in the last interglacial period (called Eem), it was 4°C hotter than now (EPICA borehole), and penguins apparently survived in good health. Climate change is not a new thing. Perhaps they won't tell you on TV, but every penguin knows that.

Penguins are endangered by warming for one more reason. A study by Peter Doran (2002) documented that, according to satellite measurements, Antarctica as a whole has cooled slightly since 1980, although climate models predict amplified warming in polar regions. "Our spatial analysis of Antarctic meteorological data demonstrates a net cooling on the Antarctic continent between 1966 and 2000... Here, we present data from the dry valleys representing evidence of rapid terrestrial ecosystem response to climate cooling in Antarctica, including decreased primary productivity of lakes (6–9% per year) and declining numbers of soil invertebrates (more than 10% per year)."[377] After 1998, even the Antarctic Peninsula cooled.[378] Doran was blacklisted as a climate change denier for this publication. He was frustrated. In order to be able to publish again, he had to prove his loyalty by turning against climate skeptics. In 2009, he wrote an article about how skeptics are a small minority not to be taken seriously.[379]

FOREST FIRES

Environmentalists demanded that no fire-fighting measures be allowed in the forests. It is not natural, they say. But now, when forest fires increased, they look for a scapegoat. And the usual suspect is global warming, of course.

In 2014, the famed actor Arnold Schwarzenegger took part in the documentary series *Years of Living Dangerously* about the horrors of global warming. "When I was the Governor of California, I saw a tremendous change from the first year I was governor to the last year I was governor. And I saw that the fire season extended. We started the fire season earlier and earlier, and it got later and later. Then eventually, I was told, governor, you have to understand, there is not going to be any fire season. I mean, the fires are going to be all year round."

In fact, the west of the USA today has the least fires in 3,000 years.[380] Around 1930, it was common for about 50 million acres of forest to be burned down every year. But then the foresters began to take care of the forests, and the fires decreased dramatically. Arnold is terrified of "doubling" the burned area from three to six million acres. But this is still very low compared to the natural conditions before the arrival of man.

Why were fires so large a hundred years ago? Probably because nobody was removing dry wood out of the forest. Nobody was cutting high and dry grass. Withered material accumulated in the forests, so a single lightning bolt was enough to ignite it. Today, we are returning to this practice. Logging is forbidden because environmentalists want to have their pristine nature. In the years 1988–2004, the US forest area in which tree cutting and pruning is duly performed decreased by 91%, from 283,000 to 19,000 acres.[381]

However, when we return to pristine nature, fire severity also returns to natural levels and at high levels. True, it may benefit nature to some extent because some trees such as redwoods cannot even reproduce without fires that make room for their seedlings.[382] But people whose farms burn to the ground are not going to be happy. One is also amazed by the impudence of the ecologists who blame the increased numbers of standing dead, dry trees—caused by their own ban of logging—on global warming. News headlines: "Climate change has doubled forest mortality."[383] If a forest is not maintained properly, it is also easier for the bark beetle to spread. But environmentalists blame global warming instead.

It is somewhat reminiscent of Michael Crichton's novel *State of Fear*.[384] It is a story of eco-terrorists who cause a series of natural disasters to convince the public of the urgency to fight climate change.

Environmentalists imposed restrictions on logging in the USA at the end of the 1980s under the pretext of protecting one owl species. It is the

Spotted Owl, which lives mainly in Washington, Oregon, and California on the Pacific coast of the USA. Inside the US Forestry Administration, there was heavy opposition because experienced foresters had a good idea of the possible consequences of such amateurism.[385]

Nevertheless, ecologists employed their usual tactics, they tied themselves to trees, vandalized the equipment of lumberjacks, etc. The dispute was taken to court, and Judge William Dwyer ruled in favor of the owl. Logging was banned (the Northwest Forest Plan), which was an economic disaster for the American countryside. Jim Geisinger, who was then director of the Northwest Forestry Association, recalls: "The net effect has been about a 90% reduction in our federal timber supply... Hundreds of mills closed, and tens of thousands of people lost their jobs, and those jobs haven't been replaced."[386]

Conservationists celebrated a triumph. The owl doesn't need to fear the woodcutters' axes anymore. Now it can just peacefully burn to death in forest fires. In Oregon, for example, three fires in the years 2001–2002 hit the hunting grounds of 80 owls. In the following years, eight out of the 24 radio-monitored owls died. This is 33% mortality.[387] Six of them underwent an autopsy, and hunger was identified as the cause of death. There was nothing to eat in the burned territory.

The situation in Europe is also interesting. In 2005, the European Commission published a comic book, *What a Terrible Heat* for schools.[388] The cartoonish fire-fighter chief says: "Mr. Mayor, we are firefighters. We are just doing our job. We see the Earth is warming. Today's forest fire was no accident. We humans probably caused it. The climate is changing!" The children, educated by the fireman, then come up with a great idea. We should thank mainly the bureaucrats from the European Commission: "Give medals to all who are trying to regulate emissions of greenhouse gases! These people are the real heroes!"

However, statistical data prove that the European Commission was just telling children fairy tales. The statistical journal *Forest Fires in Europe 2010* shows the number and extent of fires since the early 80s of the 20th century.[389] The fires do not show any upward trend. If we look at the data for the past 300 years, we even find that in the last 200 years, forest fires have decreased dramatically—by some 90%.[390] The reasons are the same as in America—human activity removes dry material from the forest, so when a spark happens, there is not much to ignite.

In summer 2019, the media created a hoax about unprecedented burning of the Amazon rainforest. BBC: "Amazon forest fires increase by 84% in one year."[391] French president Macron even criticized the Brazilian president Bolsonaro and suggested that an international emergency intervention is needed to save the rainforest. But, in reality, these fires occur every year—the farmers use the "slash and burn" method to prepare for the next growing season. True, the 2019 fire season was higher than the previous year and the highest since 2012. But the illusion of "unprecedented" disappears when you look at a longer data set. NASA'S website Earth Observatory acknowledges that the 2019 forest fires are "close to the average in comparison to the past 15 years."[392] On the website GlobalFireData.org, one can check that there have been many years with higher fire counts. But who cares! The jungle fever served its purpose—to whip hysteria before the New York climate conference where the famous activist Greta Thunberg was sailing on her eco-yacht.

AN INCONVENIENT TRUTH

Al Gore received the Nobel Peace Prize for his documentary movie, although a court decided that the film contains a number of misleading claims.

Al Gore was vice president of the United States under President Bill Clinton (1993–2001). For his election campaign in 1992, he wrote the book *Earth in the Balance*.[393] His famous quote comes from the same year: "Only an insignificant fraction of scientists deny the global warming crisis. The time for debate is over. The science is settled."

When he lost the presidential election against George Walker Bush in 2001, he returned to writing. His documentary *An Inconvenient Truth* about climate change was awarded the 2007 Oscar for Best Documentary. In the same year, the author received the Nobel Peace Prize for his contribution to raising public awareness on environmental threats.

In 2007, the Czech Minister of the Environment, Martin Bursík, decided to subsidize the Czech edition of the book. He told the media: "We want to provide teachers with quality materials for lectures on applied ecology... We will subsidize the publication of the book *An Inconvenient Truth*, in which Al Gore explains very well the impacts of climate change. We are also preparing a DVD film version for schools."

But there were objections to the plan. Czech journalist Ivan Brezina, in the article *Self-Defense Against a Climatic Liar*,[394] described the book as political propaganda that does not belong in schools. "And if Gore's book can go to schools, why not the neo-fascist literature on Holocaust denial, the creationist propaganda of militant Catholics, or, let's say, the teachings about Lizard People from Space?"

The British government also wanted to get Gore's book into schools as a teaching aid. However, one of the parents, Stewart Dimmock, a truck driver, sued the government, demanding a court ban on showing the film to children. Dimmock's lawyer said: "Lots of parents have written to him supporting his application. They do not want our children brainwashed in this way by the New Labor Thought Police."

In the end, the British High Court did not prohibit film screening in schools because we have freedom of speech. However, he ordered that students be warned in advance that the film contains nine falsehoods. Since then, whenever a school wants to show *An Inconvenient Truth* to kids, they must first explain to the students that the film itself is not quite true. These are the nine inconvenient truths:

1. Greenland: Gore's claim that Greenland will melt and cause a sea-level rise of seven meters "in the near future" is nonsense. The oceans have been rising at the rate of three millimeters a

year for the last 150 years. An increase of seven meters would take thousands of years.

2. Pacific Islands: The case where islanders were evacuated because of rising sea levels (caused by warming) was made up by Gore. Coral islands are growing despite rising sea levels, as evidenced by satellite imagery. Corals are living organisms, and so, they can grow and adapt.

3. Gulf Stream: Scientists don't expect the Gulf Stream to shut down in the foreseeable future due to warming. Its speed fluctuations are natural. They are not a sign that it is going to shut down. The main driver of the Gulf Stream is rotation of the Earth around its axis, and it certainly will not stop.

4. CO_2 controls temperatures: In fact, it's the opposite of what Gore said. In the ice ages and interglacial periods, which the author speaks about in the film, the temperatures first changed, and only then the CO_2 levels rose, not the other way round. This is evidenced by glacier boreholes such as Vostok.

5. Kilimanjaro: The loss of ice in Kilimanjaro is not attributable to warming but to other local factors such as landscape changes. Gore should have chosen a different example for melting glaciers.

6. Lake Chad: The drying up of Lake Chad cannot be blamed on global warming. It is due to population growth, agriculture, and land-use change. People pump too much water from the lake.

7. Hurricane Katrina: This hurricane cannot be blamed on global warming. There have always been hurricanes. Far more powerful than Katrina was the hurricane in Miami before World War II, when CO_2 levels were low. Normalized "insured damage" caused by hurricanes has not increased in over a hundred years, as Roger Pielke states in a 2008 study.[395]

8. Drowning Polar Bears: There is actually one case where bears drowned. But they did not die because of the melting ice. They drowned in a storm. Charles Monnet wrote about it. Polar bear populations have not been decreasing over the last 20 years, and their hunting is, therefore, permitted.

9. Coral Bleaching: Other factors, such as water pollution, may be the cause of dying corals. Millions of years ago, corals survived even many times higher CO_2 concentrations than that of today. On the other hand, higher water temperatures help marine organisms with calcification of their shells.[396]

Al Gore responded to the criticism quite awkwardly: "I believe it is appropriate to have an over-representation of factual presentations on how dangerous it is, as a predicate for opening up the audience to listen to what the solutions are, and how hopeful it is that we are going to solve this crisis."[397] But when they repeatedly catch you exaggerating, they will just stop trusting you.

Brezina's comments on the whole case: "Let me be frank: I do not call for a ban on *An Inconvenient Truth* in Czech schools. On the contrary: given the huge global impact of Gore's book, children should know it as well as Hitler's *Mein Kampf* or Marx's *Capital*... A detailed analysis, including an analysis of all manipulations, lies, and subliminal manipulative practices, can become an important part of critical thinking education."

Ironically, at the same time, the court decided that the film was untrue, Mr. Gore was awarded the Nobel Peace Prize (2007) together with the IPCC chairman Rajendra Pachauri. Strangely, the UN Climate Panel did not consider it inappropriate to accept a prize alongside a convicted manipulator.

Sadly, it has a tragic subtext too. Originally, this Nobel Peace Prize was to be given to Irena Sendler, a Catholic nurse who saved 2,500 Jewish children in World War II. She helped smuggle them out of the ghetto. Gestapo finally caught her. She was tortured and was lucky to escape execution. She was hiding with fake documents until the end of the war. According to the Nobel Committee, Gore's PowerPoint presentation full of misinformation is somehow more worthy than someone who risked her life.

Gore preaches that mankind should live more modestly and lower its carbon footprint. Do as I say, not as I do. According to the Tennessee Center for Policy Research in 2006, his 20-room villa with a swimming pool consumed 221,000 kilowatt hours of electricity, roughly 20 times the US average.[398] This is actually true about most environmentally aware progressives. A 2017 scientific study called *Good Intents, but Low Impacts* documented that "individuals with high pro-environmental self-identity intend to behave in an ecologically responsible way, but they typically emphasize actions that have relatively small ecological benefits."[399] Your ecological footprint is dictated by your income, not by virtue of signaling gestures. Ironically, the wealthy middle-class people who lecture the world about green awareness usually have the worst ecological footprint.

But this progressive awareness pays. Al Gore was one of the major shareholders of the Chicago Climate Exchange.[400] He was in conflict of interest because, as a politician, he promoted regulations that benefited his business. For example, he worked for Kleiner Perkins (KPMB), which provided capital to Silver Spring Networks energy company. The companies that Silver Spring works for then received $500 million government subventions for smart grids.

These subsidies were approved thanks to politicians like Gore. When oil companies lobby for their business, environmental activists denounce it as greedy misdeeds. But if the same is done by the companies dealing in "green energy," suddenly it is fine.

THE END IS NEAR

Doomsday has been announced many times, and we are still waiting. These pessimistic prophecies only serve to depress the minds of fragile individuals.

The United Nations Environment Program adopted "doomsday scenarios" as its main method of work. Maybe you remember the once-popular slogan *"Will They Survive the Year 2000?"* In 1982, Mostafa Tolba, chairman of UNEP, scared conference delegates from more than 100 countries by saying that in the last decade, "on almost every front there has been a marked deterioration in the quality of our shared environment... Only international cooperation can save the planet. Unless governments act now... by the turn of the century, an environmental catastrophe which will witness devastation as complete, as irreversible, as any nuclear holocaust."[401]

Later, a new fashionable scare appeared—climate change. In 2013, the organizer of humanitarian concerts "Live Aid," Bob Geldof, argued that due to climate change, humanity could become extinct within 15 years.[402] James Lovelock, author of the well-known Gaia theory, said that because of warming, "billions of us will die and the few breeding pairs of people that survive will be in the Arctic where the climate remains tolerable" by the end of the 21st century. Today, he acknowledges that he exaggerated it a bit. British Prince Charles, whose father is one of the founders of WWF, said in 2009 that only 96 months remain to save the world.[403] At the time, Professor of Geophysical and Climate Hazards Bill McGuire published a book, *Seven Years to Save the Planet.*[404] In 2019, US politician Alexandria Ocasio-Cortez (AOC) argued we must adopt her costly Green New Deal policy or else the world will end: "The world is going to end in 12 years if we don't address climate change, and your biggest issue is how are we gonna pay for it?"[405]

We find doomsday prophets almost in every generation. For example, in the 1930s, the American farmer William Miller calculated that the end of the world would come in 1844, according to the Bible. A mass movement of the "Millerites" arose. Some of them sold all their property in anticipation of the end of the world. It did not come, but some of them just changed their name to Seventh-Day Adventists and kept on believing anyway.

Nowadays, we suffer from a similar delusion, as evidenced by a number of Hollywood films, such as *The Day After Tomorrow* or *Waterworld*. In predominantly left-wing Hollywood, it is difficult to find someone who does not share this belief. The warriors against global warming include Leonardo DiCaprio, Arnold Schwarzenegger, James Cameron, and many others. Many of them do not hide that environmentalism is a substitute for religion to them. Everyone needs to believe in something, fight for something. The concentration of environmentalists in urbanized areas is not accidental. Urban atheists, who live in concrete wastelands, naturally miss forests and mountains.

Handling environmental problems is one thing. Believing that these issues will bring about the apocalypse is something else. From a psychiatric point of view, it is "delusional thinking"—just as if someone thinks that he is being spied on by aliens who keep stealing his thoughts. In 2010, there was a case of an insane couple from Argentina who committed suicide in fear of global warming. They explained their motives in a farewell letter.[406]

Psychiatric clinics are slowly filling up with people who believe in a climate catastrophe. Psychiatrist M.K. Jones (2012) conducted a study of 50 patients with obsessive-compulsive behavior (OCD) who sought help at a Sydney clinic.[407] Fourteen of the 50 patients (28%) had their anxiety directly related to the media frenzy about climate change. Patients feel the compulsion to check 100 times a day if the lights are off, if the gas is off, or if the water tap is not dripping. Such behavior is common in this mental disorder. But the reasoning was surprising. They did not do it for fear of fire or thieves but because they wanted to reduce their carbon footprint.

The number of such cases is increasing. New Zealand psychiatrists also describe the case of a 17-year-old psychotic patient at the Royal Children's Hospital Melbourne who suffers from delusions of apocalypse. He believes that millions of people will die of water depletion in a few days due to his water consumption. The patient felt guilty and tried to stop drinking completely. To prevent a world catastrophe, he constantly checks to see if water is not dripping. The patient's condition improved after administration of clonazepam and olanzapine.[408]

In 2018, a Swedish girl, Greta Thunberg, described how the climate propaganda in mass media triggered her Obsessive-Compulsive Disorder: "When I was about eight years old, I first heard about something called climate change or global warming... So, when I was 11 years old, I became ill. I fell into depression. I stopped talking, and I stopped eating. In two months, I lost about ten kilos of weight. Later, I was diagnosed with Asperger's syndrome, OCD, and selective mutism."[409]

Greta became obsessed with a global apocalypse prophecy. "Around the year 2030, ten years 252 days and ten hours away from now, we will be in a position where we set off an irreversible chain reaction beyond human control that will most likely lead to the end of our civilization as we know it."[410]

Instead of giving her medical treatment, her parents encouraged her doomsday obsession, and in August 2018, her mother used the girl to promote her new book, *Scenes from the Heart*. She sent the mentally ill girl to sit in the street in front of the Swedish parliament with a cardboard sign "Climate Strike." Ingmar Rentzhog, a rich businessman, real estate tycoon, and PR agency owner (trained by Al Gore in his Climate Reality project training camp), organized a campaign on Twitter and the Internet using her as a face of his agency, *We Don't Have Time,* thus earning millions. Greta's family later distanced from this man under public pressure.[411]

In 2018, people suffering from "environmental grief" began organizing. But instead of attending something like Alcoholics Anonymous psychotherapy, they started blocking traffic. The founder and activist, Gail Bradbrook, suffers from visions of apocalypse, too: "We are killing life on Earth. We're in the sixth mass extinction event, and it's possible that human beings will go extinct." So, then she came up with an idea to block traffic and organize civil disobedience. "I'd been focused on trying to start civil disobedience since 2010, and I've tried many things, and they didn't work, so I went on a retreat and prayed in a deep way with some psychedelic medicines."[412] Bradbrook actually wants hallucinations to become part of the XR movement strategy. "I would support mass civil disobedience where we take medicine to tell the state that they have absolutely no right to control our consciousness and to define our spiritual practice," she said in 2019.[413]

This fear of extinction is not based on facts. According to IUCN—which publishes the Red Book of endangered species—some 800 known species became extinct over the last 400 years. That is less than a tenth of a percent out of the 1.9 million known species. Most of these animals were killed by hunters, certainly not by carbon dioxide. This rate of demise cannot be compared with the five previous great mass extinctions. The one at the end of Perm witnessed the demise of 90% of species documented in fossil records.

Most of the modern extinctions we hear about in the media are not even visible in fossil records. Smithsonian paleontologist, Doug Erwin, cites an example: "So there are estimates of what the standing crop of passenger pigeons was in the 19th century. It's like five billion. They would black out the sky... How many records are there of fossil passenger pigeons? Two... So, here's an incredibly abundant bird that we wiped out. But if you look in the fossil records, you wouldn't even know that they were there."[414] There are real problems like overfishing, but the mass extinction narrative is false.

V. CLIMATE SCANDALS

An average person imagines a scientist as a kind of monk who peacefully toils in the search for truth through the continuous accumulation of discoveries. In the 1960s, this noble illusion was shattered by Thomas Kuhn's book *Structure of Scientific Revolutions*. It pointed to the other face of science. Scientists form various "tribes" that fight each other to defend their pet theories. These tribes compete mercilessly. And just like in ice hockey, sometimes it is foul play.[415]

An example is global warming. From World War II until 1990, the northern hemisphere did not warm up. But greenhouse hypothesis supporters needed warming to confirm their greenhouse hypothesis. So, they searched for some confirmatory data until they were able to fabricate some warming, at least on paper.

In 1999, the climatologist Mann published a study claiming it was the hottest year in a thousand years. According to him, the development of temperatures resembled a hockey stick—for a thousand years, nothing happened, and then suddenly, the Earth began to overheat. This conclusion contradicted all previous studies that claimed the Middle Ages to have been at least as warm as the end of the 20th century.

One might say that Mann, being a beginner, probably made a mistake somewhere. But the hockey stick phenomenon was welcomed with frenetic applause by various interest groups. They propelled Mann to an astounding career. So, when it became obvious that his legendary study was a mistake, he fended off the attacks from a well-fortified position of power, although he used irony in his defense rather than facts or data.

Let us say that there were plenty of attacks on Mr. Mann. Especially, his refusal to disclose his source of data surprised everyone. His statement that people should just believe him blindly because he wears a white coat failed to persuade his critics. Opponents argued that in genuine science, you have to disclose evidence for anyone to replicate your results. A scientific article must have footnotes with sources—otherwise, it is not science. These critics, however, were immediately identified as enemies of science paid by Big Oil to attack poor scientists.

Mann's secretive behavior led the US Congress to set up an inquiry committee—actually two committees. The investigation revealed that the reviewers were Mann's friends, so nobody actually checked the "hockey stick." The authors avoided independent review for good reasons. They did not want their enemies to look for mistakes. If they should find one, it might call into question the whole CAGW (Catastrophic Anthropogenic Global Warming) concept.

Gradually, it became apparent how creatively Mann contributed to the scientific methodology. His data on whether it was warmer in the Middle Ages is so uncertain that he was actually able to choose the shape of his hockey stick at will. In addition, someone found data on the university server in Mann's file, which seemed to have censored a data period from the Middle Ages. Did he conceal this to create a neat hockey shape? Of course not. He decided not to include that data in his calculations because of "poor quality."

A few years later, it turned out that other studies used similar methods to confirm the accuracy of Mann's hockey stick. The key study by the climatologist Briffa was based on a sample of a single tree instead of tree ring data from thousands of trees, as is the usual. He deliberately chose this one tree because it was showing what he wanted to see. Perhaps sociologists will also adopt this method to make their work more efficient. Why bother doing opinion polls of thousands of people when you can just ask your grandma or yourself?

Mr. Briffa also behaved as a CIA agent, refusing to disclose his sources. He said he would love to reveal them but, unfortunately, he couldn't because of confidentiality. And his colleagues also remained silent when people asked them why the new version of their graphs looked different from the original. The public didn't understand what might possibly be so secret about thermometer measurements. Suddenly, climatologists were flooded with outraged requests to publish their data immediately. However, they refused the applications as nuisance and harassment. Eventually, someone lost patience, hacked into their computers, and published everything for them.

It was very enlightening reading. The public finally learned from the working correspondence of scientists how the hockey stick came into being. Firstly, the author processed the data using a "flat" algorithm that underestimates climate variability in the past. The algorithm also generates "hockey sticks" even from random data noise. As if that wasn't enough, the author compared apples and oranges. When the data did not confirm the "alarming" warming in the second half of the 20th century, scientists simply erased it. And they replaced it with completely different data from another source. Until then, we had seen such creative math only in criminal cases of tax evasion.

One would expect that, after such embarrassment, Mann would be kicked out of university and hired perhaps as a magician in a traveling circus. Instead, he still lectures and cruises around at world conferences. The investigation of the scandal was carried out in a friendly spirit within a community inclined to the CAGW hypothesis. The scandal was swept under the rug. At that time, too many careers and funding channels depended on climate panic.

Instead of being condemned, Mann's "trick" became common practice in climatology. The uncomfortable post-war cold period in the northern hemisphere is no longer shown to anyone. And if they do show you, data is adjusted accordingly—the older data is cooled down and newer data is warmed up in order to straighten the curve. After all, a tailor will either let your clothes out or take them in so they will fit.

HOCKEY STICK

The hockey stick graph rewrote the history of climate change. Later research did not confirm its correctness, but it was defended by other means. Whoever criticized it ended up on a blacklist.

In 1999, *Geophysical Research Letters*[416] published a study that literally rewrote the history of the last thousand years. The authors almost erased the Medieval Warm Period and the subsequent Little Ice Age (14th–19th century). According to them, these were just local phenomena, irrelevant for global average. The resulting curve created by Michael Mann et al. looked a bit like a hockey stick.

This caused a sensation and even appeared on the cover of the 1999 *World Meteorological Organization* journal.[417] The United Nations climate panel was so enthusiastic that it decided to make the hockey stick the key message of its 2001 assessment report. IPCC: "It is very likely that the 1990s was the warmest decade and 1998 the warmest year in the instrumental record since 1861."[418]

Since then, a number of reconstructions have been published, which have been declared "independent" confirmation of the hockey stick. In fact, all these "independent" reconstructions were done by members of the so-called "hockey team" themselves. According to the slogan: "I believe only the statistics which I forged myself."

In all the studies, the same names appear again and again. Jones, Briffa et al. (1998),[419] Jones and Mann (2002),[420] Mann, Bradley, and Hughes (1999),[421] Jones, Osborn, and Briffa (2001),[422] Briffa, Jones, Osborn et al. (2001),[423] Briffa, Jones et al. (1995),[424] Mann et al. (2008),[425] etc.

All these studies use similar methods. They compare apples and oranges, combine direct and indirect measurements from different locations, and replace "inconvenient" curves with others to support the CAGW hypothesis of unnatural warming. But we should compare only things that are comparable—the width of the present tree rings and the medieval tree rings. Data from today's glaciers and medieval glaciers.

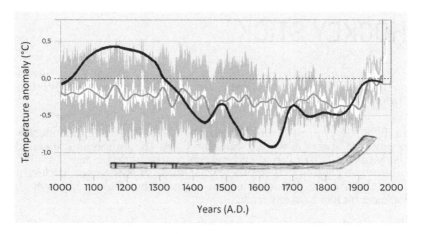

Figure 5—The hockey stick graph (green) by Michael Mann et al. (1999) erased the Medieval Climate Optimum from history as well as the Little Ice Age. The last part of the graph after 1980 (red) is not based on tree ring data but data from thermometers from other locations.[426] The black curve is Hubert Lamb's description of Central England temperatures used in the First Assessment Report of the IPCC in 1990.

However, if we do so, we find out that Mann was wrong, and the Little Ice Age really existed. This is confirmed in a study by J. Esper in 2002,[427] Moberg's 2005 study,[428] Loehle's 2007 study,[429] and Ljungqvist 2010 study.[430] The difference between today's and medieval temperatures is so small that it cannot be distinguished from mere measurement error.

The hockey team tried to prevent the publication of studies that would challenge the established hockey stick dogma. When the Esper's study was to come out, Briffa, as the reviewer, wrote to the authors: "I simply would not like to see you write a paper that puts out a confused message with regard to the global warming debate, leaving ambiguity as to your opinion on the validity of the Mann curve."[431]

In 2003, the *Climate Research* journal published a study by Soon and Sallie Baliunas "Proxy Climatic and Environmental Changes of the Past 1,000 Years."[432] The authors came up with a whole new approach. Instead of analyzing global average temperatures (which are quite uncertain for the Middle Ages due to poor global coverage), they preferred to analyze the temperatures of each region. And it turned out that almost every part of the world had experienced some time in the past millennium when it was as warm or warmer than it is today.

The community around Mann responded by attempts to destroy the publisher. We know this from correspondence that leaked later in the Climategate scandal. Mann: "So what do we do about this? I think we have to stop considering *Climate Research* as a legitimate peer-reviewed journal. Perhaps we should encourage our colleagues in the climate research community to no longer submit to, or cite papers in, this journal."[433] Former CRU head, Mr. Wigley replied: "We must get rid of von Storch too."[434] And so they did. The editors were eventually pressured to resign

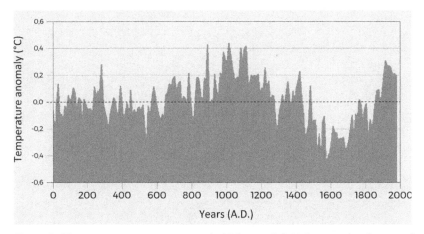

Figure 6—Newer temperature reconstruction by Moberg et al. (2005) returned to the original scientific paradigm that the late 20th century temperatures were close to the Medieval Climate Optimum temperature. This is what proxy data looks like when you don't mix it with instrumental record.[436]

This had devastating consequences for Soon. Since the publication of the article in *Climate Research*, the government has not approved any of his grant applications. He ended up on a blacklist. If it hadn't been for the philanthropy of the private companies that sponsored his research, he would have had to find another job.[435]

CONGRESSIONAL PROBE

The author of "hockey stick" tried to conceal that his work was the result of dubious data selection. The method he used generates hockey sticks even from meaningless data noise. The investigation clarified why the experts did not protest against this methodology. They are old pals.

The root problem of Mann's defective algorithm was identified by the Canadian researcher Steve McIntyre in 2003[437] and 2005.[438] His findings were also confirmed by climatologist Hans von Storch (2004).[439]

The whole method depends on correct measurement of tree ring width. When a cold country has a warm year, its trees grow better, and the tree rings are wider. We need trees that are sensitive to temperature. Therefore, when a climatologist comes to a forest, he searches for trees whose annual rings best match the thermometer records we have for the last 150 years. But there is a catch. What if it is just a coincidence? In that case, the tree would not be a good indicator of temperatures for the pre-industrial era at all. If we fall in the trap and rely on data from such a misleading tree, we get a pre-industrial temperature curve that does not reflect temperatures—it just jumps up and down randomly. Trends cancel each other, and the result is almost a straight line as if the climate in the pre-industrial era did not change at all.

Steve McIntyre, an amateur climatologist and retired mining engineer, found yet another problem. On a computer server of the University of Virginia, where Mann worked during his hockey stick years—he discovered some of Mann's files. And among them was a directory with a suspicious name: "BACKTO_1400-CENSORED."

McIntyre demonstrated that if Mann hadn't censored the data, he would have obtained a U-shaped graph instead of the hockey stick graph. He would have discovered a warm period in the Middle Ages and then cooling in the years 1400–1600 AD, followed by warming up to the initial level, which is precisely how climate history had been understood before Mann.

Apparently, there was no rigorous peer-review. Nobody checked the hockey stick study before publication. This is why McIntyre launched his Climateaudit.org website (2005) and started doing the "audit" on his own accord. In retaliation, Mann launched Realclimate.org. An online battle broke out on the Internet. In order to carry out the audit, McIntyre began sending requests to scientists, asking them to reveal the data on which they based their conclusions. The review process in climatological journals was obviously not done with due diligence. This years-long effort to improve transparency in science earned Mr. McIntyre the title "Personality of the Year 2010" in *The New Statesman* magazine.

From the beginning, it was somewhat suspicious that Mann did not disclose where he'd taken his data, so McIntyre began chasing him with questions. But in an interview in *The Wall Street Journal*, Mann publicly declared that the method used for calculations is his copyright, and he won't show it to anyone. "Giving them the algorithm would be giving in to the intimidation tactics that these people are engaged in."[440] Mann's cloak-and-dagger approach to science angered some US congressmen, who demanded Mann's investigation.[441]

At the request of Congress, a committee was set up, chaired by Edward Wegman, Chairman of the Applied and Theoretical Statistics Committee of the National Research Council (NRC). Wegman's conclusion: "We found that at least 43 authors have direct ties to Dr. Mann by virtue of co-authored papers with him."

Sociological analysis revealed that "it is immediately clear that Mann, Rutherford, Jones, Osborn, Briffa, Bradley, and Hughes form a clique, each interacting with all of the others."[442] This clique is referred to as the "hockey team." These people review each other's articles or co-author them. If the group falls into the trap of a wrong hypothesis, the pals will stick together to defend it. It is a community so small and entwined that an independent review is almost ruled out. This is why peer-review is not panacea to quality control.[443]

Also, Gerald North's committee in the National Academy of Sciences (NAS) audited the hockey stick. The committee noted that Mann's statements about temperatures of the Middle Ages cannot be taken too seriously.[444] Unfortunately, media misinformed the public about the findings of North's committee. In *Nature*, there was a misleading article *Academy Affirms Hockey Stick Graph* by an author biased in favor of Mann.

"The committee has a 'high level of confidence' that the second half of the 20th century was warmer than any other period in the past four centuries."[445] This is confusing for the reader because this has never been a controversy. Of course, it is warmer now than in the Little Ice Age, but the controversy was about comparing the climate of today with that of the Middle Ages. And here, the academy agrees with critics of the hockey stick. North: "Less confidence can be placed in large-scale surface temperature reconstructions for the period 900 to 1600." The panel also "concluded that systematic uncertainties in climate records before 1600 were not communicated as clearly as they could have been." In other words: Mann presented speculations as if they were solid facts. This is what McIntyre criticized for years.

When Susan Solomon was working on the Fourth Assessment Report in the IPCC, she was confused because she was unable to find Mann's bold claims anywhere in the draft—claims that 1998 was the hottest year in a thousand years and that the 1990s the hottest decade in a thousand years. In fact, this unsubstantiated claim (which was promoted in the Third Assessment Report) was quietly dropped from the text upon the recommendation of North's committee.[446]

Climatologist Keith Briffa of the UK Climate Research Unit replied to her like this: "The IPCC's Third Assessment Report was, in my opinion, wrong to say anything about the precedence (or lack thereof) of the warmth of the individual year 1998. The reason is that all reconstructions have very wide uncertainty ranges bracketing individual-year estimates of part temperature. Given this, it is hard to dismiss the possibility that individual years in the past did exceed the measured 1998 value."[447]

When the IPCC threw the hockey stick under the bus in 2007, Briffa apologized to Mann: "I tried hard to balance the needs of the science and the IPCC, which were not always the same. I worried that you might think I gave the impression of not supporting you well enough while trying to report on the issues and the uncertainties."[448]

It is still a mystery as to how the hockey stick could have ever passed through the IPCC review process. A British citizen, David Holland, decided to use the Freedom of Information Act (FOIA) and demanded to know if the British reviewer Mitchell did his job in the IPCC properly. But the Met Office demonstrated amazing ingenuity to find legal loopholes to avoid having to hand over the documents to Holland.

At first, the Met Office told Holland that Mitchell's records had been "deleted." Then they came up with a new excuse that the records exist, but they cannot be disclosed because Mitchell worked in the IPCC as a private individual and not as a Met Office employee.[449] Finally, it turned out that the Met Office actually paid Mitchell for his work in the IPCC and reimbursed his travel expenses. Such secrecy and abuse of legal loopholes is dishonest behavior unbecoming a scientific institution. Most certainly, it does not strengthen public trust in science.

THE MOST INFLUENTIAL TREE IN THE WORLD

The Climategate scandal broke out in 2009 when correspondences between climatologists were leaked to the public. And after reading the emails, it appeared that they cheat when they scare people with unprecedented global warming (at the beginning, the problem with data from Siberia).

Michael Mann's "hockey stick graph" has been arguing for years that Medieval Climate Optimum did not exist. He rejected all criticism by pointing out that independent studies confirmed his hockey stick. He meant a particular study by Keith Briffa of the British Climate Research Unit (CRU) in 2000.[450] But it was a bit suspicious why Briffa was hiding the data on which the study was based. He was hiding it for nine years. Specifically, it was tree ring data from the Siberian peninsula Yamal. Scientists measure the width of annual rings of old trees to deduce how warm each year was.

However, whenever Briffa wanted to use this data in another article, Steve McIntyre of Climateaudit.org, a persistent hockey stick critic, appeared and wrote to the chief editor to demand that the source data be disclosed. Briffa managed to avoid such requests for a long time. But finally, one editor complied. "We take matters like this very seriously, and I am sorry that this was not picked up in the publishing process," he replied because, in the journal's code of conduct, there is adherence to principles of science. "As a condition of acceptance, authors agree to honor any reasonable request by other researchers for materials, methods, or data necessary to verify the conclusion of the article."[451]

After months of delays, the data was released in September 2009 to Briffa's embarrassment. His study fell apart. It turned out that the hockey stick shape of the often-quoted study depended on a single tree. It was a tree marked YAD061.[452] Of course, one specimen is not a statistically representative sample. Similarly, it is not enough to ask just one person when you do a public opinion survey. If we use the entire Schweingruber database of hundreds of trees, the hockey stick shape will disappear (that's why the Ural database was never published).[453]

Briffa probably believed that if a tree in the database of Russian scientists Hantemirov and Shiyatov corresponds well to the temperature curve of the first half of the 20th century, that tree will be a good indicator of temperature. But what if it is just a coincidence? When Hantemirov and Shiyatov published their own study (2002) and used all the trees, the illusion of the hockey stick disappeared.[454]

For years, Briffa violated the Freedom of Information Act (FOIA). He made excuses about not being able to disclose the data for copyright reasons. Now, however, the years of data hiding, which was common practice in CRU, no longer appeared as mere laziness but rather as an attempt to conceal serious errors. Finally, an unknown person, nicknamed FOIA, lost patience and hacked the Climate Research Unit computers. In November 2009, he released a selection of email correspondence of these climate scientists.

When journalist Fred Pearce telephoned Phil Jones, the boss of the CRU scientists, and asked why anyone would steal the emails, Jones said clearly, "I think it's about Jamal."[455] Mr. FOIA, the hacker, sent the following message to the climate skeptic blog Air Vent: "We feel that climate science is, in the current situation, too important to be kept under wraps. We hereby release a random selection of correspondence, code, and documents. Hopefully, it will give some insight into the science and the people behind it." This was accompanied by a link to a ZIP file with data stored on a server. A commented selection of emails explaining the context of each statement was published by J. Costello.[456]

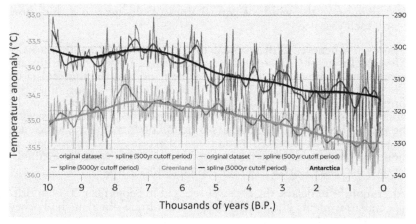

Figure 7—The longest climate change history is known from drilling in the glaciers of Greenland (green) and Antarctica (black). Judging by these sources, there is nothing unusual about the recent climate change. Greenland data is from the NorthGRIP site. Antarctic data comes from the Taylor Dome site. Both adapted from the Holocene Climate Atlas.[457]

The hacker published two more batches of emails in 2011 and the last one in 2013. To the last one was attached a farewell letter. He did not reveal his identity. He writes only that he is not from the USA or Britain, and his mother tongue is not English. He acted on his own, with no accomplices.[458] FOIA also explains what motivated him: "It makes a huge difference whether humanity uses its assets to achieve progress, or whether it strives to stop and reverse it, essentially sacrificing the less fortunate to the climate gods."

Climatologists have not learned anything from the scandals and still cheat the law. Steve McIntyre's rejected requests for data in 2011 confirm that the Siberian tree ring data is still kept a secret. Climatologists refused to disclose the Yamal data because, as they say, they want to sell them ("expectation of making financial gains").[459]

UNDERCOVER SCIENCE

Climatologists can hardly be seen as trustworthy if they keep their data secret. People just wonder what could be so confidential about thermometer measurements.

Lack of transparency in climatology was criticized by the World Federation of Scientists (Permanent Monitoring Panel for Climatology) as early as 1999. The document *Enabling Science Through Data Access in the Face of Increasing Protectionism* complained about increasing inaccessibility of data, often motivated by profit.

"The increasing commercialization of factual databases by both private and public sector institutions, supported and encouraged by the introduction of highly protectionist legal regimes and unfettered licensing rights, is antithetical to the tradition of full and open exchange of data. This is a threat to fundamental scientific research and education."[460] It is, therefore, no coincidence that the president of the World Federation of Scientists (established 1982), the Italian physicist Antonio Zichichi, is one of the renowned climate skeptics.

The Climate Research Unit (CRU) at the University of East Anglia is one of the institutions where lack of transparency became a big problem. This is the home of pioneering reconstructions of world temperature development in the 20th century. But when somebody asked them how exactly they calculated these global temperatures, they were unable to answer.

In 2005, Phil Jones, the director of CRU, wrote to the researcher Warwick Hughes: "We have 25 or so years invested in the work. Why should I make the data available to you when your aim is to try and find something wrong with it."[461] Such thinking goes against the true spirit of science. Finding mistakes is the very purpose of peer-review. Besides, isn't the public entitled to the data of measurements paid from their taxes?

Canadian researchers McIntyre and McKitrick also wanted to check if the CRUTEM global temperature graphs were correct. They asked for the global warming data, and the scientists refused to oblige for unknown reasons. Climatologist Phil Jones wrote fearfully to his colleague in an email: "And don't leave stuff lying around on anonymous download sites—you never know who is trawling them. McIntyre and McKitrick have been after the Climatic Research Unit... data for years. If they ever hear there is a Freedom of Information Act now in the United Kingdom, I think I'll delete the file rather than send it to anyone." He continued as follows:

"Does your similar Act in the United States force you to respond to inquiries within 20 days?—Ours does! The United Kingdom works on precedents, so the first request will test it. How uncivilized: Actually being forced to respond to inquiries! We also have a Data Protection Act, which I will hide behind."[462]

In summer 2009, CRU director Phil Jones, flooded with data requests, finally announced that he couldn't explain to anyone how he had created the CRUTEM's global temperature charts because he lost the calculations. Therefore, he was unable to explain how he came from raw data to the product presented to the public. Climatologist Pat Michaels wrote a mocking article about it called "Dog Ate Global Warming."[463] That is a typical excuse of why small children do not have their homework—the dog ate it.

In another Climategate email, Phil Jones writes to one of his colleagues: "I have a few things in mind—don't say anything to anyone... You can delete this attachment if you want. Keep it to yourself, but it is the person who, under the Freedom of Information Act, makes requests to publish the emails Keith and Tim wrote about Chapter 6 of the IPCC Fourth Report. I think we've found a way to get around it." Jones's email jokingly ends with a quote from the spy movie *Mission Impossible*: "This message will self-destruct in ten seconds."[464]

If climatologists base their claims on data that is inaccessible to the public, the reader cannot check if the author is telling the truth. But real science must be transparent. The World Meteorological Organization (WMO), in Resolution 40 of 1995, promised:

"As a fundamental principle of the World Meteorological Organization (WMO), and in consonance with the expanding requirements for its scientific and technical expertise, WMO commits itself to broadening and enhancing the free and unrestricted exchange of meteorological and related data and products."[465] Whereby "free and unrestricted" is defined as "non-discriminatory and without charge." This applies in particular to CLIMAT type data such as monthly temperatures from terrestrial weather stations.

Unfortunately, as we have seen, the reality was different. And the credibility of climatology was certainly damaged by such secrecy. Since then, the situation has somewhat improved not only thanks to the Internet but also due to the pressure of climate skeptics like Steve McIntyre.

MIKE'S TRICK

Scientists erased inconvenient data and replaced it with data from other sources from other locations. They wanted to cover up the findings that there was no warming in some parts of the world.

The hockey stick graph claimed that the climate warmed dramatically in the second half of the 20th century. But when British scientists Jones and Briffa of the Climate Research Unit (CRU) tried to replicate Mann's research, they hit a roadblock. In his 1999 tree ring study, Jones showed stagnation in temperatures throughout the second half of the 20th century.[466] And Briffa's 2000 study even showed cooling after World War II if only tree ring data is used.[467]

At a meeting in Arusha, Tanzania (1999), UN climate panel staff began to panic. Mann advocated that the inconvenient part of the Briffa's graph be concealed and erased: "Otherwise, the skeptics will have a field day casting doubt on our ability to understand the factors that influence these estimates and, thus, can undermine faith in the paleoestimates. I don't think that doubt is scientifically justified, and I'd hate to be the one to have to give it fodder!"[468]

Keith Briffa was troubled by conscience: "I know there is pressure to present a nice tidy story as regards 'apparent unprecedented warming in a thousand years or more in the proxy data,' but, in reality, the situation is not quite so simple... I believe that the recent warmth was probably matched about 1,000 years ago."[469] Phil Jones, CRU director, finally found a solution. He wrote to his colleagues: "I've just completed Mike's Nature trick of adding in the real temps to each series for the last 20 years (i.e., from 1981 onwards) and from 1961 for Keith's to hide the decline." The trick is to replace the original non-warming data with different data from another source that does show warming.

In the publication for World Meteorological Organization, he simply erased the inconvenient part of the graph.[470] Instead, he added thermometer readings from other locations. Moreover, he modified the charts so that the reader won't notice that they are comparing apples and oranges—the splicing of two different curves is not visible. Thereby, he enhanced Mann's trick... I mean method. Moreover, the scale of the chart was subjectively stretched as high as possible to make the warming look more pronounced. If a student of statistics did something like that, he would probably fail the exam. It is not acceptable to replace medieval temperatures measured by annual tree rings (locally) with temperatures measured by modern instruments (globally).

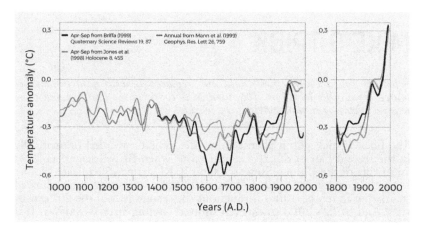

Figure 8—This is Mike's trick to hide the decline. On the right, you can see Figure 2-21 of the IPCC's Third Assessment Report (2001) with apparent warming. However, on the left, you can see what the curves originally looked like before the "trick." Briffa's study (solid black line on the left) showed 1945–1990 cooling by about 0.4 °C in the examined part of the world. In this trick, they erased Briffa's curve after 1961. Instead, they added instrumental measurements from quite different parts of the world. A 0.4 °C cooling suddenly transformed into a 0.4 °C warming. However, the studies by Mann (dashed) and Jones (green) do not confirm such warming either.[471]

Instead of honestly acknowledging that the annual tree rings are not quite reliable for measuring global temperature—neither now nor in Middle Ages, they decided on a cover-up. By doing so, they crossed the Rubicon. From the peaceful world of research laboratories, they stepped out into the political world of collusion, conspiracy, and espionage.

When Steve McIntyre became interested in who "erased" the proxy data (mainly tree rings) from the second half of the 20th century, climatologists became worried. Phil Jones (head of the English CRU) tried to cover up his tracks. He asked Mann and other colleagues by email to delete all correspondence on sensitive issues.

Jones: "Can you delete any emails you may have had with Keith regarding the latest IPCC report? Keith will do likewise... Can you also email Gene and get him to do the same? I don't have his new email address."[472] Those who investigated the Climategate scandal somehow forgot to ask about this. Only a year later, the NOAA inspection questioned Eugene Wahl, a climatologist, who confirmed that he had received a request to destroy the evidence, and he complied with it.[473]

THE LORD OF TREE RINGS

Tree rings are used in paleoclimatology as a natural thermometer because, in warm and humid years, vegetation thrives more, and tree rings grow wider. However, a tree can only indicate local microclimate, not the world "average" temperature.

In the second half of the 20th century, tree rings—as an indicator of temperature—do not reflect any dramatic "global warming," although instruments do. Scientists discussed this "divergence problem" as early as the 1990s. They thought the "treemometers" (pun intended) no longer measure the temperature correctly, a malfunction of some sort. Therefore, it has become a custom to ignore annual rings in the second half of the 20th century. Scientists simply erased the "colder" data and instead simulated "warmer" data from other regions and other types of measurements.

Whenever the public complained that this is blatant fraud, climatologists argued: "The so-called trick was nothing more than a statistical method used to bring two or more different kinds of data sets together in a legitimate fashion by a technique that has been reviewed by a broad array of peers in the field."[474] The Willis's UK parliamentary committee concluded its investigation into the Climategate affair like this:

"Professor Jones's actions were in line with common practice in the climate science community."[475] Mann explained: "Scientists often use the term "trick" to refer to "a good way to deal with a problem," rather than something that is "secret," and so there is nothing problematic in this at all."[476]

The trick might be considered legitimate if we were certain that the tree rings in the 20th century really malfunctioned and if we knew the cause of this malfunction. But such is not the case. Keith Briffa: "As yet, the cause is not understood, but a number of factors such as increasing atmospheric CO_2, higher levels of pollutant (i.e., nitrates or phosphates) transport, other changes in soil chemistry, or increased UV-B levels might be involved."[477] Rosanne D'Arrigo wrote about the "divergence problem" in an entire study claiming that it was an "anomalous" decrease in tree sensitivity and that it occurred "since the mid-20th century."[478] The culprit might be air pollution, maybe.

However, there is an even better explanation—that it is a statistical error. Perhaps trees are still good indicators of temperatures, as they have always been, and the "divergence problem" does not exist. The difference between the global instrumental data and the annual tree ring data is just due to different locations. Keep in mind that proxy measurement of temperature uses trees from cold regions, usually Nordic, because trees are most sensitive to climate change in harsh living conditions, i.e., in the cold north.

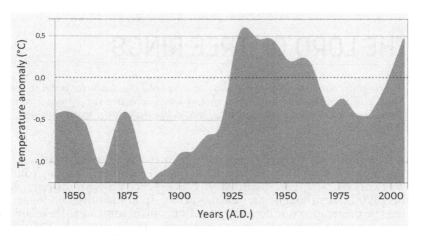

Figure 9—Instrumental temperature measurement from Greenland shows that the Nordic countries did not warm between World War II and the establishment of the IPCC (1988). The northern hemisphere was cooling for most of this period.[479]

Thermometers in Nordic sites confirm that there was no net warming between 1945 and 1990. In the first half of the "Cold War," the climate was cooling; in the second half of the period, temperatures were slowly climbing back up. The annual tree rings reflect this correctly. During this period, according to thermometers, there was no net warming in Greenland, the United States of America, or Scandinavia.[480] Why do the Nordic tree rings not reflect the global average temperature? Because a tree has no idea how warm it is on the other side of the planet. Unless a tree has psychic abilities such as telepathy, it is just an indicator of local microclimate.

When the "hockey stick" was created in the 1990s, it only covered data until about 1990. And this was mainly data from the Nordic regions, where no net warming occurred between the Second World War and the collapse of the USSR. Therefore, the tree rings showed non-warming correctly, and there was no legitimate reason to erase the data.

However, it is true that thermometer readings often differ slightly from proxy tree ring data. But why should we be surprised? After all, different tree ring data differ from each other too. How can someone blame the "divergence problem" on industrial pollution when pre-industrial data shows exactly the same "divergence problem"? The same "divergences" can be seen in a thousand years of data prior to 1880. Temperature reconstructions from each scientific team say something different. It is not an anomaly; it is common. Annual rings have never been and never will be an absolutely accurate indicator of temperature.

Actually, we should be surprised by the exact opposite. How the hell is it possible that in the period 1880–1950, the data does not show divergence? Isn't it weird that only in this single time period all reconstructions by all authors are in perfect agreement? The explanation seems to be human factor. It is called statistical cherry-picking. The researchers wanted to find trees where tree rings give the same curve as the thermometer measurements in the 1880–1950 period. And they kept searching until they found some. If you torture data long enough, it will confess to anything.

IN HER MAJESTY'S SECRET SERVICE

The suspect scientists handled the Climategate scandal in a do-it-yourself style. They asked their pals to investigate them, and the inquiry took place behind closed doors. One can surely imagine how "impartial" it was.

When emails of climatologists leaked to the public, the head of the Climate Research Unit at the University of East Anglia, Professor Phil Jones, was ashamed. His conspiracy statements such as "I've just completed Mike's Nature trick... to hide the decline" or "I think I'll delete the file rather than send it to anyone" made history.

What was his employer's first response to the Climategate email affair? Did the University of East Anglia initiate disciplinary proceedings to punish the scientists for unethical conduct? Not so. Instead, they hired media experts to help them sweep the scandal under the rug. The advisor, the Outside Organization agency, sent them the tabloid journalist Neil Wallis, with the poetic nickname "The Wolfman."[481] He is the same person who was investigated in 2011 for illegal wiretapping committed by *News of the World*. The involvement of this agency in whitewashing Climategate was revealed by their director Edwards, who could not resist and bragged about it in an interview for *Music Week*.[482]

"Don't tell the conspiracy theorists," the article begins. "But one PR company was at the center of the Michael Jackson funeral, Climategate, and Naomi Campbell's appearance at Charles Taylor's trial in The Hague." Its name is Outside Organization. It was also hired by the University of East Anglia to handle the media disaster of the Climategate scandal.[483] Had it not been for Edwards's huge ego, the operation would have remained unknown. "We don't advertise a lot of the things we do," Edwards says. "That was really interesting. It's very high level, and you're very much in the background on that sort of thing."

For example, Wolfman was asked to prepare scientists to be questioned by Willis's committee at the House of Commons—to rehearse their public statements like in a theater. The parliament investigated Climategate only briefly because there was no time.[484] Elections were looming. "Clearly, we would have liked to spend more time on this... We had to get something out before we were sent packing." So, the investigation was limited to a one-day—carefully rehearsed—theater performance.[485]

The suspects answered the questions in front of TV cameras, but no one verified their claims. They avoided problematic issues just as Wolfman had taught them. The conclusion of the investigation? Climategate practices are "in line with common practice" in climatology, which is unfortunately true.

159

Willis's parliamentary committee did not spend a lot of time on this because they hoped that the university would carry out a more detailed investigation anyway. That was naive in the first place—to believe that a university would investigate its own staff impartially, although their natural interest is to whitewash the scandal. It's like expecting a criminal to arrest himself. Such disciplinary investigations can perhaps work in a field where an isolated individual breaks the rules, and the university can distance itself from it. Climatology is something else, where bad behavior is common practice. If they punished one person for such conduct, they would have to punish also everybody else—including themselves.

The University of East Anglia (which includes the CRU) set up two inquiry bodies (Muir Russel's and Oxburgh's). The committees were reporting to Vice-Chancellor Acton, who had been helping the scientists to get around the Freedom of Information Act for years. It seems they have never heard the term "conflict of interest." The first committee was chaired by Lord Ron Oxburgh, who was said to be completely objective with no interest in maintaining climate panic. Except that he is the director of GLOBE, an eco-lobbying organization, president of the Carbon Capture and Storage Association, and president of Falck Renewables, which operates in the windmill industry.[486] It was like asking Mr. Rockefeller to carry out an audit of his own Standard Oil Company.

And Oxburgh's conclusions? His report says that the climate researchers' work is a mess ("slightly disorganized"). And the methodology of their figures would make a statistician weep ("not done in close cooperation with professional statistics"). They do not archive data, so they cannot explain how they had calculated their results ("they are not ready to be the center of public attention").[487]

Let us remember that we are talking about a pioneering reconstruction of global temperatures, which they have been doing since the 1980s. The Oxburgh committee had the term "Science Appraisal" in its name, so MEPs naively believed that the commission would check the accuracy of studies and CRU figures.[488] But that didn't happen. Phil Willis of the House of Commons was surprised by the Oxburgh report: "Quite frankly, I couldn't believe it! …There has been a sleight of hand in that the actual terms of reference were not what we had been led to believe.[489] Sleight of hand is a trick used by magicians on stage to confuse the public.

The Oxburgh Commission was supposed to assess scientific accuracy of selected CRU studies. However, they let the accused scientists select these studies at will. And then they made a phone call to the president of the Royal Society asking him whether they could pretend that it was the idea of the Royal Society. The president agreed to play along.[490] But in the end, it does not matter, as the report does not evaluate the correctness of these studies anyway. The Oxburgh report is an eight-page long essay about how a good climatologist should work, without commenting on whether this is really being followed in practice. It reads like a child from kindergarten telling you what daddy does at work.

The second UEA committee was chaired by Sir Muir Russel. Its independence is also in dispute. One of its members was Geoffrey Boulton, who taught at the Department of Environment at UEA for 18 years (which he "forgot" to mention). In recent years, he had been a loud activist and performed publicly with a CRU member on several occasions (another "omission"). One member of the Muir Russel committee, David Eyton, was from the R&D department of the British Petroleum (BP) oil company, which had sponsored CRU for years. Well, a sponsor who invested a lot of money in UEA is not a very impartial arbitrator.[491]

Although the committee clearly was not independent, they at least put the word "independent" in its official title (Independent Assessment of Climate Change Emails).[492] Sir Humphrey from the TV series *Yes Minister* would understand: "Always dispose of the difficult bit in the title. Does less harm there than in the text. The less you intend to do about something, the more you have to talk about it."

The committee produced a detailed 60-page report and correctly described many instances of improper conduct of scientists, always ending in a tolerant tone—actually, the researchers did not murder anyone, so it's no big deal. Sure, there are legal loopholes, and many reprehensible deeds are not illegal. But are they ethical? The committee completely avoided investigation of the main scandals. For example, it completely "forgot" to question Phil Jones on why he was asking his colleagues to delete the emails.[493]

Although none of the investigations were independent, the media claimed the scientists were exonerated. Grist: "'Climategate' scientists cleared of all charges by independent review."[494] Scientific American wrote: "Climategate scientist cleared in inquiry, again."[495] Journalists followed their usual work procedure—parrot official statements of authorities without questioning. Just print whatever the ruling elite says, and don't ever dare ask inconvenient questions!

The situation in the media is so bad that genuine investigative journalism must be done by citizens themselves—by bloggers like Steve McIntyre. The rigged investigation, therefore, only deepened the suspicion that something sinister was happening. If the climatologists had nothing to hide, they would have agreed to a true independent investigation. But one thing has to be appreciated. At least all "investigative" committees acknowledged that climatologists should be more open.

STATE PENN OR PENN STATE?

The climatologist Mann, author of the hockey stick graph, will sue anyone who doubts that the investigation really "exonerated" him. But the whole so-called investigation consisted of just one friendly chat over a cup of tea.

The University where Michael Mann was working swept the whole Climategate affair under the rug as well. In January 2010, the university president Spanier said: "I know they have taken the time and spent hundreds of hours studying documents and interviewing people and looking at issues from all sides." In reality, the whole investigation was a two-hour friendly chat with Mike. Mann's critics were not invited for questioning, not even Steve McIntyre, whose requests for data were avoided by the secretive scientists for years.

If there is no plaintiff, there is no judge. And they really did not invite any victim of the scientific misconduct, nor any accuser of the scientists. The only climate skeptic that was brought in was Professor Lindzen. When he heard that the committee had already found Mann innocent on three of the four charges, Lindzen exclaimed in disbelief: "It's thoroughly amazing. I mean, these are issues that he explicitly stated in the emails. I'm wondering what is going on!"[496]

Marc Morano, editor-in-chief at *Climatedepot.com,* commented briefly: "This is not surprising that Mann's own university circled the wagons and narrowed the focus of its own investigation to declare him ethical. The fact that the investigation cited Mann's 'level of success in proposing research and obtaining funding' as some sort of proof that he was meeting the 'highest standards' tells you that Mann is considered a sacred funding cash cow. At the height of his financial career, similar sentiments could have been said about Bernie Madoff."[497]

Attorney Ken Cuccinelli was not satisfied with how Penn State University handled the scandal. He wanted to reopen Mann's case; so, he asked the University of Virginia—where Mann worked at the time of the hockey stick research—for access to Mann's emails and documents from that time. He wanted to investigate whether Mann's "trick" constitutes a crime because by creating a false alarm, Mann gained fame and a lot of grants he wouldn't otherwise have received.

Such misappropriation of taxpayer money is illegal under the 2002 Fraud Against Taxpayers Act. However, the university refused to release the documents. What are they hiding? What is so important that they are willing to spend half a million dollars on a lawsuit?[498]

Actually, Penn State had another scandal from 2009 to 2012. It turned out that the university covered the sports coach Sandusky, who sexually abused kids on the university team. The commentators noticed similarities between the two cases. Mark Steyn from *National Review* wrote about the university: "If an institution is prepared to cover up systemic statutory rape of minors, what won't it cover up?... His "investigation" by a deeply corrupt administration was a joke."[499]

Mann sued Steyn for these statements. No one has the right to criticize him because "an independent investigation exonerated him." In the book *The Hockey Stick and the Climate Wars* with the subtitle *Dispatches from the Front Lines,* Mann describes himself as a heroic freedom fighter assaulted viciously by the henchmen of Big Oil.[500]

Mann can afford expensive lawyers like John. B. Williams of Cozen O'Connor law firm, who previously represented tobacco and oil corporations. Mann wants to silence his critics with the threat of a protracted court battle. At other times, Mann threatened to sue the authors of the satirical video clip "Hide the Decline" because they were using his photo without authorization. The authors were ordinary citizens (Minnesotans 4 Global Warming) who had no money for lawyers. They got scared of the lawsuit from a wealthy climatologist and retracted the video.[501]

Mann clearly thinks more like a ruthless Wall Street lawyer rather than a scientist. Years ago, when mathematician Doug Keenan criticized Mann's colleagues Jones and Wei Chyung Wang for having poorly measured urban heat islands in China,[502] Mann proposed to send his lawyers (2007):

"Wei Chyung needs to sue them or, at the least, threaten a lawsuit. If he doesn't, this will set a dangerous new precedent. I could put him in touch with a leading attorney who would do this free of charge. Of course, this has to be done quickly. The threat of a lawsuit alone may prevent them from publishing this paper, so time is of the essence."[503] Yet, in a later interview for *Nature,* Jones admitted that Keenan's criticism was justified.[504]

After several years, Mann's desperate effort to bury his data became suspicious even to journalists. In February 2014, representatives of 18 world media such as *Reuters, The Associated Press, The Washington Post, The Newspaper Association of America,* and *The Reporters Committee for Freedom of Press* encouraged the court to disclose Mann's data that was paid from taxpayers' money.[505]

But Mann was so afraid of disclosure of his data that he would rather lose a court battle. Mann sued Tim Ball, a Canadian scientist, for his insensitive statement that Mann "belongs in the state penn, not Penn State." Meaning: belongs in prison, not university. In the end, Mann lost the lawsuit (2019). The court declared it was unable to ascertain if Mann is a fraudster who belongs in the state penn, because Mann—committing contempt of court—refused to disclose his data for verification.[506] The court decided that Mann must pay all court expenses to Mr. Ball. In spite of the happy ending, many considered it a cynical SLAPP (Strategic Lawsuit Against Public Participation)—the court case dragged on for years, which was a financial burden for a retired person like Ball.

POST-NORMAL SCIENCE

When hiring a scientist as an expert advisor, a politician does not want to hear about uncertainty of the models. The client wants results and wants them right away!

The UN climate panel scandals resemble political scandals for a good reason. The Intergovernmental Panel on Climate Change was established in the United Nations in 1988. Ten years later, climate scientist Hans von Storch and sociologist Dennis Bray identified the institution as a model example of the so-called post-normal science, which is a hybrid of science and politics.

In the article *Climate Science: An Empirical Example of Post-normal Science,* the authors warn that politicians love simple solutions. They quote a policymaker: "I would love to have a one-handed scientist because a scientist will testify and say, 'on the one hand,' such and such and then 'on the other hand,' such and such and that doesn't give any policy guidance."[507]

The concept of post-normal science was developed in the 1980s by mathematicians Silvio Funtowicz and Jerome Ravetz. Their 1993 article, *Science for the Post-normal Age,* is still the most cited article in the history of the Futures journal.[508]

After the tragic crash of the Challenger space shuttle and the Chernobyl explosion, Ravetz and Funtowicz concluded that Kuhn's theory of "normal" science was no longer enough. Science is no longer about competing paradigms that result from puzzle-solving in the peace of a laboratory. Scientists now work for employers and work under pressure. This sometimes forces scientists to downplay uncertainties or risks; Funtowicz and Ravetz, therefore, advocate the democratization of science—it should be open to scrutiny by citizens that form an "Extended Peer Community."

Climate alarmists say that "uncertainty" in science is a fabrication manufactured by "climate deniers." But Ravetz was discussing uncertainty in science long before climate warming debate started. In 1971, he published an influential book on uncertainty in science called *Scientific Knowledge and Its Social Problems.*[509] He has always realized that science is not an island, entire of itself, and is influenced by society.

In particular, post-normal science deals with risk assessment where stakes are high, decisions are urgent, but facts are uncertain and values in dispute. Jeroen van der Sluijs calls this high risk surrounded with uncertainty an "uncertainty monster." These are things that many scientists fear.[510] There are several ways how to deal with such monsters. You can try to banish the monster and get rid of it. You can learn to live with it.

You can just modify how it is described to make it look less threatening. Some people are even able to embrace it as good news.

The best solution is not passivity—we need to acknowledge uncertainty and learn to deal with it. According to Sluijs, this means we should follow the precautionary principle—when in doubt, act so as to minimize the damage. However, if risk protection costs more than the risk itself, you would worsen the damage instead of mitigating it. Unfortunately, many proponents of the precautionary principle forget this—and they demand that risk must be lowered at any cost, not even caring if the cure kills the patient.

Fear sometimes leads scientists to exaggerate in order to make the public notice something. Legendary is the quote of climatologist Stephen Schneider, which I shall—to avoid excuses about a misquote—reprint in full: "On the one hand, as scientists, we are ethically bound to the scientific method, in effect promising to tell the truth, the whole truth, and nothing but—which means that we must include all doubts, the caveats, the ifs, and the buts. On the other hand, we are not just scientists but human beings as well. And like most people, we'd like to see the world a better place, which in this context translates into our working to reduce the risk of potentially disastrous climate change. To do that, we need to get some broad-based support to capture the public's imagination. That, of course, means getting loads of media coverage. So, we have to offer up scary scenarios, make simplified, dramatic statements, and make little mention of any doubts we might have. This 'double ethical bind' we frequently find ourselves in cannot be solved by any formula. Each of us has to decide what the right balance is between being effective and being honest. I hope that means being both."[511]

Such a scientist no longer acts as a scientist but as a politician who diplomatically chooses when to hide the truth and when to exaggerate. The theory of post-normal science is, therefore, perceived by its critics as an insidious attempt to make the politicization of science seem legitimate. British journalist James Delingpole wrote angrily: "In 1991, a Marxist philosopher called Jerome R. Ravetz had helped to invent a seductive and dangerous new concept called 'post-normal science' (PNS). No longer was it considered essential that scientists strive after objectivity. Their new duty, Ravetz held, was not to 'truth' but to what he called 'quality.' And by 'quality' he meant something more akin to rhetoric—the ability to manipulate evidence and present it in such a way as to achieve particular political ends."[512]

Indeed, some authors advocate replacing the traditional ethical standards of scientific research with something else. Robert Merton declared in the 1940s that a scientist should be impartial, share his data for free, and scientists should not discriminate on the basis of faith or nationality. A scientist should prefer skeptical thinking to belief in authority. These principles are known by the acronym CUDOS. Some believe that modern post-normal science can no longer honor these classical demands and, therefore, needs to set different goals such as sustainability, robustness, flexibility, etc.[513] Climategate scientists, however, did not respect even these milder standards; in particular, they failed to transparently admit uncertainty. Proper uncertainty handling is paramount in post-normal science.

The creator of post-normal science theory did not intend to legitimize unscientific conduct. Ravetz likes to explain his theory with the water dam construction parable. The principle of hydroelectric power plants is a question of pure science. It is important not to make a mistake in the calculations. Designing a specific dam in a specific location is a task for professional consultants. They must consider the interests of the client. For example, there may be pressure to use cheaper material to save money.

If the dam is to flood a village or a war heroes cemetery, it becomes a question of post-normal science, a problem on the border of science and politics. "The thought of putting party hacks or eco-activists in charge of explaining the science of the dam or creating its design was very far from my intention. As it happens, dams can be intensely political indeed, as some peoples' lands and homes are drowned so that others far away can benefit from their products; should we leave all those decisions to scientists and engineers?"[514]

The post-normal science concept is often misunderstood, just like Kuhn's theory about the rivalry of paradigms in science. Some see it as a tragic description of how bad the situation is, while others consider it a prescription of something that is desirable.

Post-normal science theory is often used by environmentalists to justify the precautionary principle. Many were, therefore, surprised by Ravetz' praise for critics of climatology when the Climategate affair broke out. In the article *The Climate Crisis Could Be Solved by Courteous Communication,* published by the British Guardian, he wrote: "Science is no longer an affair of isolated individuals discovering their facts. With external funding for big projects, the pressures on scientists to behave like authoritarian managers rather than free inquirers are strong and growing. There are many cases of abuse of the principles of scientific debate."[515]

Ravetz criticizes climatologists for hiding the uncertainties and weaknesses of their models from the public. "It's ironic that I got my real breakthrough in understanding what is going on with Climategate when I identified all the critics on their blogs (and especially this one) as the new Extended Peer Community in this post-normal science situation. For they have been doing the job of quality assurance that, in some cases at least, was not done by the mainstream. They might have to decide now whether they really want to belong to an Extended Peer Community, and thereby validate post-normal science."[516]

A year later, Ravetz held a symposium in Lisbon with the support of the European Commission. He invited leading skeptics and alarmists to settle their disputes. Journalist Fred Pearce wrote: "The meeting was the brainchild of University of Oxford science philosopher Jerry Ravetz, an 81-year-old Greenpeace member who fears Al Gore may have done as much damage to environmentalism as Joseph Stalin did to socialism. Post-Climategate, he found climate science characterized by "a poisoned atmosphere" in which "each side accuses the other of being corrupt."[517]

Although the conference had an optimistic title, Reconciliation in the Climate Change Debate, none of the mainstream climatologists arrived. UN climate scientists did not indicate any interest to debate anyone. Gavin Schmidt (a colleague of Michael Mann) turned down the invitation because science is settled, and there is nothing to discuss. Even Pearce's report was deleted from *NewScientist* as if it never happened.

VI. CLIMATE MODELS

Climatologists have always been warning that climate change may endanger food production. They just couldn't decide whether "climate deterioration" meant cooling or warming. In the 1970s, many scientists warned that post-war climate cooling brought droughts, floods, and other weather extremes. Then it began to warm up, and scientists changed their minds. Floods, droughts, and other natural disasters are the result of warming, not cooling. And only investment in research of the greenhouse effect can prevent this warming.

In full circle, the age of superstition is back with a vengeance. In the 18th century, science rejected the idea that weather is somehow controlled by gods and supernatural forces. People were slowly getting used to the idea that weather was governed by impersonal laws of nature. But after two centuries, the belief that bad weather is unnatural has returned. That clouds in the sky are some kind of punishment for our sins. The belief in the anthropogenic origin of "climate disruption" is simply as old as mankind itself.

In the Middle Ages, people used to watch storms and lightning with awe, convinced that witches were certainly responsible. Today, such behavior might be the subject of ridicule. But deciding how much climate and weather variations are of natural or unnatural origin is difficult even with the latest technology. The climate system is a complicated beast, full of feedbacks that amplify or neutralize each other.

A climatologist who predicts future climate scenarios sometimes finds himself in a similar position as astrologers with their crystal balls. What is a clairvoyant supposed to tell the king when the stars do not speak clearly? If I admit the uncertainty, won't I lose all my funding? One must tread carefully in this minefield—instead of one forecast, let us make dozens of scenarios for various conditions that may or may not occur. Are you saying they contradict each other? Great! You will always be able to pull one out of the hat and say: I told you! Your client will be completely baffled by this confusing mumbo-jumbo. So, you give him an answer, but you make sure he won't understand. Then he can't complain if the prediction turns out wrong.

Another problem is groupthink. Scientists may become overconfident if one clan of scientists wins with their pet theory. As long as they wield control of their field, they do not want to hear about any other factors other than CO_2, as this would undermine the importance of their research. The resulting climate models are so simplified that they have little to do with reality.

Water vapor is a stronger greenhouse gas than carbon dioxide. But the models ignore it, although any sun-induced warming must be intensified by water vapor. No wonder that the models make no sense. Although the climate has always been regulated by various ocean cycles and phenomena such as El Niño, they are absent from the models. We do not know what causes them, so we cannot fit it into global circulation equations.

You won't ever see scenarios of what would happen if solar activity dropped. We cannot predict how solar activity will develop. We don't even know why it fluctuates. The scenarios of future changes in cloud cover are contradictory. When the cloud cover increases, we do not know whether the climate will warm or cool or not change at all. Now imagine how insiders must laugh when they hear on television that "science is settled."

Physical models of the atmosphere use the latest technology and complicated mathematical equations. It is certainly enough to impress the ordinary Joe. Unfortunately, the equation is worthless if you cannot measure the variables in the formula. When climate scientists reach such a dead end, they simply estimate the unknown variables. The accuracy of such estimates is often similar to a coin-toss.

The models estimate that carbon dioxide is as powerful as Hercules. It plays the role of a Deus ex Machina. When the inputs and outputs in a model do not match because something is missing there, you can just wave your magic wand and say that "greenhouse gases" are to blame. Nobody has measured their effects and feedback precisely. Estimates—how much a doubling of CO_2 would warm the atmosphere—have been for forty years in almost the same range between 1.5°C and 4.5°C (Charney Report 1979). There are also higher or lower estimates.

When real temperatures differ from what the model predicted, one doesn't say the model is "worthless" but that it is "drifting." The models did not expect a pause in warming after 1998, one generation long. The scientists were taken aback. First, they denied the existence of this "pause," then reluctantly acknowledged it and started a desperate search for—sometimes contradictory—explanations. Eventually, they decided that there was never a pause. The pause was just a myth perpetrated by Big Oil. And how come the measured data say the opposite? Never mind, data can be "corrected," historical records can be reimagined. History is written by the winners.

GREENHOUSE EFFECT

In the ice ages, atmospheric greenhouse gases always increased in response to warming, not the other way around. Without the "evil" greenhouse effect, it would be too cold on Earth to be habitable.

Scientists have long wondered that due to the distance from the sun, Earth should be much cooler. It was not until the 19th century when the French scientist Joseph Fourier suggested an explanation—atmosphere functions as thermal insulation and retains heat. Like a greenhouse. This phenomenon may have played an important role in the history of the planet. In 1896, the Swedish scientist Svante Arrhenius came up with the theory that it was these fluctuations of greenhouse gases in the atmosphere that caused the waxing and waning of ice and interglacial periods.

At that time, the greenhouse effect was seen as a beneficial phenomenon, without which Earth would be less hospitable to life. In his 1908 book, Arrhenius expressed the hope that industrial coal combustion could release enough carbon dioxide into the atmosphere to avert onset of the next ice age. "We often hear lamentations that coal stored up in the earth is wasted by the present generation without any thought of the future... We may find a kind of consolation in the consideration that here, as in every other case, there is good mixed with evil. By the influence of increasing percentage of carbonic acid in the atmosphere, we may hope to enjoy ages with more equable and better climates, especially as regards the colder regions of the earth, ages when the earth will bring forth much more abundant crops than at present, for the benefit of rapidly propagating mankind."[518]

In 1957, Roger Revelle and Hans Suess (both employees of the Scripps Institute of Oceanography, California) published an article arguing that the oceans are unable to absorb all human CO_2 emissions, resulting in carbon dioxide accumulating in the atmosphere. This discovery was a side-effect of their work for the army. Originally, they were investigating how, after nuclear tests, radioactive substances remain on the surface of the ocean instead of dropping rapidly to the seabed.

At the Scripps Institute, they started to measure atmospheric CO_2 growth continuously. The project was commissioned by Charles D. Keeling, who established an observatory on Mauna Loa Island in Hawaii. Keeling's measurements have shown that the planet seems to "breathe." In other words, the CO_2 concentration in the atmosphere fluctuates during the seasons. Most of the vegetation is in the northern hemisphere, and in winter, when the plants are "asleep," there is no one to consume CO_2, which then accumulates in the atmosphere. It is an irony: The highest concentrations of this greenhouse gas are in winter, when the temperatures are the lowest.

The annual measurement of increase in CO_2 concentration of the atmosphere is called the Keeling Curve. When Keeling started in 1958, he measured less than 320 ppm of carbon dioxide, whereas, in 2014, it was 400 ppm. By way of comparison, in the 18th century, the concentration of carbon dioxide in the atmosphere is estimated to have been about 280 ppm. Anyway, today's levels are still low compared to the Jurassic epoch, when atmospheric CO_2 concentrations were over 2,000 ppm.[519]

The concentration of carbon dioxide in prehistoric times can be estimated when we examine air bubbles trapped in old glaciers—it is a sort of natural archive. In the Antarctic glaciers, the Soviets were the first to drill at the Vostok station (1970), gradually acquiring data of nearly half a million years. The Vostok borehole reached a depth of over three kilometers. The results were analyzed and published in the late 1990s. Although carbon dioxide is a greenhouse gas, its direct effect on temperatures appeared to be modest. The climates of the glacial era were dominated by exactly an opposite relationship.

"High-resolution records from Antarctic ice cores show that carbon dioxide concentrations increased by 80 to 100 parts per million by volume 600 to 400 years after the warming of the last three deglaciations."[520] In ice ages, CO_2 changes occurred hundreds of years after temperature changes, as confirmed by the study of authors like Caillon[521] and Petit.[522] There is speculation about how much the released CO_2 acts as a feedback. We may certainly talk about it, but the measured data show only the effect of temperatures on CO_2, not vice versa.

The effect of temperatures on carbon dioxide can be easily verified by anyone. Henry's law says that when heated, the solubility of gas in water decreases (outgassing). If you leave a soda bottle in the sun, the cork will soon pop out like opening a champagne bottle. That is why from today's sea-level temperature, a scientist can predict how its pCO_2 (partial pressure of CO_2) will change tomorrow.

Of course, people are also contributing to the rise in CO_2 levels by burning fossil fuels, yet even today, the influence of temperatures on CO_2 is still relevant. The year-on-year rate of atmospheric CO_2 change depends on how warm each year was, not vice versa. Year-on-year CO_2 fluctuations always begin in the warm ocean of the southern hemisphere near the equator, not in industrial areas.[523]

About 38,000 gigatons of carbon are stored in the oceans. Atmospheric CO_2 concentrations respond to global temperature changes with a delay of about six months.[524] We were able to test this in a natural open-air experiment. Volcanic cooling after the explosion of Pinatubo volcano in 1991 brought a sharp decline in the annual growth of atmospheric CO_2, despite the continuing rise of fossil fuel emissions.

For the pioneer of CO_2 measurement Charles D. Keeling, this was unexpected. In his study in *Nature* (1995), he concluded that natural factors played a greater role in this change of atmospheric CO_2 growth than changes in fossil fuel combustion, which means that you cannot predict growth in atmospheric CO_2 levels based solely on expected industrial activity.[525]

Roger Revelle also warned of hasty conclusions. In an interview with *Omni* in 1984, Revelle objected to the carbon hypothesis: "I estimate that the total increase [in CO_2] over the past hundred years has been about 21%. But whether the increase will lead to a significant rise in global temperature, we can't absolutely say." When asked what such warming would mean, Revelle responded: "There may be lots of effects. Increased CO_2 in the air acts like a fertilizer for plants... you get more plant growth. Increasing CO_2 levels also affect water transpiration, causing plants to close their pores and sweat less. That means plants will be able to grow in drier climates."[526] *Omni*: "Does the increase in CO_2 have anything to do with people saying the weather is getting worse?" Revelle: "People are always saying the weather's getting worse. Actually, the CO_2 increase is predicted to temper weather extremes."[527]

GLOBAL COOLING

From the Second World War until the 1970s, the northern hemisphere was cooling considerably, given the growth in greenhouse gases.

In 1939, after lengthy analysis of meteorological station data in Britain, amateur meteorologist Guy Callendar concluded that temperatures had risen since the 19th century. As a possible explanation, he proposed the so-called Callendar effect, i.e., the effect of coal combustion, which causes greenhouse gases to be released into the atmosphere. In 1938, he wrote:

"In conclusion, it may be said that the combustion of fossil fuel... is likely to prove beneficial to mankind in several ways, besides the provision of heat and power. For instance, the above-mentioned small increases of mean temperature would be important at the northern margin of cultivation, and the growth of favorably situated plants is directly proportional to carbon dioxide pressure. In any case, the return of deadly glaciers should be delayed indefinitely."[528] But a few years later, climate began cooling, and Callendar, in his later, years began to doubt his own theory. One photograph shows him in 1962 at the very end of his life, shoveling away record snowdrifts.

The irony is that cooling occurred during the greatest increase in greenhouse emissions—after World War II, there was a boom in automobilism and oil pipeline construction. Why the warming stopped is not entirely clear. According to Wallace Broecker (1975), the post-war cooling was due to ancient climate cycles (Camp Century Cycles), which, among other things, affect cloud cover.[529] According to glacier boreholes in Camp Century, Greenland, the climate has been oscillating like that for centuries. Today we call this cycle AMO (Atlantic Multidecadal Oscillation).

Others believed that the cooling was caused by industrial air pollution. An effect similar to nuclear winter (global dimming). In 1971, Rassool and Schneider's article, *Atmospheric Carbon Dioxide and Aerosols: The Effects of Large Increases on Global Climate,* claimed that dust particles from industrial smokestacks shielded the sun like some artificial clouds.[530] Schneider even made the documentary *The Weather Machine* for the BBC about the threat of cooling. Later he changed his mind and became the herald of global warming.

The aerosol theory has not been unequivocally proven until today. The global measurement of atmospheric transparency (Optical Atmospheric Thickness) shows every volcano eruption, but there is no industry-related dust particle trend. It is possible that the dust had only a local effect. "Global dimming" (a decrease in the surface solar radiation) might also have been caused by natural increase in cloud cover.

Many scientists like Mikhail Budyko believed that the warming effect of CO_2 would soon prevail over the cooling factors, whatever they are. But journalists prefer bad news, so they gave more room to pessimists like Hubert H. Lamb. In 1972, he established the main climatological institute in Britain (Climate Research Unit) and today the building bears his name. In 1966, Lamb writes about global cooling: "On this evidence, something like the climatic regime of the years since 1960 should probably be expected to persist till the end of the century or beyond."[531]

In his 1977 book *Climate: Present, Past and Future: Volume 2,* he refers to the World Meteorological Organization's predictions (WMO, Working Group on Climatic Fluctuations and Man). Lamb: "There is a considerable measure of agreement between the 24 forecasts listed. Expectation of a trend toward colder climates with weakened general atmospheric circulation from 1950 or 1960 onwards seems to have been well verified by the actual weather to date. Most forecasts expect this regime to continue into the 21st century, possibly into the second half of that century, in some cases with a further sharp cooling around 1980, and somewhat easier conditions for a time in the first half of that century."[532] Today, the World Meteorological Organization acts as if none of these cooling predictions ever existed.

The US State Climatology Program—now focused on global warming—was created in the 1970s to deal with global cooling. A key role was played by the Quaternary geologist George Kukla. In the early 1970s, he estimated from the length of past interglacials that the current one seems to be coming to an end. After migrating from communist Czechoslovakia to the United States, he did research for the Lamont-Doherty Earth Observatory. In 1972, along with Robert Matthews, he convened a conference: The Present Interglacial: How and When Will It End?

This resulted in an urgent letter to President Nixon about the conclusions of the conference: "The present rate of cooling seems fast enough to bring glacial temperatures in about a century if continuing at the present pace." Nixon's government responded by convening an extraordinary research panel: Ad Hoc Panel on the Present Interglacial. The experts concluded that the climate was cooling at a rate of 0.15°C per year and that this cooling would last until 2015.

Also, the National Science Board, an advisory body to the Congress and US president, stated in its report *Science and the Challenges Ahead* in 1974: "During the last 20–30 years, world temperature has fallen, irregularly at first, but more sharply over the last decade. The cause of the cooling trend is not known with certainty. But there is increasing concern that man himself may be implicated."[533] So, we don't know what is happening, but we would love to blame it on mankind. Otherwise, the story would not be compelling enough, and we wouldn't get subsidies for research.

Even the CIA felt the need to participate, and in 1974, they prepared an internal analysis: *A Study of Climatological Research as It Pertains to*

Intelligence Problems.[534] They relied on the research of Reid Bryson, who founded the Center for Climate Research at the University of Wisconsin in 1963. Bryson was—by today's terminology—a climate skeptic. "You can go outside and spit and have the same effect as doubling carbon dioxide," he said.

In the book *Climates of Hunger,* 1977, Bryson warned that climate cooling has always led to crop failures.[535] According to a CIA report, "a forecast by the University of Wisconsin projects that the earth's climate is returning to that of the neo-boreal era (1600–1850)—an era of drought, famine, and political unrest in the Western world."[536] The report illustrates the danger of cooling by the same types of "disasters" that today are associated with global warming.

"Costa Rica and Honduras (1973)—the worst drought in 50 years. Pakistan (August 1973)—the worst flood in 20 years affected 2.8 million acres... Six West African countries south of the Sahara, known as the Sahel... became the first victims of the climate change. The failure of the African monsoon beginning in 1968 has driven these countries to the edge of economic and political ruin... Early in the 1970s... the Moscow region suffered the worst drought in three to five hundred years," the CIA reports.[537]

Based on these findings, the White House Domestic Council in 1974 launched government-sponsored climate research. Deterioration of climate and its impact on food production appeared to be a question of national security. Congress approved this plan in 1978 (National Climate Program Act). The government was to invest about $50 million a year to the urgent research of global cooling.[538] As soon as these maneuvers were initiated to save us from the imminent ice age, the very opposite happened of what the science had predicted. The climate began warming up.

PAUSE IN GLOBAL WARMING

A pause in global warming between 1998 and 2012 baffled the climatologists and sparked a number of theories to explain it. Eventually, they found a way around it. They rewrote the temperature records and simply erased them.

On June 23, 1988, the climatologist James Hansen from NASA gave a speech at the US Congress. In the past, he studied the planet Venus with its strong greenhouse effect. Now, he was coming with a warning that unless we stop burning coal, we will have drastic global warming, just like Venus. He presented three scenarios generated by his computer model.[539] Scenario A ("business as usual") said what would happen if the growth of CO_2 emissions kept accelerating (at a rate of 1.5% per year). Scenario B said what would happen if annual CO_2 emissions no longer increased. Scenario C said what would happen if CO_2 emissions were falling. Then the warming would stop.

He chose a hot summer day for his presentation, and it seemed that a mere glance out of the window proved him right. Robert Jastrow, the founder of NASA's Goddard Institute, repeatedly criticized his successor Hansen for such dramatic gestures. Hansen was even repeatedly arrested by the police at demonstrations or riots against coal-fired power plants. Since burning of coal releases greenhouse gases, he declared coal "the greatest threat to civilization and life on this planet." In his book *Storms of My Grandchildren,* Hansen recalls how cargo trains ferrying coal reminded him of death. "But it was that day in Iowa when we visited our parents' gravesites that I realized those coal trains are death trains. The railroad cars may well be loaded with the species themselves, carrying them to their extermination."[540]

A few years after the climax of the global warming awareness campaign, the United States was hit by a series of very harsh winters that included blizzards, huge snowdrifts, and public transport collapse. For example, in February 2010, the USA was hit by a "Snowmageddon," three large snowstorms in a single month! Snowstorms also increased in Siberia. In the winter of 2009 to 2010 in Asia, especially Mongolia, millions of cattle died in an unexpectedly stiff blizzard.[541]

Proponents of the global warming hypothesis did not know how to deal with this situation. So, they said that cooling does not disprove warming; it actually confirms it. In early 2009, *Scientific American* wrote: *Why Global Warming Can Mean Harsher Winter Weather.* [542] They explain the issue away as a consequence of jet stream behavior becoming more erratic due to increased global temperature. But that hypothesis would also need to work in the opposite direction too. Is that supposed to mean that in the Little Ice Age, winters were generally warmer and milder? Because they weren't. It seems that the global warming crowd decided that their pet theory cannot be refuted by any observation, which is certainly very comfortable. But according to Karl Popper's demarcation criteria, a hypothesis that cannot be falsified by any observation is not science at all.

Historian Paul Johnson describes his experience with the green movement similarly.[543] "That's the Greens' stock response to anything weather-related. Too much sun? 'Global warming.' Too little sun? 'Global warming.' Drought? 'Global warming.' Floods? 'Global warming.' Freezing cold? 'Global warming.'" And Johnson concludes: "Marxism, Freudianism, global warming. These are proof—of which history offers so many examples—that people can be suckers on a grand scale. To their fanatical followers, they are a substitute for religion."

At first, the scientists downplayed the pause in global warming because a few years don't mean much. Benjamin Santer et al. (2011) said that at least 17 years must have passed since the end of warming in order to distinguish between climate signal and noise.[544] Finally, the UN Climate Panel acknowledged in its Fifth Assessment Report (2013) that over the previous 14 years (1998–2012), the warming trend had been close to zero. Specifically, from –0.05 to +0.15°C in ten years. This is called a "hiatus" or a warming pause.

Temperatures were at or near the lower limit of predictions of different models. In view of these developments, the UN climate panel in its Fifth Assessment Report (2013), shifted its lower estimate of future warming down from 2°C to just 1.5°C. This is already approaching the climate skeptic upper estimate of 1.1°C.[545]

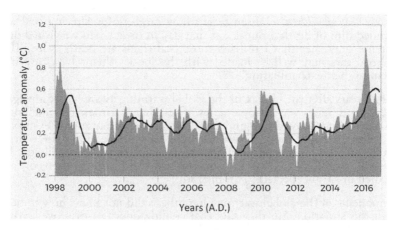

Figure 10—Global temperatures as measured by satellites, RSS (Remote Sensing Systems), TLT satellite channel. From 1998 to 2016, the so-called hiatus in global warming can be seen. The warming stopped for a full one generation.[546]

Emissions increased more than in Hansen's pessimistic scenario A, but warming is between scenarios B and C. Also, most of the 73 climate models in the CMIP-5 database from the whole world overestimated the warming. This discrepancy is the worst around the equator at higher tropospheric levels, as Roy Spencer, the creator of the satellite temperature measurement method, pointed out.[547]

Fifteen years later in *Scientific American* (2004), Hansen admitted that he had been exaggerating a bit: "Emphasis on extreme scenarios may have been appropriate at one time, when the public and decision-makers were relatively unaware of the global warming issue, and energy sources such as "synfuels," shale oil, and tar sands were receiving strong consideration. Now, however, the need is for demonstrably objective climate forcing scenarios consistent with what is realistic under current conditions."[548]

The alarmists began to look for an explanation why warming had stopped for so long. There was an idea that warming might still be here, just hiding. Some called this a warming "in the pipeline"—coming but not yet here.[549] Climatologist Trenberth was lamenting: "Well, I have my own article on where the heck is global warming? We are asking that here in Boulder, where we have broken records the past two days for the coldest days on record. We had four inches of snow... The fact is that we can't account for the lack of warming at the moment, and it is a travesty that we can't."[550]

Trenberth was clinging to the idea that warming had hidden in the depths of the oceans. That global warming continued unnoticed and unseen by anyone. This was allegedly indicated by the increasing heat content in the seas. But the oceans have great thermal inertia, and the accumulated energy does not reflect current climate change. Instead, it reflects a delayed response to long-term changes in the past. For example, ocean levels rise during warming (thermal expansion of water), but with a delay of about a hundred years.

Clueless scientists produced a storm of contradictory ad hoc explanations as to why it had not warmed. Anthony Watts, editor-in-chief of *Wattsupwiththat.com*—the world's most visited climate server—counted more than 50 such excuses.[551] For example, cooling is just "masked warming." Or that warming hid in the ocean. Or that the wind was responsible for the warming pause.[552] Or smoke from Chinese factories.[553] I consider the most curious explanation about pine trees. It was claimed the climate stopped warming because the pine trees smell too much, and aerosols are released from them.[554]

Later, the problem was elegantly eliminated by erasing the pause from historic records. In the end, they started to claim that there was no pause; it was merely a measurement error. When British scientists developed the HadCRUT4 dataset, they suddenly discovered some warming that they had not noticed before in their HadCRUT3 dataset. Perhaps they misplaced it somewhere in their office. But you need to know where to look. For example, the Arctic data coverage, where warming is greater, is improving, but the Antarctica coverage, which is cooling, remains scarce. The more warming regions I add to the database, the more the global average will go up, of course.

Another example is the analysis published by the US NOAA (National Office for Oceans and Atmosphere) in the summer of 2015, which managed to double the warming trend for the years 2000–2015 by a slight "adjustment" of data.[555] When they merged older measurements (from ships) with newer data (from buoys), they made adjustments, which reduced the older ocean temperatures (1990s) and raised the newer ocean temperatures (after 2000).[556] This study was called "Pausebuster." The authors argue that warming never slowed down because the warming rate of 2000–2015 was not less than the average warming rate of 1950–1999. But to get this convenient "average," the authors had to include the period 1950–1975 when the climate was cooling significantly, and people were worried about the next ice age.

Two years later, a former NOAA official complained that the author of this study, Thomas Karl, did not adhere to the principles of data archiving, making the study difficult to verify. The study was deliberately timed to be published just before the Paris climate conference.[557]

Mainstream climatologists are also uneasy about NOAA's efforts to "erase" the hiatus. Fyfe et al. (2016) believe that the warming pause really existed, and it occurred because of the Pacific Decadal Oscillation cycles.[558] "We're presenting results to support previous findings of reduced rates of surface warming... That essentially refutes the Karl et al. paper," said lead author John Fyfe. Its co-author, Michael Mann, added: "We shouldn't sweep the early 2000s warming slowdown under the rug."[559]

Satellite data from UAH (University of Alabama in Huntsville) show global temperature stagnation until the year 2016. The average temperature of 2016 was 0.02°C higher than in 1998, which is not statistically significant and less than the uncertainty of the measurement.[560]

Satellite measurements are also not error-free. The satellite orbit may degrade, but it has several advantages. In particular, it has greater coverage than ground measurements, which leave large swaths of Earth's surface blank. There is no terrestrial data from much of Africa and South America, and scientists just estimate it based on theoretical models. The satellites do not depend on an arbitrary choice of a ground station for a location to include in the statistics. It measures in the upper layers of the troposphere. The marginal effect of the stratosphere is carefully filtered, and the measurements are not affected by the effect of urban thermal islands.

Anyway, the fairest conclusion is that we have no reliable global temperature measurement. We only have a lot of conflicting data from different teams. All you can do is look at the photos of old glaciers and say, "Yes, it seems they were bigger in the 19th century."

DRIFTING MODELS

Ninety-eight percent of models did not predict a 14-year pause in warming (1998–2012). There is obviously something missing in the models as many natural factors were not included, as if the authors believed the atmosphere was composed only of carbon dioxide and nothing else.

In its Fifth Assessment Report (2013), the UN climate panel had to admit that from 1998 to 2012, the trend of temperature rise was around zero, despite a strong increase in CO_2. Climatologist Hans von Storch said that climate models did not expect such a pause in warming. "So far, no one has been able to provide a compelling answer to why climate change seems to be taking a break. We're facing a puzzle... At my institute, we analyzed how often such a 15-year stagnation in global warming occurred in the simulations. The answer was: in under 2% of all the times we ran the simulation."[561]

Apparently, something was missing in the climate models. "There are two conceivable explanations," Storch continues. "The first possibility is that less global warming is occurring than expected because greenhouse gases, especially CO_2, have less of an effect than we have assumed... The other possibility is that, in our simulations, we have underestimated how much the climate fluctuates owing to natural causes."

Why are climate models so inaccurate? No one knows the real effect of carbon dioxide on temperature ("climate sensitivity"), inferring that a given model can calculate 0.5°C or so rise in temperature when CO_2 doubles, while other models expect warming of almost 6°C. With every model, you get a different result. It is like not knowing if your train arrives at lunchtime or after dinner.

Knowing the laws of physics alone is not enough. A large number of phenomena and processes are still not accurately measured or mathematically described sufficiently, meaning that the numbers we put into equations are only estimates. For example, we all know from our own experience how it cools down when the sky is overcast. But scientists do not know whether the overall increase in cloud cover will lead to net warming or cooling or how big this effect will be.

Physicist Freeman Dyson is skeptical about climatologists: "I just think they don't understand the climate... The models are extremely oversimplified... They don't represent the clouds in detail at all. They simply use a fudge factor to represent clouds."[562]

According to Professor J. Scott Armstrong, founder of the Journal of Forecasting, this shows that climate models are untrustworthy. In his article *Let's Deal in Science and Facts* (2010)[563] he writes: "We published a peer-reviewed paper showing that the forecasting procedures used by the UN's Intergovernmental Panel on Climate Change violated 72 of 89 relevant principles (e.g., "provide full disclosure of methods"). The IPCC has been unable to explain why it violated such principles."[564]

Armstrong continues: "In testing the models on global temperature data since 1850, we found that the long-range (91-to-100-years ahead) forecast errors from the IPCC's projection were 12 times larger than the errors from our simple model."

Climatologists are not eager to speak about the weaknesses of their models. The situation has improved somewhat, but it has long been customary for simulations to diverge completely from reality—it was euphemistically said that the model was "drifting." When oceanic global circulation models (GCMs) and atmospheric GCM models were combined, the drift was often larger than the whole simulated climate change.[565]

In their jargon, an error is called flux. For example, regarding the British Hadley Center model, HADCM2, scientists said, "We find that the global-average temperature response of our model to CO_2 increasing at 1% per year is about 30% less without flux adjustment than with flux adjustment."[566] In order to make the models usable at all, the error (flux) must be corrected (adjusted).[567] Flux adjustment means that "suitable" parameter values are added to the model to get a result that seems plausible.

Engineers call such "suitable" numbers a "fudge factor." This factor assumes whatever value you happen to need in the equation to get the result you want.[568] But you don't know in advance how badly your model will drift. That is why climatologists are able to predict events only after they have happened.

Unfortunately, journalists tend to take climate scenarios too seriously, although a scenario represents just one of many possible futures. Czech meteorologist Metelka explains: "A scenario tells us what would happen if... We all sometimes think like that: If the weather is nice next week, I will take a walk, but if it rains, I will go to the pub... Similarly, climate scenarios do not tell us what will happen; they only say what might happen if greenhouse gas concentrations followed the emission scenario A1FI or scenario B1."[569]

Computer simulations of climate are still rather primitive, which is fine. Nobody is born wise. But if something shaky is presented as accurate forecasts, it will backfire. Hans von Storch comments in the above interview: "It's not a bad thing to make mistakes and have to correct them. The only thing that was bad was acting beforehand as if we were infallible. By doing so, we have gambled away the most important asset we have as scientists: The public's trust."

CLOUD COVER

We are always reassured that climate scientists have reached a consensus and the climate debate is over, which is odd because they do not understand even the clouds. It is unknown if an overall increase in cloud cover would lead to warming or cooling or how large this effect would be.

The IPCC 2007 report (Working Group 1, Chapter 1-5-2) admits: "The amplitude and even the sign of cloud feedbacks was noted in the Third Assessment Report as highly uncertain, and this uncertainty was cited as one of the key factors explaining the spread in model simulations of future climate for a given emission scenario." We need more research to understand how clouds work. For example, cosmic radiation affects the clouds. Cosmic radiation changes due to solar activity. Particle stream from the sun, "solar wind," shields Earth from cosmic rays. So, when the solar wind calms down, more cosmic rays penetrate Earth's atmosphere, creating radioactive isotopes in the atmosphere. These isotopes facilitate the formation of clouds, and as the cloud cover increases, our climate cools.

The influence of "space weather" on Earth's atmosphere is investigated by so-called cosmoclimatology. The founder of this field is the Danish physicist Henrik Svensmark. It is not yet clear how strong the effect of the cosmic rays is, and we need more research here, but such research is inconvenient for some. The UN climate panel chairman Bert Bolin argued that this hypothesis was "scientifically extremely naive and irresponsible" because it only serves to distract focus from the much-needed reduction of greenhouse gas emissions.

In an interview with *Discover* magazine, Svensmark recalls how this surprised him: "I was just stunned. I remember being shocked by many thoughts of what I was doing was terrible. I couldn't understand it because when you are a physicist, you are trained that when you find something that cannot be explained, something that doesn't fit, that is what you are excited about. If there is a possibility that you might have an explanation, that is something that everybody thinks is what you should pursue. Here was exactly the opposite reaction. It was as though people were saying to me, 'This is something that you should not have done.' That was very strange for me, and it has been more or less like that ever since."[570]

When Svensmark wanted to test his hypothesis experimentally, he ran into problems. The European Union refused to fund research that casts doubt on the very purpose of the European anti-greenhouse-gas policy. Svensmark was saved only by sponsorship from the Carlsberg brewery. In the end, an experiment at CERN was able to verify Svensmark's hypothesis, but the director general of the institute, Mr. Heuer, was cautious about the politically incorrect research: "I have asked the colleagues to present the results clearly, but not to interpret them... That would go immediately into the highly political arena of the climate change debate. One has to make clear that cosmic radiation is only one of many parameters."

When the BBC reported on the Svensmark hypothesis test, it chose a strange way to do so.[571] They interviewed Svensmark´s scientific adversary, Lockwood, and asked him to give his interpretation. And the *Nature* article written by Jasper Kirkby about the CERN experiment does not mention Svensmark at all, which is strange because it was his hypothesis and bears his name.[572]

OCEAN CYCLES

When the UN Climate Panel was established (1988), no one knew about the existence of the Pacific Decade Oscillation (PDO). Yet, it has a major impact on climate and on salmon fishing.

There are powerful forces in the climate system that scientists like Guy Callendar, Roger Revelle, and Bert Bolin were not aware of in their time. It was not until the mid-1990s that Steven Hare, in his PhD thesis, investigated the cause of dramatic fluctuations in the Alaska salmon population from one generation to another.

It turned out that there is an ancient ocean cycle in the Pacific, warming up for about 20–30 years and then cooling down for about 20–30 years. It is called Pacific Decadal Oscillation (PDO). This fluctuation in sea level temperature triggers significant fluctuations in the fish population of oceans, as reported by Kljashtorin in a 2001 study.[573] No wonder that even the United Nations Food and Agriculture Organization (FAO) became interested in this phenomenon.

The economic impact of this cycle may have been known for a long time, but no one was aware of the climate connection. Already between the World Wars, the Russian economist Kondratev postulated a cycle of major economic crises, which come like every 60 years. [574] This theory was later popularized in the West by Josef Schumpeter, although it is not universally accepted.[575] It is noteworthy that in the last two centuries, the economic crises in this cycle (Modelski 2012)[576] coincide with periods of decline in fish stock associated with climate cooling (e.g., around 1850 or around 1900 or around 1970), as reported by Klyashtorin.

In recent centuries, this cycle has had a period of about 60 years—30 years of cooling after 1946, 30 years of warming after 1976. After 1998, the PDO switched back to its cold phase, and warming has slowed down or halted. Science does not know the cause of the Pacific Decadal Oscillation (PDO) or the similar Atlantic Multidecadal Oscillation (AMO). The cause of the El Niño and La Niña phenomena, which determine shorter global annual temperature fluctuations, remains unknown too.

At the beginning of these fluctuations, there are always changes in atmospheric pressure in the Pacific Ocean. The cause of this climate cycle may be astronomical because this cycle also manifests itself in the fluctuations seen in the "northern lights" (Aurora Borealis), which are regulated by solar wind.[577]

It appears that, at first, the planet's rotation rate changes and affects the length of day (LOD). Consequently, the pressure over the ocean changes, followed by temperature change. Only then, CO_2 concentration in the atmosphere responds, as sea temperature affects solubility of gas in water. At the same time, the sea-level growth rate fluctuates.[578] For example, between 1900 and 1930, Earth's rotation accelerated, and the length of the day became shorter. An increase in global temperatures, sea levels, and salmon stock followed. What causes the planet's rotation speed to change is not clear. Maybe tidal force from surrounding cosmic bodies— the moon, sun, and Jupiter.

Already in 1976, Lambeck and Cazenave predicted global warming[579] because of the length of day (LOD) variations, not greenhouse gases. In 1976, Lambeck and Cazenave wrote: "Whatever mechanism is finally proposed, it will have to explain the apparently significant lag that is found between the LOD and the various climatic indices, temperature, and excitations. The interest of this lag suggests that the LOD observations can be used as an indicator of future climatic trends, in particular, of surface warmings." When Bert Bolin—the first chairman of the United Nation's climate panel, predicted warming, and when the warming did come, it was considered as proof that the greenhouse hypothesis was right. But other theories predicted warming, too—for completely different reasons.

THE SUN

The cause of global warming? How about this: Between 1964 and the end of the 20ᵗʰ century, the intensity of the magnetic field increased by 40% due to solar activity.

In the 20ᵗʰ century, solar activity increased to its highest level in hundreds of years—over the century, the solar activity doubled. Scientists at the Max Planck Institute in Germany say: "According to our reconstruction, the level of solar activity during the past 70 years is exceptional, and the previous period of equally high activity occurred more than 8,000 years ago."[580]

In 1989, solar eruptions were so severe that they caused a power outage throughout Quebec and, because of the "blackout," even Toronto stock trading had to be interrupted. The cause was strong solar wind, the charged particles flowing from the sun. This affects the variations in the Earth's magnetic field, which, in turn, influences the zones of low and high pressure and wind patterns.[581] This was studied, among others, by the Czech researcher Václav Bucha. Solar wind can also induce current in power lines (GIC: Geomagnetically Induced Current). That is why astronauts have to watch out for "space weather" to avoid short-circuiting of their electrical equipment.

When we measure the variations in Earth's geomagnetic field, we indirectly measure changes in solar activity. Georgieva (2004) reports that the correlation between Earth temperature and the sun's influence on Earth's magnetic field is 0.85 at $p < 0.01$.[582] The correlation $r = 0.85$ is tight (the best possible correlation is 1.0). The value of p determines statistical significance. If p is less than 0.05, we consider the results to be plausible. This close relationship between Earth's temperatures and influence of the sun on Earth's magnetic field was confirmed by further research.

"Extrapolating the aa-temperature correlations to Maunder Minimum geomagnetic conditions implies that solar forcing can account for ~50% or more of the estimated ~0.7–1.5°C increase in global surface temperature since the second half of the 17ᵗʰ century."[583] The geomagnetic aa index is measured every three hours at opposite stations in England and Australia. From 1964 to the end of the 20ᵗʰ century, the intensity of the sun's magnetic field increased by 40%.[584] This increase coincides with the global warming period in the years 1976–1998.

Eigil Friis-Christensen, director of the Danish Space Research Center, has been doing this research since the 1970s and was able to personally witness the power of magnetic storms caused by solar wind. One day, he was in Greenland setting up magnetometer stations on the west coast for the Danish Meteorological Institute. He remembers "watching the ink pens... going so wild that they nearly tore the paper chart apart—we had no digital recording at that time—and I wondered whether such big events could also have an influence in the lower atmosphere, on weather and climate. That storm cut off my contact to the outside world for nine days—all radio communication was blacked out—so I had lots of time to reflect on the enormity of the forces at play."[585]

Christensen is the author and co-author of more than 100 scientific articles. One of the most influential was his article of 1991, in which he pointed out how climate was affected by the sun.[586] The temperatures on Earth usually correspond to the changing length of the solar cycle. The sunspot cycle is 11 years on average but, in fact, varies between nine and 13 years.[587]

The shorter the cycle, the stronger is solar activity and the more the climate warms up in the next cycle. Anyone can check it by looking at astronomical tables. The solar cycle that peaked around 1970 was 11.6 years long, and the cycle that peaked around 1990 was just 9.6 years long—the shortest and, therefore, the strongest in a hundred years.

The recent solar cycles after 2000 were weak, which may have been related to the warming "hiatus." Some researchers like Abdussamatov expect climate cooling in the next decades. However, this effect could be counteracted by increasing carbon dioxide levels. Only the future will tell.

Also, Earth temperatures do not copy the sunspot cycle exactly. For example, they do not drop to zero every 11 years. Moreover, the various indicators of solar activity differ from each other. And the climate is influenced by factors other than the sun, be it oceanic cycles, cloud cover, volcanic eruptions, greenhouse gases, etc.

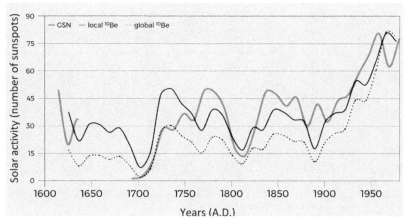

Figure 11– Solar activity in the 20th century reached the highest levels in many centuries. It shouldn't be a surprise that the climate has warmed up. The green line shows the number of groups of sunspots. The more sunspots, the stronger the solar activity. The other two curves show isotopes of Berylium. Changes in solar activity and cosmic radiation influence the rate at which isotopes form in the atmosphere.[588]

Solar impact is especially long-term—like in the 17th century when the sunspots disappeared completely, solar activity decreased, followed by the coldest part of the Little Ice Age. German and Finnish researchers report: "The long-term trends in solar data and in northern hemisphere temperatures have a correlation coefficient of about 0.7–0.8 at a 94%–98% confidence level."[589]

Unfortunately, climate models do not fully include solar forcing in the models. Ladislav Metelka from the Czech Hydrometeorological Institute notes: "The models presented in the IPCC summary do not count with significant systematic change(s) in solar radiation... However, if astronomers provide credible data that solar activity is going to increase, we may build this factor into the climate models and take it into account in our forecasts."[590] If one of the strongest drivers of climate is not included in the climate models, one can hardly expect the models to have good predictive skills.

VOLCANOES

In the 1990s, volcanic activity subsided, the atmosphere became less dusty, and this may have contributed to warming.

Proponents of the greenhouse hypothesis do not want to admit that the sun could have an impact on the climate in the past. Although, it used to be common to attribute the Little Ice Age to the decline in solar activity, especially the solar Maunder Minimum in the 17th[th] century. At that time, sunspots disappeared from the sun, and the Earth cooled.

But they are looking for another culprit instead. "Scientists suggest that the Little Ice Age was triggered by an unusual, 50-year episode of four massive volcanic eruptions" (NCAR 2012).[591] Newspaper headlines declare: "Volcanic origin for Little Ice Age"[592] Volcanoes may have contributed to cooling, but if the volcanoes are the suspect, does it rule out the influence of the sun? In fact, volcanic activity is regulated by solar activity because the sun affects the Earth's crust in many ways.[593] It is a similar phenomenon to the cracking sound you hear in central heating when it cools down and the metal is contracting. When the Earth's crust is heated—due to solar warming—and then it cools down, the crust expands first and then begins to contract. Tension in the Earth's crust rises, and then it releases in the form of volcanic eruptions.[594] We could observe this in the 20th[th] century when the largest volcanic eruptions always arrived in the period of cooling after the solar cycle peak.

- 19th[th] solar cycle (1954–1964) culminated in 1958. This was followed by the eruption of the Agung volcano in Bali in 1963.

- 20th[th] cycle was weak.

- 21st[st] cycle (1976–1986) culminated in 1979. This was followed by the eruption of El Chichon volcano in 1982 in Mexico.

- 22nd[nd] cycle (1986–1996) culminated in 1989. The Pinatubo volcano erupted in the Philippines in 1991.

In the years 1963–1987, the sun's magnetic field (open solar flux) strengthened by 29%.[595] Yet in the years 1980–1997, there was not much global warming, probably because of the large volcanoes (El Chichon 1982, Pinatubo 1991) spewing heaps of dust into the stratosphere. Large volcanic eruptions can cool the world climate by 0.2–0.3°C for several years.[596]

Climatologist Richard Keen from Colorado pointed out that in the late 1990s, volcanic activity declined, the atmosphere cleared, and that is why the global temperature jumped up.[597] That was the 1998 warm year with the mighty *El Niño*. When a large volcanic eruption occurs with a suitable composition of volcanic dust, the earth's surface is shielded from the sun, and it cools down. When the atmosphere later clears, warming may occur without any further increase in solar activity.

WATER VAPOR

The strongest greenhouse gas is water vapor. However, because it is often left out of the reports, it looks as if the main greenhouse gas is carbon dioxide.

Water vapor is a greenhouse gas you do not hear about very often. The UN climate panel categorically stated: "The models fail to reproduce the observed warming when run using only natural factors. When human factors are included, the models also simulate a geographic pattern of temperature change around the globe similar to that which has occurred in recent decades."[598] However, these models do not consider all-natural influences, so this comparison is meaningless.

When IPCC compares various climate factors, water vapor is not explicitly mentioned anywhere.[599] IPCC reviewers complained in vain about this double standard. Dr. Vincent Gray criticized the IPCC Fourth Report: "The chief defect of this Chapter is the total absence of the main greenhouse gas, water vapor. By comparison, the others are insignificant."[600]

The IPCC argued that water vapor is not explicitly listed as forcing but is implicitly counted as "feedback." However, the problem is that this feedback is counted in only on one side of the equation. It is taken into account that water vapor intensifies the human impact (CO_2 emissions) on climate. But the model ignores the fact that water vapor also intensifies the influence of the sun on climate. If you erase a significant factor from your model, you cannot be surprised that the model cannot explain a thing. It reminds us of Darrell Huff's book *How to Lie with Statistics*. This is creative accounting, like comparing my salary before taxes with your salary after taxes.

Instead of a full overview of all greenhouse gases, only the anthropogenic ones are often reported without any note or warning to the reader. For example, the publication of the European Commission with the title *You Control Climate Change. Make a Pledge!* (2006) misleads schoolchildren by saying that carbon dioxide accounts for 80% of the greenhouse gases in the atmosphere. That would be almost like Venus! In fact, carbon dioxide represents just 0.04% of the atmosphere. It is a trace gas.

Water vapor concentration in the atmosphere in the 20th century increased by 5%.[601] Maybe due to solar warming too. That's not a small number. Neglecting the role of water vapor is sometimes justified by the fact that its concentration can easily and quickly return to the "original" level if cooling comes, whereas you can't get carbon dioxide out of the atmosphere quickly. Maybe that's true. However, the water vapor content in the atmosphere did increase, and its effect on temperatures should be reported honestly.

JUPITER

Every 200 years, solar activity drops significantly. According to one hypothesis, the gravitational effect of large planets—especially Jupiter—is responsible for that. One of these minima should occur in the first half of the 21ˢᵗ century.

Science does not yet know why solar activity is fluctuating. However, at least, the barycentric hypothesis of SIM (solar inertial motion) is worth mentioning. Already in his *Principia,* Newton noticed that large planets appear to apply traction on the sun. In particular, the gravitational force of the giant Jupiter drags the sun back and forth. Therefore, the sun does not sit at the center of gravity (barycenter) of our planetary system but dances around this center of the system along complex circular paths.

P.D. Jose noticed in 1965 that the cycle of these movements was as long as the 180-year cycle of sunspots (the Suess cycle). Every 200 years, solar activity declines significantly for several decades and cools down the climate. These minima have their names—Dalton's minimum (early 19th century), Maunder's minimum (17th century), Spoerer's minimum (15th century), etc. It obviously cannot be the only thing that controls solar activity—otherwise, it would be completely identical every 200 years.

Rhodes W. Fairbridge, a climatologist and well-known editor of the *Encyclopedia of Earth Sciences,* was among those who studied the solar inertial motion.[602] Fairbridge was the first to measure the long-term fluctuations of sea level over thousands of years (Fairbridge Curve of the Holocene Eustatic Fluctuations, 1958). He discovered that the sea level had risen significantly since the Ice Age, and he also noticed periodic oscillations. His research then attempted to explain these oscillations by changes in solar output.

Czech researchers were also involved in the research of SIM. Ivanka Charvátová from the Geophysical Institute of Academy of Sciences of the Czech Republic noticed that once every 180 years when the solar activity is high, the sun's "dance" around the barycenter follows a regular "trefoil" path.[603] Due to gravitational pull of the planets, the inertial motion of the sun accelerates and decelerates.

However, the physical mechanism remains unclear, and it is still "just" a hypothesis. According to Einstein's physics, it is the state of "free fall," meaning that it should not affect solar activity. Space has no up and down, and when one object passes another in space, it is hard to say which of them is stationary and which one is moving. On the other hand, it would not be the first thing in physics that Einstein's theory cannot explain (note the duel between string theory and loop theory).[604] Theoretically, Jupiter could also affect the sun via tidal forces, but they appear very weak at this distance.

This solar inertial motion would require more research, but instead, it is rather frowned upon. Charvátová recalls: "There have been significant difficulties with publication of my (our) articles. Some editors returned an article without a review, saying that their readers would not be interested. Another editor said openly that their journal won't allow anything about SIM! I even remember a peer-review consisting of single sentences: 'Articles about solar inertial motion should be banned!'"[605]

This is really happening. In 2014, the scientific journal *Pattern Recognition in Physics* dedicated a special issue to natural climatic cycles. Among other things, the barycentric hypothesis and its impact on solar activity was discussed. Chief Editor Martin Rasmussen then disbanded the journal, saying that when PRP was established, it was not with the intention to promote theories that contradict the IPCC and the anthropogenic cause of warming.

VII. POLARIZATION OF SOCIETY

Ensuring high-quality news service is not like a walk in the park. This noble effort is much too often foiled by people who disseminate doubt and misinformation. Sadly, it is difficult to deal with them because it is no longer legal to send them to a Gulag. What is more, some confused people mistakenly think this quality assurance effort is some kind of censorship.

First of all, it is necessary to ensure quality in the media so that only genuine truth can be published. Who decides what is true? Well, every political regime has a different version of the truth, but the general rule of thumb is that whatever the power elite says is true. Ask experienced journalists who have survived several regimes. They will tell you: A journalist who is incompetent to flexibly adapt to changing regimes can be sent to a re-education camp to understand what happens to be true this week.

In new media, like Wikipedia, the situation is even more complicated. Anyone who is able to catch a mouse, a computer mouse, can contribute to the Internet encyclopedia—which is the source of wisdom for most of the population. Quality is ensured by editors who are authorized to delete contributions that are inappropriate. Since the creator of Wikipedia has the right worldview, he will appoint editors who are "reasonable." So, don't be surprised when you spend a week editing a Wikitext, and the next day you discover that the whole thing has vanished.

At first sight, it may appear that scientific journals exist in their ivory tower, far from politics. A scientist must have accurate measurements before he or she publishes anything. There is no room for bias, is there? But the editors are not ghosts; they need food and air like other humans. They need funding for their salary and to pay the print. And they have a publisher. If a magazine is owned by a sensible person, he or she will appoint a chief editor who is also sensible. And he will see to it that studies that might confuse the public somehow will not be published.

The question remains, what to do with meteorologists who appear on TV and stubbornly refuse to believe that the sky is falling down? One can barrage their employers with angry letters and demand that such a person be fired. Better yet, one can send angry letters to sponsors of such an employer—and threaten to boycott their products until an unreasonable meteorologist is sent to a suicide mission into a hurricane.

If it is not possible to silence the inconvenient people, they can be at last properly discredited. Try digging up some dirt—perhaps unpaid fees from the library—then you won't have to debate them at all. Or you can accuse them of being paid by a corporation. Philanthropy is a standard part of corporate public relations these days, so it should be easy to find some donations. Even if the guy received a free pencil, you could destroy his reputation.

Just remember to appeal to people's desire to be on the winning side. The basic survival instinct tells people that it is unsafe to protect the underdog. Keep saying that your opponent is in the minority and that they are a tiny rag-tag band of contrarians and crackpots. Try finding a convert whose eyes opened to see your truth and who deserted from the thinning ranks of your opponent. Present it as if their ship is sinking. If you don't find a convert, you can hire an actor to play one on TV. But make sure it is in the newspapers. Insist that the scientific consensus, the consensus of thousands of top experts, can never be wrong. If someone brings a list of how many times the consensus was wrong, apologize for having to leave because you don't want to miss your train or plane or something.

You can use opinion polls or statistics of scientific studies to show that you have mass support. By cleverly selecting "unbiased" questions, you can achieve any result you want. For instance, you ask people if they believe that water is wet, and if they say yes, you can claim it proves their support for your policy, which does not concern water at all.

In an ideological discussion, you do not debate your opponent politely as your peer. You speak from the heights of your moral superiority. Here, an invaluable source of inspiration is the popular "argumentum ad Hitlerum," where you compare your opponents to the Nazis. If their opinion differs from yours—for example, they do not think fish and chips is tasty—they deny the facts and are deniers, like the Holocaust deniers.

SKEPTICAL SCIENTISTS

In his essay on pseudoskepticism, Marcello Truzzi writes: "In science, the burden of proof falls upon the claimant and the more extraordinary a claim, the heavier is the burden of proof demanded. The true skeptic takes an agnostic position, one that says the claim is not proved rather than disproved... Since the true skeptic does not assert a claim, he has no burden to prove anything. He just goes on using the established theories of conventional science."[606] Climate has always been changing. And it has always been changing from natural causes. This is the so-called null hypothesis, which shall remain valid until the opposite is proven. If someone claims that something unusual is happening to the climate, it is an anomaly, and it demands evidence. Truzzi: "The ground rules of science are conservative, and in so far as these place the burden of proof on the claimants and require stronger evidence the more extraordinary the claim, they are not neutral."[607]

Today, however, we are living at a time when scientific evidence is being replaced by political mechanisms. They use the precautionary principle to indicate that in urgency, there is no time to wait for scientific evidence. Scientific method is circumvented by voting, by international conferences, and by meetings. So, instead of proof, we hear that some scientists have reached a "consensus" on how much they believe in something.

Proponents of the null hypothesis about predominantly natural climate change are slowly dying out. They are being replaced by a new generation that is raised at school to believe in the climate apocalypse. As Thomas Kuhn wrote in *The Structure of Scientific Revolutions* citing the physicist Max Planck: "A new scientific truth does not triumph by convincing its opponents and making them see the light, but rather because its opponents eventually die, and a new generation grows up that is familiar with it."[608]

The generation of scientists born before World War II was used to a different organization of science. During their lifetime, however, they gradually witnessed a growing problem, which was already mentioned by President Dwight Eisenhower in his farewell speech when he was leaving office in 1961:

"Today, the solitary inventor, tinkering in his shop, has been overshadowed by task forces of scientists in laboratories and testing fields. In the same fashion, the free university, historically the fountainhead of free ideas and scientific discovery, has experienced a revolution in the conduct of research. Partly because of the huge costs involved, a government contract becomes virtually a substitute for intellectual curiosity. For every old blackboard, there are now hundreds of new electronic computers. The prospect of domination of the nation's scholars by Federal employment, project allocations, and the power of money is ever-present and is gravely to be regarded."[609] General Eisenhower was concerned that the products of the war effort, such as the A-bomb or the first ballistic computer ENIAC, forged an unholy alliance between science and government. He was calling it "the military-industrial complex."

However, climatology proves that the loss of academic independence is not isolated to military technology R&D only. Science now depends on government funding, and applications for grants have become a standard part of everyday life in academia. Managers of scientific institutions abandoned value-free science as an ethical norm and instead issued public endorsements of political parties in elections.

Ivar Giaever (b. 1929) received the Nobel Prize in physics. Later, he withdrew from the American Physics Society to protest its declaration about the need to immediately reduce greenhouse gas emissions regardless of the cost.[610] The APS statement said that environmental and social systems are likely to be seriously disrupted due to warming. Giaever argued that temperatures had risen in the last 150 years, and there was no "disruption." Instead, people's standard of living and health had improved.

The team of Republican senator Inhofe in the US Senate Environment and Public Works Committee collected a list of over 400 scientists from around the world rejecting the so-called consensus on climate change, which is more than the about 50 people who write the "Summary for Policymakers" for the UN climate panel.[611] The opponents of climate alarmism included such scientific celebrities as the historical climatologist Hubert Lamb, oceanographer Roger Revelle, founder of the Goddard Institute of NASA, Robert Jastrow, a pioneer of seasonal forecasts of hurricanes, William Gray, founder of the first TV channel about weather (The Weather Channel), John Coleman, chairman of the World Federation of Scientists, the physicist Antonio Zichichi, creators of the method of satellite measurement of global temperatures, Roy Spencer and John Christy, and Richard C. Willson and his team of satellite measurement of solar activity (ACRIM). Let's look at the ideas of some of these scientists in more detail.

When **Hubert Lamb** (b. 1913) enrolled in the Climatology Department of the British Meteorological Service, he was a bit of an outcast there. Meteorologists did not believe that the climate had been changing over the last millennia, and they did not believe that it would have any effect on human civilization. This illusion that the climate used to be stable in the past is still believed by environmentalists to this day. He eventually left that office when he was offered an opportunity to establish a specialized Climate Research Unit (CRU) at the University of East Anglia.

In the 1970s, he published his life work, *Climate: Present, Past and Future*. He analyzed the records from Central England and reconstructed the changes of the local climate over the last thousand years. He discovered that it was warmer in the Middle Ages and called this period a Medieval Climate Optimum. The subsequent period of Little Ice Age, which ended only in the mid-19th century, was considered by him as deterioration of the climate. This was how the first IPCC report in 1990 depicted climate change—before the Hockey Stick graph rewrote history.

The 1970s was an era of great cooling. Lamb noted: "The observed decline of global temperature since 1945 implies some other factor exercising about three times as strong an effect (in the opposite direction) as the carbon dioxide increase."[612] However, as soon as the cooling ended, the World Meteorological Organization immediately changed its mind. And they began to emphasize the potential threat of greenhouse gases. To Lamb's disappointment, funding for research on natural climate change suddenly faded. If human influence on the climate is going to prevail soon, there is no point in exploring the natural factors—that was the logic of the reasoning.

When he retired in 1978, his successor Tom Wigley went with the flow in order to ensure funding for CRU. Lamb was not happy about it: "Since my retirement from the directorship of the Climatic Research Unit, there have been changes there... My immediate successor, Professor Tom Wigley, was chiefly interested in the prospects of world climate being changed as a result of human activities... After only a few years, almost all the work on historical reconstruction of past climate and weather situations, which had first made the Unit well known, was abandoned. There was an exception in the case of tree-ring studies."[613]

Lamb noted that "the prospects of global warming are now spoken of on every side and are treated by many, including people whose decisions affect millions, as if the more alarming forecasts were already established as fact."[614]

When he died in 1997, the obituary in *Nature* only cautiously mentioned Lamb's "climate skeptical" views: "During his later years, Lamb was skeptical of certain claims regarding the dangers posed by global warming. An empiricist at heart and well aware of the complexities of the climate system, he felt that climate models were limited in their ability to provide accurate forecasts... He had found a new orthodoxy to challenge."[615]

Lamb would probably turn in his grave if he knew that the Climate Research Unit, which he founded and which bears his name today, has become the symbol of fraud due to the Climategate scandal. For CRU, its founding father has become a skeleton in the closet. The CRU building is named after Lamb, but their website is silent about his skepticism of "global warming."

Another skeptic was the climatologist **Roger Revelle** (b. 1909). He was the director of the Scripps Institute for Oceanography (1950–1964) at a time when Keeling began measuring carbon dioxide there. It was Revelle who proved that the oceans cannot absorb all human carbon dioxide emissions. At the same time, however, he rejected the conclusions of the climate alarmists as premature.

In the summer of 1988, NASA climatologist James Hansen spoke in Congress to warn against global warming, and Revelle considered such claims to be premature. He wrote a letter to Congressman Jim Bates on August 14, 1988: "Most scientists familiar with the subject are not yet willing to bet that the climate this year is the result of 'greenhouse warming.' As you very well know, climate is highly variable from year to year, and the causes of these variations are not at all well understood. My own personal belief is that we should wait another ten or 20 years to really be convinced that the greenhouse is going to be important for human beings, in both positive and negative ways."[616] And let me remind you that between the 1930s and 1988, there was no net warming in the USA (although it did warm globally).

In 1991, shortly before his death, Revelle and Fred Singer published an article in Cosmos magazine: *What To Do about Greenhouse Warming: Look Before You Leap.*[617] They wrote: "Drastic, precipitous and, especially, unilateral steps to delay the putative greenhouse impacts can cost jobs and prosperity and increase the human costs of global poverty, without being effective. Stringent controls enacted now would be economically devastating, particularly for developing countries."

The article was inconvenient for Al Gore's election campaign. The prospective vice president of the United States presented himself as an environmentalist, and he appealed to the authority of his teacher at Harvard. But now, it seemed that Revelle turns against Gore's alarmist message. So, the election campaign staff changed their strategy. Revelle was no longer a wise genius. Now, he was depicted as a confused senile grandpa. What was in the article was not written by Revelle. It was written by Singer, who cheated the old man into signing it later. However, Fred Singer defended himself in court and won. Dr. Justin Lancaster, who was spreading these rumors, had to publicly apologize to Singer on April 29, 1994. The investigation even found written evidence that Lancaster was acting on orders of Al Gore's staff.[618]

Fred Singer (b. 1924) helped set up the US satellite service in the 1960s and was its first director (National Weather Bureau's Satellite Service Center). In the 1960s, he also founded the School of Environmental and Planetary Sciences at the University of Miami. In

the 1970s, he worked for the US Environmental Protection Agency. Until 1994, he was a professor at the University of Virginia (UVA).

In 1990, he founded the Science and Environmental Policy Project (SEPP). In response to the Earth Summit in Rio de Janeiro, he organized the Heidelberg Appeal against radical environmentalism (1992). Dozens of Nobel Prize holders signed the protest. The text says: "We are, however, worried at the dawn of the 21st century, at the emergence of an irrational ideology which is opposed to scientific and industrial progress and impedes economic and social development."

He also organized protests against the Kyoto Protocol (1997) and collected signatures of thousands of Americans with academic degrees in The Oregon Petition. The cover letter to The Oregon Petition (www. petitionproject.org) was written by Fred Seitz, former president of the

National Academy of Sciences. It says: "There is no convincing scientific evidence that human release of carbon dioxide, methane, or other greenhouse gases is causing or will, in the foreseeable future, cause catastrophic heating of the Earth's atmosphere and disruption of the Earth's climate. Moreover, there is substantial scientific evidence that increases in atmospheric carbon dioxide produce many beneficial effects upon the natural plant and animal environments of the Earth."

Singer is the co-author of the book *Unstoppable Global Warming: Every 1,500 Years* with Denis Avery on the climatic cycle of Bond Events. In 2009, with the help of the Heartland Institute, SEPP helped to organize a team of scientists who wrote a 1,000-page *Climate Change Reconsidered* analysis that can compete with major UN reports.

Singer has often faced obstacles from the mainstream. For example, when he was due to give a lecture in Brussels in September 2011, the IPCC vice president van Yperselle contacted the organizers (Société Européenne des Ingénieurs et Industriels) and asked them to withdraw Singer's invitation. He used slander to persuade them. "His activities of disinformation are financed by the fossil fuel lobbies, and it is scandalous that such a person could be remotely or closely associated with the SEII and to the Fondation Universitaire," Yperselle wrote.[619]

William Niernberg (b. 1919) was director of the Scripps Institute for Oceanography (1965–1986). Today, Scripps awards the Niernberg Prize for contributions to science every year.

In 1983, Niernberg chaired the climate committee, which came to a moderate conclusion: "Overall, we find in the CO_2 issue reason for concern, but not panic... Both climate change and increased CO_2 may also bring benefits... A program of action without a program for learning could be costly and ineffective."[620]

In 1984, he co-founded the George C. Marshall Institute, a non-profit educational organization, along with Fred Seitz and Robert Jastrow, founder and long-time director of NASA's Goddard Institute. The Marshall Institute was named after the World War II general and later Secretary of State, who was the father of the so-called Marshall Plan for post-war economic aid.

The Institute became interested in climate change due to Reagan's Strategic Defense Initiative (SDI), nicknamed Star Wars. The SDI was supposed to build a defensive shield that would destroy Soviet nuclear missiles while still in the air, for example, satellites armed with a laser. The Marshall Institute defended this vision as a guarantee of national security against the threat of attack by the Soviet Union. However, the SDI program was heavily criticized by astronomer Carl Sagan, who viewed Reagan as a warmonger. Sagan used climate models of "nuclear winter" as an argument.[621]

When nuclear bombs explode, tons of dust are ejected into the air, overshadowing the sun for months. According to Sagan's team, even a relatively moderate 100-megaton bomb could trigger such nuclear winter.[622] But the eruption of the Krakatoa volcano in 1883 released energy equivalent to about 200 megatons of TNT.[623] The eruption was 13,000 times more powerful than the bomb dropped on Hiroshima, and it did not trigger any nuclear winter.

Sagan's team used an equation where variables are the number and size of nuclear warheads, the height for detonation, flammability of the target, duration of burning of the target, particles entering the atmosphere, reflectivity of the particles, lifetime of the particles, etc. However, the researchers are unable to know any of these variables because the war has not started yet. They just made up the numbers. They say that these are just different "scenarios." They also forgot to point out that if the explosion occurred in winter, when nature is asleep anyway, it would have almost no effect on the growing season.

Sagan's team spent more time on media promotion than the research itself. Sagan first published an article in a popular magazine and then spoke at a conference side by side with the celebrity Paul Ehrlich, and only months later, the scientific study came out.[624] It was very convenient. At the time of heated media debate, no one could verify on what data the whole theory stood. Sagan also had a loyal ally in the Union of Concerned Scientists, which later moved to the issue of global warming.

Henk Tennekes (b. 1936) used to be a director of the Dutch meteorological service KNMI. His 1972 book *A First Course in Turbulence* still belongs to the main textbooks in the field.[625]

However, when the UN established a climate panel and the field began to politicize, Tennekes publicly criticized the greenhouse hypothesis. "I worry about the arrogance of scientists who blithely claim that they can help solve the climate problem, provided their research receives massive increases in funding. I worry about the lack of sophistication and the absence of reflection in the way climate modelers covet new supercomputers," he wrote in the 1990s.[626]

He was then fired because his views were politically uncomfortable. It was hard to break through. "KNMI'ers still avoid me like the plague because I say something different from the group dogma. First, you must believe in something; only then are you allowed to participate in their discussion."[627] Tennekes is quoted in Timmer's article in *De Telegraaf*.[628]

In 2010, he resigned from the Dutch Academy of Sciences to protest against the politicization of science. Two years later, he was one of the signatories of the letter *No Need to Panic about Global Warming*, published by a group of scientists in *The Wall Street Journal*. [629]

Swedish climatologist **Lennart Bengtson** (b. 1935) was Director of the European Center for Medium-Range Weather Forecasts (founded 1975) in the 1980s. He then chaired the Max-Planck Institut für Meteorologie in Germany for nine years. In 2006, he received an award from the World Meteorological Organization for pioneering research in numerical weather forecasting.

In 2014, he joined the British climate skeptic group called Global Warming Policy Foundation (GWPF). What followed was a shock to him. Climate alarmists started a bullying campaign against him. "I have been put under such an enormous group pressure in recent days from all over the world that has become virtually unbearable to me. If this is going to continue, I will be unable to conduct my normal work and will even start to worry about my health and safety. I see, therefore, no other way out, therefore than resigning from GWPF. I was not expecting such an enormous world-wide pressure put at me from a community that I have been close to all my active life. Colleagues are withdrawing their support; other colleagues are withdrawing from joint authorship, etc. I see no limit and end to what will happen. It is a situation that reminds me of the time of McCarthy. I would never have expected anything similar in such an original peaceful community as meteorology. Apparently, it has been transformed in recent years. Under these situations, I will be unable to contribute positively to the work of GWPF, and, consequently, therefore, I believe it is the best for me to reverse my decision to join its board at the earliest possible time."[630]

SOCIAL DIMENSION
OF SKEPTICISM

Climate skepticism among the general public results mostly from political belief that higher taxes and more bureaucracy are no good.

In the 2014 documentary series *Years of Living Dangerously*, Hollywood stars like Harrison Ford jumped on the bandwagon of climate apocalypse. The first episode of the series shows climate skeptics as illiterate rural rednecks devoted to religious superstitions. Then a wise scientist arrives in the village and opens the eyes of these simple people, obvious propaganda where the villains are two-dimensional characters with no soul.

Out there in the real world, however, surveys have shown that climate skeptics have equal or better general scientific knowledge than climate alarmists. In a 2012 study, psychologist Dan Kahan of Yale University writes: "Seeming public apathy over climate change is often attributed to a deficit in comprehension. The public knows too little science, it is claimed, to understand the evidence or avoid being misled," but their research did not confirm that. "Members of the public with the highest degrees of science literacy and technical reasoning capacity were not the most concerned about climate change. Rather, they were the ones among whom cultural polarization was greatest."[631]

Sociological surveys show that public attitude to climate change does not depend on education but on cultural values and political orientation. The climate change dispute is fueled by cultural war about what an ideal society should look like. The left-wing liberals "will be inclined to accept environmental risks because they resent unrestrained commerce and self-interested behavior and readily accept that such activities are dangerous and worthy of regulation,"[632] says the sociologist Andrew J. Hoffman from the University of Michigan.

By contrast, right-wing conservatives do not want to acknowledge the existence of environmental problems as this could be an excuse to restrict trade and personal freedom. This represents a schism that is difficult to overcome. "Each side views the other with suspicion, even demonizing the other, leading to a strong resistance to any form of engagement, much less negotiation and concession," Hoffman continues.

The language used by climate activists is politically very divisive. Compare what UN Secretary-General Ban Ki-Moon said at the 2011 Davos conference:[633] "Climate change is also showing us that the old model is more than obsolete. It has rendered it extremely dangerous. Over time, that model is a recipe for national disaster. It is a global suicide pact...

We need a revolution. Revolutionary thinking... It is easy to mouth the words 'sustainable development,' but to make it happen, we have to be prepared to make major changes—in our lifestyles, our economic models, our social organization, and our political life." Statements like this make an impression that the fight against climate change is only an excuse for political coup and elimination of market economy.

A century ago, V.I. Lenin declared that "communism is government by the Soviets plus the electrification of the whole land." Similarly, liberals today love to mix technical solutions with revolutionary plans, thus making them toxic for conservatives. In 2019, the Green New Deal proposed in the United States by Congresswoman Alexandra Ocasio-Cortez was a fine example. Only a handful of its proposals had anything to do with climate. Instead, it was a blueprint for socialist revolution. "Free college... Check... Guarantee of high-paying jobs for everyone? Check. Free healthcare? Check. Free housing? Check. And to sum it all up: Free lunch? Check."[634] Tempting promises, but in stark contrast to the American tradition of individualism.

The liberal left considers plans like the Green New Deal as a legitimate reform effort. After all, why would anyone not want sustainable development? Some sociologists like Anthony Giddens see environmentalism as a reasonable path to "reflexive modernity." Modern civilization forged in the fire of industrial revolution needs to pause a bit and reflect on the side-effects of its so-far blind pursuit of economic growth. Ulrich Beck warns that our Frankenstein technology creates new risks, previously unknown. We live in a "risk society," he says. In the Middle Ages, you didn't have to worry about plane crashes, nuclear bombs, or plastic waste.

These risks may be real, but somebody must decide which one is the top priority. The perception of risk changes in each generation; it is a social construct. Cultural theory of risk,[635] formulated by anthropologist Mary Douglas and political scientist Aaron Wildavsky, explains the attitude to environmental risks by emotion—egalitarians or individualists see things differently. The theory was designed to explain the paradox of why the American youth decided to riot at the peak of prosperity in the 1960s. The environmental movement was part of this wave of protests. One would expect a general relief that life is safer, child mortality lower, and famines are a thing of the past. Instead, people became worried about "consumer society."

In the 1982 book *Risk and Culture,* the authors divided the US political landscape into Center and Periphery (they say Border). In those times, the political center was occupied by the individualistic "market" and the conservative "hierarchy." In the 1960s, egalitarian organizations similar to religious sects began to appear in opposition to this center.[636] They castigated our spoilt society and demanded return to nature.

Sects maintain loyalty of their fan base by whipping up feelings of acute threat. This is why they usually resort to prophecies of the end of the world. Their attitude to modern technology is strikingly similar to the taboos of primitive tribes, as described by anthropologists. Their thinking revolves around purity—whether physical, ritual, or ecological.[637] Anomalies that do not fit in the natural order are seen as impure—such as plastics. Diseases and natural disasters are attributed to violations of traditional social order—in our case, the disruption of pre-modern Gemeinschaft by the advent of modern technology.

However, much has changed since the 1960s. A small sect sometimes grows into a powerful church. Where once was just a bunch of hippies, there is a powerful environmental bureaucracy today. This may be related to a change in social stratification. New middle class appeared on the world stage as a new entity. These are the "white collars" described by Charles Wright Mills already in the 1950s.

The old middle class consisted mostly of small family farms and businesses. The new middle class consists mostly of educated employees of the state and large companies. They think differently. For a businessman, risk means opportunity. For a bureaucrat, risk is justification for more regulations, more paperwork, and more jobs for fellow clerks.

The emerging social strata use criticism of capitalism to advance their cause. They reject the recent "dominant social paradigm" based on the ideals of enlightenment.[638] They consider the belief in progress, growth, and modernization as "myths" invented by the bourgeoisie. The pursuit of happiness by uneducated merchants is not seen as creative force driving unparalleled prosperity. Instead, it is framed as destructive greed, which created the risks that only new thinking—by educated experts—can solve. Thus, the emerging social groups justify their takeover of political power.

As the role of production in post-industrial society decreases, the importance of working class goes downhill too. Even traditional labor parties betray the workers now. Whereas the old left placed the interests of the labor first, the new left is Malthusian, and it asks the workers to reduce their consumption to save the planet. The roles have turned upside down. Suddenly, the conservatives defend the poor people and their jobs—which is now labeled as "populism." They warn that the climatic regulations push energy prices up and jeopardize jobs. For instance, in the open letter to Pope Francis, they write: "Severe poverty, widespread hunger, rampant disease, and short life spans were the ordinary condition of humankind until the last two-and-a-half centuries... It follows that reducing fossil fuel use means reducing economic development, condemning poor societies to remain poor, and requiring poor people of today to sacrifice for the sake of richer people of the future—a clear injustice."[639]

The affluent elites of the West believe in "post-material values" now, as sociologist Ronald Inglehart calls it. Their living standards are so high that they don't understand what hunger means anymore. So, they urge the poor to also give priority to "spiritual values" over a slice of bread. Surprisingly, post material values do not prevent the educated elites from filling in applications for subventions. A woke progressive intellectual will buy overpriced eco-bio-organic food, the production of which is sub-sidized. And with this "conspicuous consumption," one can kill two birds with one stone—to signal one's high social status and also one's humble virtues.

The conflict between the pro-growth Old Left and anti-growth New Left values can be illustrated in the case of Caleb Rossiter, Professor of Statistics. Rossiter was one of the well-known liberal peace activists criticizing the Vietnam and Iraq war (calebrossiter.com). In May 2014, however, he published an article in *The Wall Street Journal: Sacrificing Africa for Climate Change*. As a man of social conscience, he warned left-wing parties against the asocial aspects of climate policy.

He was shocked in 2010 when left-wing liberals campaigned for the World Bank to stop funding a new coal power plant in South Africa. "The left wants to stop industrialization—even if the hypothesis of catastrophic, man-made global warming is false... Where is the justice when the US discourages World Bank funding for electricity-generation projects in Africa that involve fossil fuels, and when the European Union places a 'global warming' tax on cargo flights importing perishable African goods?... Western policies seem more interested in carbon-dioxide levels than in life expectancy."[640]

A few days after publishing this opinion, he was notified by email that his membership in Institute for Policy Studies was terminated. Rossiter says, "If people ever say that fears of censorship for 'climate change' views are overblown, have them take a look at this. Just two days after I published a piece in *The Wall Street Journal* calling for Africa to be allowed the 'all of the above' energy strategy we have in the US, the Institute for Policy Studies (IPS) terminated my 23-year relationship with them... because my analysis and theirs 'diverge.'"

"I have tried to get [IPS] to discuss and explain their rejection of my analysis... When I countered a claim of 'rapidly accelerating' temperature change with the [UN] IPCC's own data showing the nearly 20-year temperature pause—the best response I ever got was 'Caleb, I don't have time for this.'"[641]

PUBLISH OR PERISH

The scientific journal Nature is owned by a German media corporation. On politically sensitive issues, it only publishes what is in line with orthodoxy.

The media landscape has changed a lot since the times of Bob Woodward and Watergate journalism. In 1983, about 90% of the US media was owned by about 50 companies. In 2013, it was only six companies (GE, News Corp, Disney, Viacom, Time Warner, and CBS).[642] A handful of people decide what you can see and hear. But even the media tycoons themselves are under pressure. If they allow opposition views in their press, they will become outcasts like the climate skeptic Rupert Murdoch and his *Fox News*.

Climatologist Richard Lindzen used to work in the UN climate panel (the IPCC). In the article *Climate of Fear in The Wall Street Journal* (2006), he described extensively how science magazines dislike anything that goes against the doctrine of man-made warming. "At *Science* and *Nature,* such papers are commonly refused without review as being without interest. However, even when such papers are published, standards shift... Normally, criticism of papers appears in the form of letters to the journal to which the original authors can respond immediately. However, in this case (and others) a flurry of hastily prepared papers appeared, claiming errors in our study, with our responses delayed months and longer. The delay permitted our paper to be commonly referred to as 'discredited.'"[643]

Problems with the publishing of skeptical articles were also reported by paleontologist Robert M. Carter, who chaired the School of Earth Sciences at James Cook University in Australia from 1981 to 1999. In 2009, Bob Carter, John McLean and Chris de Freitas described how temperatures can be predicted from ocean oscillations, regardless of greenhouse gases.[644]

Their opponents hurried to write a critique of this study in record time. It usually takes six months or a year for an article to go through the peer-review process. Instead, they personally handed the article over to their friend Mike McPhaden, who happens to be president of the American Geophysical Union (AGU), which happens to publish the JGR journal. The editor, who approved McLean's article for publication was suddenly fired. And only "reliable" reviewers were carefully selected for Foster's critique. When the article was published and McLean and the team wanted to respond to their critics, the editors did not permit.[645]

Since the mid-1990s, *Nature* and *Scientific American,* the most influential of scientific journals, have been owned by the German media corporation Verlagsgruppe Georg von Holtzbrinck GmbH, named after its Nazi founder.[646] The purchase of *Nature* was probably a priority for the Germans because they wanted to do something for climate change awareness. This is evident from the fact that the new editor of *Nature*, Phillip Campbell, was appointed as climatologist. Two years later, Mann's hockey stick graph was published there with its claims that the present climate is unprecedented. The editorial staff did not ask the author for documentation on how he reached his bold conclusions. They published the ground-breaking article without proper peer-review.

When the Climategate scandal was investigated, Campbell was disqualified from Muir Russel's inquiry committee because of his alarmist bias.[647] But your bias apparently doesn't bother anyone when you run a top scientific journal. It was Campbell who, after the Climategate affair, wrote an editorial in which he was rude to critics of climatology.[648] The journal completely abandoned the ethics of impartial, neutral, and value-free science under his reign. In the 2012 presidential election, editors even recommended to scientists which political party to vote for if they wanted more government subsidies.[649]

WIKI BIAS

The internet encyclopedia is governed by ideological censorship and biased selection of information. Don't believe everything you read.

Wikipedia (founded in 2001) is an Internet encyclopedia that most people rely on whenever they need to find out something fast. It grew so rapidly because anyone can contribute to it. However, a team of censors watches over and can erase any inappropriate opinion.

William M. Connolley, a member of the British Green Party, has made about 40,000 edits to Wikipedia, created or rewritten nearly 5,500 articles, most of which are about global warming, including the Climategate scandal. In 2006, he gained administrator rights.

Unfortunately, the editing rules at Wikipedia are rather flexible, and Connolley was out of control. "When Connolley didn't like an article, he simply deleted it without scruples—more than five hundred of them. Authors who created content that was in disagreement with the green activist and Wikipedia administrator Connolley, such contents were banned, and the authors could no longer edit articles. He has blocked over 2,000 people," writes Czech journalist Oldřich Klimánek.[650] It took a long time before Connolley lost his editor rights due to his unprofessional conduct.

Unfortunately, Connolley is not the only one who does this to Wikipedia. Almost all of the climate change figures and graphs on Wikipedia (the Global Warming Art, since 2003) were created by the alarmist Robert Rohde (nickname: Dragon's Flight). The Berkeley physicist later worked with Richard Muller on the BEST project to confirm the existence of warming after the Climategate scandal.

The most interesting part of the Global Warming Art is what is missing there. You will not find any graphs of natural climate cycles, or else people might notice that global warming is largely just another natural fluctuation. You cannot find the 200-year Suess solar cycle, or else people might see that Alpine glacier melting responds to the sun. You won't find the 1,500-year-long cycle of Bond Events, or else people might notice that the Little Ice Age and the recent warming are mostly natural fluctuations. The year-on-year rate of CO_2 increase is missing, too, because then people might notice that CO_2 responds to last year's temperatures—and not the other way around.

There is no graph of ocean level fluctuations encompassing thousands of years because people might notice that the oceans were higher in the Middle Ages or in antiquity than they are today. There is also no figure of sea-level fluctuations over the last 150 years because then people would see that these fluctuations are driven by a 60-year natural climate cycle, not by humans.[651] Glacier melting graphs begin only in 1960, or else people might notice that the melt began in the mid-19th century when CO_2 levels were low. And, of course, there is no comparison of the exaggerated warming prophecies (CMIP-5 models) with a completely different reality.

Unfortunately, this malpractice has the support of Wikipedia leadership. In 2005, Jim Giles' article *Internet Encyclopaedias Go Head to Head* was published in *Nature,* saying that Wikipedia can now proudly compete with the legendary Encyclopedia Britannica for accuracy.[652] Wiki was especially praised for its consistency with the greenhouse hypothesis. Jimmy Wales is quoted as saying: "Connolley has done such amazing work and has had to deal with a fair amount of nonsense." Jim Wales is the founder of Wikipedia.

SAFEGUARDING IMPARTIALITY AT BBC

Once a shining example of journalistic integrity, now BBC is being lectured by ideologues. They even decided that impartiality and balance no longer belong to journalism. Instead, they prefer to broadcast commercials masquerading as news because it is cheaper.

The British television channel BBC used to be the epitome of quality journalism that is impartial, objective, and balanced. The past tense "used to be" is important grammar here.

Peter Sissons spent 30 years on the screen of BBC as a host and journalist. In his memoirs, he remembers what happened in 2007 when IPCC published its Fourth Assessment Report on climate change. "Back in the studio, I suggested that we line up one or two skeptics to react to the report, but received a totally negative response, as if I was some kind of lunatic. I went home and wrote a note to myself: 'What happened to the journalism? The BBC has ¬completely lost it.'"[653]

In my country, when the Communist Party was in power, everybody, including factory workers, had to attend mandatory (and mostly boring) training in Marxism-Leninism. It is surprising to learn that this practice has been recently adopted in the West, in British BBC. Journalists should be the watchdogs of democracy. They should investigate suspicious activities of the climate lobby. Instead, the lobby just dictates to them what to think and print.

In 2007, Roger Harrabin of the BBC and Joe Smith of the CMEP (Cambridge Media and Environment Program) organized the training "Real World" for BBC journalists. It was about global warming, and it was paid, among others, by the University of East Anglia.[654] This is the very university that was involved in the Climategate scandal.

The training was very fruitful. In June 2007, the BBC published a document entitled *Safeguarding Impartiality in the 21ˢᵗ Century*, stating: "The BBC has held a high-level seminar with some of the best scientific experts and has come to the view that the weight of evidence no longer justifies equal space being given to the opponents of the consensus."[655] It reminds me of the Soviets who also claimed their regime is built on "scientific communism," based on hard facts of science. Letting anti-communists speak on TV would have been unscientific.

However, it was not known who the experts were on whose recommendation the BBC introduced censorship. The BBC even went to court because it didn't want to disclose the identity of the so-called experts.[656]

Only years later, their list was discovered or leaked. And it turned out that the so-called top experts were, in fact, activists from Greenpeace, an MP, an insurance company guy, representatives of the Church of England, activists from Stop Climate Chaos, etc. Among the dozens of "experts," there were only three scientists—all of them proponents of the greenhouse hypothesis.[657]

These training seminars help the journalists to exercise self-censorship in their work. When an unknown hacker stole email correspondence from climatologists in 2009 and wanted to publish what he discovered, he sent it to the BBC first. But the BBC didn't show any interest in the Climategate affair, so after weeks of futile waiting, the hacker just posted everything on the Internet directly.

Paul Hudson, who was in charge of the weather at the BBC, admitted on his blog: "I was forwarded the chain of emails on the 12th October, which are comments from some of the world's leading climate scientists written as a direct result of my article *Whatever Happened to Global Warming*. The emails released on the internet as a result of CRU being hacked into are identical to the ones I was forwarded and read at the time, and so, as far as I can see, they are authentic."[658] But Hudson did not inform the public about the email scandal as a proper journalist would do. He kept it to himself.

Ideological bias is also evident in BBC programs about wildlife. Just compare the fate of David Bellamy and David Attenborough, who have been hosting these shows for decades. Botanist David Bellamy has written over 40 books about nature. His smiling bearded face has become synonymous with BBC's natural science programs, of which he has made several hundred. He is one of the best-known conservationists in Britain. For example, he was arrested in 1983 when he and other activists demonstrated against the construction of a dam on the Franklin River.

His career ended in the mid-1990s when he began to express criticism of the environmental policy. For example, he criticized wind farms that kill birds. In 2004, he publicly described man-made warming in the media as nonsense.[659] Because of his views, he was immediately sacked from the position of Plantlife International director. He also lost the presidency of the Wildlife Trusts, which manages nature reserves.[660]

Compare this with another colleague of Bellamy's who remained loyal to the mainstream. David Attenborough was quick to understand the winds of change. He joined a eugenics organization called the Optimum Population Trust, saying that the number of people needs to be reduced. He is allowed to host wildlife programs on TV, but he must add alarmist bits to his shows so as to retain his job.

In the Planet Earth program, for example, he claimed that polar bears cannot find food anymore because of melting ice, and so they desperately attack walruses who would normally be a taboo for them. In fact, bears have been hunting walruses for thousands of years. And we have had accurate observations of this phenomenon since the 1950s.[661]

The BBC also broadcasts misleading programs because such shows are subsidized by lobbyists and, therefore, cost less. For example, the BBC broadcast FBC Media's documentaries that celebrated wonderful biofuels. Not a word about the fact that biofuels pushed up food prices in developing countries. The BBC aired these documentaries because they were cheap. And they were cheap because they were sponsored by the biofuel lobby, the Malaysian government.[662] But this is just one example.[663]

The BBC also aired the documentary series Earth Reports by TVE. This television was founded by UN politicians, namely the UN Environmental Programme founded by Maurice Strong.[664] Remember that he also helped establish the Climate Exchange, aka the first climate casino. So, the BBC was actually broadcasting political propaganda paid by politicians. Almost the entire annual TVE income is not payments from viewers, but subsidies from the UN and the like. The reputation built by BBC in old times is now being exploited to spread propaganda.

HOLOCAUST DENIERS

A climate change denier is a fictional character. In fact, such people live only in the imagination of environmental activists.

"Gossip is a major part of human communication. If all mankind suddenly came together in one place, and we couldn't speak about anyone behind their back, we would soon run out of talking points." This is an old observation of the Czech writer Jan Neruda. Slander is also a crucial part of climate change communication. When Professor Miroslav Kutílek received state honors from the president of the Czech Republic, *The Referendum* daily wrote that "Klaus also honored a climate change denier."665 But Professor Kutílek has never denied that climate change has been occurring. In his book *Thinking Rationally about Global Warming* (2008), he actually details how the climate has been changing throughout history, in prehistoric times or in the Middle Ages, long before the first coal-fired power plant was built.

In 2007, another newspaper claimed that "Klaus promoted a film of a climate change denier."666 But director Durkin, the author of the *Great Global Warming Swindle* movie, does not deny that the climate has always been changing. He merely doubts that man is the main cause of the recent warming. Petr Mach, head of the Center for Economics and Politics (CEP), objected to the defamation in the article "Editors of *Lidové noviny* should apologize."667

Sociologists O'Neill and Boykoff frown upon such language. "Using the language of denialism brings a moralistic tone into the climate change debate that we would do well to avoid. Further, labeling views as denialist has the potential to inappropriately link such views with Holocaust denial."668 Other sociologists like Peter Jacques, however, advocate comparisons of climate skeptics to Holocaust deniers quite openly and are unapologetic about it.669

Abraham Foxman, the president of the Anti-Defamation League, once complained that it had become a custom to compare one's opponents to Nazis. Any quarrel today ends with *argumentum ad Hitlerum*. According to him, such comparisons are not only inappropriate, they sort of downplay the Holocaust.670 Unfortunately, the Anti-Defamation League uses double standards. Why doesn't ADL intervene when climate skeptics are compared to Holocaust deniers?671 There is much talk today about how unacceptable "hate-speech" against a group of people is. However, hating conservatives is just fine, it would seem.

Eco-activist Lynas wrote: "I wonder what sentences judges might hand down at future international criminal tribunals on those who will be partially but directly responsible for millions of deaths from starvation, famine, and disease in decades ahead. I put this in a similar moral category to Holocaust denial."[672] Chief editor of the web journal *Grist* wrote: "It's about the climate-change 'denial industry.' We should have war crimes trials for these bastards—some sort of climate Nuremberg."[673]

British lawyer Polly Higgins proposed in 2010 that the International Criminal Court (ICC) should include ecocide on the list of crimes against peace. Just as genocide is being prosecuted, "ecological genocide" should be prosecuted too. *The Guardian* wrote: "Supporters of a new ecocide law also believe it could be used to prosecute "climate deniers" who distort science and facts to discourage voters and politicians from taking action to tackle global warming and climate change."[674]

It is interesting to note the people behind this effort to criminalize critical thinking in science. The above-mentioned Polly Higgins is on the board of Desertec, who planned to build giant solar power plants in the Sahara Desert. Few people know that this is a project by the Club of Rome—the organization that published the famous *Limits to Growth*. I am sure the green rent-seekers would be most happy if they could jail anyone who stands in their way.

SKEWED SURVEYS

Sometimes you can hear that 97% of scientists agree that people are somehow involved in climate change. Yes, they certainly do and are. But there is no consensus on how big the anthropogenic contribution is.

A survey by Naomi Oreskes (2004) argued that there are no scientific studies that would reject the "consensus."[675] Climate change deniers have no supporters among scientists. But Oreskes' research was quite strange, as it somehow missed to mention most studies on which the skeptics rely.

Among the overlooked studies is, for example, Henrik Svensmark's *Cosmoclimatology: A New Theory Emerges,* according to which warming is a consequence of increase in solar activity and intensification of solar wind.[676] Oreskes ignores this study because it does not contain the keywords "global climate change" in the abstract. Oreskes also suggests that climate skeptics don't believe that climate sometimes changes. However, such a dumb opinion is attributed falsely to skeptics. This weird idea is not supported by Václav Klaus, Stephen McIntyre, or Luboš Motl. Deniers of climate change exist only in Ms. Oreskes' fantasies. Oreskes' research is invalid because she misdefined the subject of her survey and studied something else, not climate skeptics.

Tricks like that were also used in Peter Doran's 2009 study. "Doran found that climatologists who are active in research showed the strongest consensus on the causes of global warming, with 97% agreeing humans play a role."[677] Sure, even most skeptics believe that humans play "a role," but there is no consensus that humans play the dominant role.

Doran conducted a questionnaire survey of 79 people who anonymously described themselves as "experts" on the Internet.[678] But you can impersonate anyone on the Internet. He did not ask them whether humans are responsible for most of the warming. He only asked if people made a "significant" contribution to climate change. But what is "significant"? If people contribute 25% to the warming, it probably is statistically significant, but it means that 75% is caused by nature.

Fortunately, there are more reasonable surveys. Klaus Martin Schulte reviewed scientific articles on "global climate change" in the ISI 2004–2007 database and found that "only 2% offer new field data or observations directly relevant to the question whether anthropogenic warming has prevailed over natural climatic variability in the past half-century."[679] That explains a lot. Roughly 97% or 98%% of the literature does not question the "consensus" because it does not deal with the subject at all.

Proponents of rational scientific skepticism summarize the current state of scientific knowledge in a thousand-page long synthesis *Climate Change*

Reconsidered II, published in 2013 by the International Non-Governmental Panel on Climate Change (NIPCC): "Doubling the concentration of atmospheric CO_2 from its pre-industrial level, in the absence of other forcings and feedbacks, would likely cause a warming of -0.3 to 1.1°C, almost 50% of which must already have occurred... Though a future warming of 2°C would cause geographically varied ecological responses, no evidence exists that those changes would be net harmful to the global environment or to human well-being."[680] This is not a denial that climate change is real. NIPCC, a project chaired by Fred Singer, documents its conclusions with hundreds of scientific peer-reviewed studies, which, according to Oreskes, do not exist.

MERCHANTS OF DOUBT

We are told that the skeptics are paid by Big Oil to sow doubt and confusion. In reality, oil companies give most of their donations to environmentalists.

Australian science journalist Joanne Nova writes in her *Skeptics Handbook*: "Non-believers don't have to prove anything. Skeptics are not asking the world for money. Believers need to explain their case, so let them do the talking... It's entirely reasonable to ask for evidence. If you are met with dismissive, intimidatory, or bullying behavior, don't ignore it. Ask them why they're not willing to explain their case. In scientific discussions, no theory is sacrosanct. Dogma belongs to religions."[681]

Today's mainstream view is exactly the opposite. Anyone who asks inconvenient questions and demands evidence is accused of delaying and wasting everybody's time. Such people are said to help polluters to manufacture doubt in order to avoid penalties. People who refuse to blindly believe the authorities are now described as troublemakers standing in the way of progress.

When sociologists write about climate skeptics, they usually do so from the point of view of "public sociology," which is activist sociology in the service of social change movements.[682] So, climate skepticism is usually not analyzed in terms of the sociology of scientific knowledge but rather in terms of class struggle. Climate skepticism is then referred to as a "countermovement" that opposes the much-needed social change.[683] Depicting climate skeptics as bad people who oppose progress is quite a surprising strategy because skeptics defend industrial modernization, which was the greatest social change since the invention of agriculture. This transformation was a positive force in history that eradicated famine and most of the world's poverty.

Climate skepticism is interpreted as a manifestation of the effort of traditional institutions—such as oil companies or government agencies—to defend the status quo and resist change. For example, sociologists have described the political pressures of the Bush administration, which sought to silence some "alarmist" climatologists.[684] However, sociology turns a blind eye to political pressures that come from the side of alarmists. Besides, environmentalists themselves declare that they are fighting "global change" (their term). So, in fact, they are the ones who defend the status quo.

Sociologists have analyzed what power mechanisms the climate skeptics use to enforce their policies. It is said the skeptics try to slow down the decision-making process and "manufacture uncertainty" on purpose.[685] However, this can also be seen from the other angle. The alarmists manufacture fear. The concerns about greenhouse gases are similar to FUD strategy (Fear, Uncertainty, Doubt). It is a kind of marketing that seeks to give the consumer an impression that something bad might happen if they do not buy our product. This is how insurance companies operate. Another example is Microsoft, which used FUD to make people fear compatibility issues and stay loyal to Microsoft products.[686]

According to environmentalists, the tactics of climate skeptics are similar to that of the tobacco industry, which used to question the health hazards of smoking. This idea was an inspiration for Naomi Oreskes' and Erik Conway's book *Merchants of Doubt* (2010). However, they have not been able to prove the link between climate skeptics and tobacco companies. Although there was once a research committee chaired by the climate skeptic Fred Seitz, that study did not deny the harmfulness of smoking. Even Oreskes admits that Seitz "coordinated a report, *Links between Passive Smoking and Disease,* which frankly acknowledged the abundant scientific evidence linking ETS to lung cancer in adults, and to respiratory illness, asthma, and ear infection in children, and even to perinatal death."[687]

If Oreskes really wanted to dig out some sensational links to the tobacco industry, I would recommend writing about the World Wildlife Fund, whose funding was provided by South African tobacco tycoon Anton Rupert. WWF is the world's wealthiest environmentalist group, by the way. It is the one with a panda in its emblem. Charles de Haes, an employee of Rothmans Tobacco, was the general director of WWF for 18 years. "Charles traveled the world using Rothman boardrooms and a Rothman expense account, and with Prince Bernhard's calling card in his pocket." Rupert gave Charles the job to gather 1001 wealthy sponsors for WWF.[688] Note that South Africa used to be a Dutch colony and Prince Bernhard of the Netherlands was the first president of WWF and also Rupert's friend.

Or Oreskes—if she is still obsessed with guilt by association—could write about the environmentalist hero Al Gore, whose family owned tobacco plantations for generations. During the 1988 election campaign, Al Gore told local farmers that he was actually one of them: "Throughout most of my life, I've raised tobacco. I want you to know that with my own hands, all of my life, I put it in the plant beds and transferred it. I've hoed it. I've chopped it. I've shredded it, spiked it, put it in the barn and stripped it and sold it."[689]

Whereas the supposed tactic of climate skeptics is manufacturing doubt, the strategy of the mainstream (such as gate-keeping) is not analyzed at all. What is worse, such research efforts are even frowned upon and labeled as "crackpot conspiracy theories." On the other hand, the efforts of climate skeptics are routinely interpreted as a sinister conspiracy of the industry to avoid responsibility for "externalities." So, the study of the climate skeptic community is mostly limited to a paranoid search for links to the oil and tobacco industries. And nobody cares what these people believe, what their grievances are, and what motivations really drive them.

Greenpeace even produced the website Exxonsecrets (2004), accusing the climate skeptics of being paid by the Exxon oil corporation. However, they have not been able to find more than one million dollars annually from Exxon to skeptics over the past 20 years. For comparison, it corresponds to one tiny grant in climate research worldwide. However, we can see in Exxon's annual reports that they donate over $100 million to charity, AIDS medicine research, handicapped people, scientific research, etc. If they really wanted to support climate skeptics heavily, they could. But they don't.

In 1999, US courts found tobacco companies guilty as RICO (Racketeer Influenced and Corrupt Organizations). For decades, they have known about the negative health effects of smoking but concealed the evidence. In 2015, based on this precedent, efforts were made to crush the oil company Exxon under this RICO act too. The accusation goes like this. When their own researcher James F. Black confirmed the harmful effects of greenhouse gases, the company fired him in 1983 and canceled the research program to cover their tracks.

In reality, Exxon really did sponsor climate research in the early years because oil companies wondered if melting Arctic might become accessible to oil drilling once the ice is gone. When they sponsored the research, they were the first ones who could observe first-hand how weak the climate models are. But Black had never published anything about climate science because he was just a corporate clerk, and it wasn't his research. He just told the managers what he had read in newspapers. He was also not firedbut retired. The research ended because the government stopped subsidizing this program.[690] In those years, the government launched its own National Climate Program Act (1978) and redirected funding there. To sum up, the theory about criminal racketeering conspiracy fell apart like a house of cards. The charge that Exxon "knew" about climate change is not enough. The climate has always been changing. It is not a sort of secret that someone could hide.

Ever since the beginning, oil companies sponsored mainstream climatology. For example, they funded the establishment of the Climate Research Unit at the University of East Anglia, the venue for the later Climategate scandal. The largest sum of petrodollars that Greenpeace discovered is the $100 million that Exxon gave to Stanford University alarmists for the Global Climate and Energy Project.[691] That's several times more than Exxon has ever given to all skeptics combined. Similarly, in 2007 BP (British Petroleum) gave to the California University at Berkeley a $500 million grant for biofuel research.[692] It was used to establish the Energy Bioscience Institute.

The selective blindness of climate activists is surprising. In their paranoia, they see Big Oil behind every corner, but they do not notice that they have Big Oil among the leaders of environmentalism. Rajendra Pachauri, chairman of the Intergovernmental Panel on Climate Change (IPCC), was one of the directors of Indian Oil Ltd (1999–2003). Maurice Strong, who founded the UN Environmental Programme (UNEP) was the president of the nationalized oil company PetroCanada after 1976. Even the climate activist Al Gore eventually decided that oil money does not smell bad. When his boring Current TV with its climate change shows failed, he sold it to Al Jazeera television, owned by the oil sheik of Qatar.

Climatologist Peter Gleick was so eager to reveal an oil conspiracy that he resorted to online fraud (phishing). He stole financial accounts of the climate skeptical Heartland Institute (by pretending to be the institute's employee in an email). It turned out that Heartland had an annual budget of just $5 million a year. Most of this goes to the organization of international climate change conferences. By comparison, Greenpeace has $200 million a year and the World Wildlife Fund some half a billion.

Gleick placed the stolen documents on the Internet for everyone to see that there is no oil company among the sponsors.[693] So, the eco-activists said, at the very least, that Heartland is "paid by coal companies." But in fact, there was only one coal company among the sponsors, and it donated less than any other donor (a few dozen thousand dollars). Among the sponsors is, for example, the company Pfitzer, yet nobody says that climate skeptics are puppets of Viagra producers.

Thanks to Gleick, environmental activists obtained a list of donors of the Heartland Institute, and they used it to threaten them. Heartland's president, Joe Bast, was worried: "Greenpeace has contacted the employers of every scientist who works for us, demanding that they be fired for having the temerity to question the official dogma of global warming. Can you imagine a more egregious attack on free speech and open academic debate? Donors to Heartland in the past two years have been the subject of hate mail, letter-writing, and telephone campaigns, and online petitions demanding that they stop funding us."[694]

In addition, Gleick produced a forgery, which he published along with stolen accounts. However, it is clear that the document *Confidential Memo 2012: Heartland Climate Strategy* could not have been written by a genuine climate skeptic. A skeptic would never write that he wanted to discourage teachers from teaching science or that he wanted to "undermine" science. Climate skeptics don't consider apocalyptic raving as science. In the document is mentioned only one scientist, Gleick himself. It is clear that Gleick wrote it himself because none of the skeptics would have described this crackpot as a "top scientist."

Gleick finally confessed to the theft and apologized.[695] "In a serious lapse of my own professional judgment and ethics, I solicited and received additional materials directly from the Heartland Institute under someone else's name." He justified his behavior by his firm belief in conspiracy theories. "My judgment was blinded by my frustration with the ongoing efforts—often anonymous, well-funded, and coordinated—to attack climate science and scientists and prevent this debate, and by the lack of transparency of the organizations involved." In fact, it was Gleick who "prevents debate"—Heartland invited him, and he declined.

Due to the scandal, Mr. Gleick's project, "Integrity of Science Initiative," ended. It would have been awkward for a thief and falsifier to give moralizing speeches as its chairman. The project, by the way, was a follow-up to the "Climate Change and the Integrity of Science" declaration, where Gleick defended scientists from the Climategate scandal. It is ironic that he was the one who claimed that scientists never cheat.[696]

Both camps accuse each other of being paid by Big Oil corporations. Frankly, it is pointless to investigate who gets what funding. There is always some funding bias these days. What matters is fact-based debate and scientific evidence. Slander does not belong in academia. Even if you had funding from Satan himself (given how many bankers are in hell), you may be scientifically correct anyway.

And, also, it remains unclear why money from the sale of coal and oil should be considered dirty or bloody. These companies fuel your car so you can get from point A to point B, and they feed your boiler, so you do not freeze in winter. How is that worse than a baker who makes bread or a tailor who sews clothes for us? Crude oil is used to produce tires, plastic bottles, lubricants, stockings, candles, cosmetics, golf balls, shampoo, and many other useful items of daily use. To condemn oil companies while still using their products is a bit hypocritical. It is like a man eating a steak while having a passionate speech about the importance of vegetarianism. What is most hilarious is the virtue signaling of individuals who turn off all electricity during Earth Hour to prove how they despise fossil fuels. And then they spend a dark hour without electricity, only with candles made from... oil.

THE SKEPTICAL
ENVIRONMENTALIST LOMBORG

The book The Skeptical Environmentalist (2001) by the Danish statistician Bjorn Lomborg caused quite a stir. The author originally wanted to write a book about the deteriorating state of the world, but while studying the facts, he discovered the opposite is true. The green movement cast him out as a traitor.

At an autograph session in Oxford, eco-activist Mark Lynas even smashed a whipped cream cake into his face, like you see in silent slapstick movies. Ironically, a few years later, Lynas himself became a renegade when he publicly apologized for his earlier resistance to nuclear energy and genetically modified crops (GMO). Today, Lynas remembers his earlier fanatical attitude with shame.[697]

In the spirit of McCarthyism, Lomborg was investigated by the Danish Research Agency's Committee on Scientific Dishonesty (DSCD). According to the verdict, Lomborg's book contains misinformation, but this claim was not supported by any quotes or evidence. A judgment without justification is quite unusual under the rule of law. Several hundred scientists petitioned against the behavior of DSCD and demanded that this inquisition should be disbanded. Lomborg appealed, and the verdict was ultimately retracted due to being too "emotional."

That wasn't all. In *Scientific American,* Lomborg's opponents published an article subtitled *Science Defends Itself against The Skeptical Environmentalist,*[698] which is a pretty startling name. If somebody publishes an opinion—even a wrong one—why should it somehow threaten science? Isn't actual science based on free exchange of opinions? The editor-in-chief of the journal also behaved in an unusual manner.

Instead of playing the role of an impartial referee, he supported Lomborg's critics in an editorial: "And it is hard not to be struck by Lomborg's presumption that he has seen into the heart of the science more faithfully than have investigators who have devoted their lives to it." But Lomborg based his data on peer-reviewed sources from such experienced experts. This is why his book is so powerful.

The attacks continued in the years to come. Kareen Fog published her criticism of Lomborg at lomborg-errors.dk. Howard Friel wrote a book called "The Lomborg Deception." Lomborg dealt with Karen Fog on 180 pages in the book *Godhedens pris* (available online)[699] and responded to Friel's objections on 27 pages.[700]

A layman will probably find it hard to know which side to trust. Let us give just one example of this battle of statistics. Friel is shocked how Lomborg can claim that poverty in the world is falling because his numbers show that in some parts of the world the number of starving people has clearly risen (by 60 million). Sure, but Friel forgot to mention that poverty decreased in other places, most places. Lomborg speaks of the total number of undernourished people, and their overall number has fallen from 980 to 850 million people in developing countries between 1990–1992 to 2011–2013.[701]

"Czech president Klaus is losing allies, the denier environmentalist Lomborg changed opinion," wrote the newspaper *Lidové noviny* in 2009.[702] But readers of *The Skeptical Environmentalist* (2001) know that Lomborg has never questioned man-made warming. Nor is it true that he changed opinion. He has always been arguing that reducing carbon emissions is costly and ineffective. He says that we should simply adapt to warming or cool the climate (for example, by creating artificial clouds). But even such a compromising (lukewarm) attitude is not acceptable to climate radicals. In 2011, the new Danish government cut all funding for Lomborg's institute Copenhagen Consensus Center. Ida Auken, as a representative of the new government, did not even try to hide that the reasons were political.

GREAT GLOBAL
WARMING SWINDLE

The documentary film by controversial director Durkin was an antidote to Al Gore's An Inconvenient Truth. Instead of criticizing the movie itself, the alarmist tried to slander him personally.

Director Durkin has been a scourge of environmentalists for years. In *The Rise and Fall* of GM, he criticized the campaign against genetically modified crops. In the film *Storm in a D-Cup* (1998), he debunked the claim that silicone breast implants cause cancer. He was right. Silicone is not translucent to X-rays, making tumors harder to detect. But silicone itself does not cause tumors.[703]

When he made the film *Great Global Warming Swindle* (2007), he became the target of a smear campaign. The Czech newspaper *Lidové noviny* wrote: "President Klaus presented a film by a climate change denier."[704] The journalists probably didn't even see the film since the film states that the climate is always changing.

Journalists argued: "It is a paradox, as President Klaus... has compared environmentalists to Marxists several times. But, in fact, it is the director of this film who is close to Marxists." It is a little complicated. Durkin used to write for *LM* magazine, which was originally founded by a Trotskyist group. In the 1980s, this group transformed into a libertarian movement, which is why the name of the magazine changed from *Living Marxism* to only *LM*. How on Earth can left-wing Trotskyites become right-wing libertarians? Well, both share resistance to Big Government meddling in the lives of individuals. Such change of heart is not unprecedented. Even Irving Kristol's neoconservatives in the USA started as liberals but moved to the right when the left-wing support for tyrants and cultural revolution became too much.

Since no skeleton was found in Durkin's closet, the Czech branch of Friends of the Earth at least tried to smear the magazine where Durkin once worked. "*Living Marxism* claimed, among other things, that reports of genocide in Rwanda or of internment camps in Bosnia were just a hoax perpetrated by the media."[705] *Lidové noviny* took this campaign even a step further. "The director denied the genocide in Rwanda."

But Durkin had nothing to do with the Rwanda article. It was written by Fiona Fox, and the article does not deny the massacre of the poor Tutsis; it only explains why it happened. The Tutsis once ruled in Rwanda with an iron fist until the Hutus overthrew their dictatorship. In 1990, the Tutsis tried to return to power.[706]

Why did most of the attacks focus on Durkin's privacy and his activities? Because there is very little in the film that could be criticized, let alone debunked. The only serious mistake in the film is a chart that has an incorrect timescale in the second half of the 20ᵗʰ century, which was corrected in re-runs of the movie. Professor Wunsch also said that he would never have interviewed the filmmakers if he had known that the film would be skeptical. Concerns about being blacklisted as a "climate denier" are understandable.

Durkin responded briefly: "The remarkable thing is not that I was attacked, but that the attacks have been so feeble. The ice-core data was the jewel in the global-warming crown, cited again and again as evidence that carbon dioxide 'drives' the earth's climate. In fact, as its advocates have been forced to admit, the ice-core data says the opposite. Temperature change always precedes changes in CO_2 by several hundred years. Temperature drives CO_2, not the other way around. The global-warmers do not deny this. They cannot."[707]

SKEPTICAL WEATHERMEN

According to a survey by George Mason University, over 60% of TV weather broadcasters who are members of the American Meteorological Society (AMS) believe that global warming is predominantly of natural origin.[708]

The world's most-viewed climate skeptic website, Wattsupwiththat.com, is run by meteorologist Anthony Watts. With the help of volunteers, he created the Surface Stations project, where he mapped poorly located weather stations in the USA. Weatherman John Coleman, founder of The Weather Channel, the first television channel about weather, is also a climate skeptic.

The management of the American Meteorological Society (AMS), however, supports the theory of CAGW (Catastrophic Anthropogenic Global Warming). William Gray, the pioneer of seasonal hurricane predictions in the Atlantic, was outraged when AMS awarded the Rossby Medal to James Hansen, who is famous for his apocalyptic warming scenarios and who is not a meteorologist. "We AMS members have allowed a small group of AMS administrators, climate modelers, and CO_2 warming sympathizers to maneuver the internal workings of our society to support AGW policies, irrespective of what our rank-and-file members might think. This small, organized group of AGW sympathizers has indeed hijacked our society."[709]

In 2012, activists established a Forecast-the-Facts organization that intimidates TV stations whose meteorologists express skeptical views. Activists released a blacklist of meteorologists who are said to be "climate deniers."[710] They send letters with demands that people committing a thoughtcrime be thrown out of work.

Although Forecast-the-Facts looks like a normal NGO citizen association, there is actually a political party behind it. This pressure organization was chaired by Brad Johnson, a long-time employee of the Think-Progress environmentalist magazine that is published by the Center for American Progress (CAP). And this CAP is run by John Podesta, the right hand of Presidents Clinton and Obama.

Forecast-the-Facts is a project of the CEL (Citizen Engagement Laboratory) media company, located near Berkeley. The director of CEL, James Rucker, is not a private person either. He is an associate of Van Jones, who was the environmental adviser to US president Obama.

Rucker and Jones are experienced in intimidation. In 2005, they launched a Color-of-Change campaign to silence the conservative media in the US. Their turnofffox.org campaign aimed to destroy Fox, the only right-wing nationwide television in the US. They managed to persuade the

MSNBC channel to fire its conservative commentator Pat Buchanan. He once ran for president and is the author of the famous book The Death of the West.

By threatening and intimidating sponsors, activists achieved the firing of one of Fox News' leading hosts, Glenn Beck. He was one of the brave few who informed the American public about the Climategate scandal. The bastadobbs.org campaign used threats to get rid of the TV host Lou Dobbs, who criticized illegal immigration. He was eventually fired from CNN.

Van Jones lost the position of Obama's eco-adviser when it turned out that after the 1992 racial riots, he was involved in a sort of revolutionary communist guerrilla (STORM: Standing Together to Organize and Revolutionary Movement). Jones admitted to journalists in 2005: "I met all these young radical people of color—I mean really radical, communists and anarchists. And it was, like, 'This is what I need to be a part of.'... spent the next ten years of my life working with a lot of those people I met in jail, trying to be a revolutionary... I was a rowdy nationalist on April 28th... by August, I was a communist."[711]

THE CASE OF ROGER PIELKE

The witch-hunt made the well-known hurricane expert withdraw completely from the climate debate, and today he has a completely different job.

Roger Pielke Jr, a Professor of Environmental Studies at University of Colorado, described himself as a climate heretic in an article for the *Wall Street Journal*.[712] While he believes climate change is real, his research has not confirmed the idea that extreme weather events such as hurricanes are getting worse in the USA.

These conclusions led to an "intense media campaign" that he should be fired from Nate Silver's well-known *FiveThirtyEight* online journal about statistics. Nate Silver is known for his successful predictions of election results, hence the name of the site (538 is the number of US presidential electors). The campaign was effective. Pielke was downgraded from an editor to an external correspondent and later he left upon realizing that the editors would no longer publish anything he wrote.

The attacks on Pielke began mainly because of his article *Disasters Cost More Than Ever—But Not Because of Climate Change* from 2014. According to Pielke, the increase in insured damages over the past 50 years was caused by increasing population density, inflation, and rising income, not by climate change. When the same hurricane of the same strength hits the same community 50 years later, it finds denser housing and more expensive equipment in each house.

But to question the CAGW dogma is politically dangerous, and Pielke could feel the consequences. In the end, the editorial board of *FiveThirtyEight* succumbed to pressure and published a "refutation" of Pielke's thesis, written by the usual suspects (Mann, Trenberth, and Abraham)—the most discredited alarmist activists in the world. Mann is the author of the hockey stick graph.

We learned more about the political background of Pielke's professional assassination before the US presidential election in 2016. Hackers at Wikileaks posted emails of presidential candidate Hillary Clinton, including the communication of her campaign manager, John Podesta.[713] The editor of the journal *ThinkProgress* (John Legum) boasted in an email that Pielke was gagged thanks to his efforts. "I think it's fair to say that, without Climate Progress, Pielke would still be writing on climate change for *FiveThirtyEight*."

On Twitter, Pielke commented: "Propaganda works: I count more than 160 articles at the Center for American Progress trashing me over the years." Because of this slander campaign, Pielke even had to defend himself in a Congress investigation, as he was accused of being funded by Big

Oil—the investigation did not find any evidence of such funding, but the damage to his reputation had already been done. At first, Pielke tried to fight. In 2010, he challenged Romm (editor-in-chief of *ThinkProgress*) to a public debate in Romm's hometown, saying that the loser should contribute $10,000 to a charity of the winner's choice. Romm, however, rejected the challenge and avoided confrontation.

The media was able to destroy the career of a man who was a leading expert in his field. Roger Pielke Jr. studied mathematics and political science. He focused mainly on the economic assessment of natural disasters. In 1993 and 2000, he was a research fellow at the National Center for Atmospheric Research (NCAR). Between 2002 and 2004, he was a postgraduate student in environmental studies at the University of Boulder, Colorado (he was awarded the prize for best lecturer). In 2006, he received the Eduard Brückner Prize in Munich for his contribution to interdisciplinary climate research.

Pielke—exhausted by personal attacks and the never-ending lies about his alleged denial of climate change—ultimately decided to change his job. Today, as a political scientist and economist, he does research about steroids and drug-abuse supervision in sports. Investigating fraud in sports—which is a multi-billion-dollar business today—is apparently safer than writing about the weather.

VIII. WHO PAYS THE PRICE?

Selling fear has many advantages over other commodities. Unlike iron ore, you do not need to mine anything. You do not need to build processing factories. You can do without warehouses and cargo transport. All you need is to make up a creepy scenario of what might happen, and, as soon as people are scared enough, you offer them protection. Protection for money, of course. You know, like the extortion money collected by the mafia.

There is a long tradition of fear-mongering in various churches, which threaten you with hell in the afterlife. Then they promise to save your soul for a certain generous amount. But beware of angry customers who want a refund. If you sell a cure for global warming, make sure to explain to your clients that the effects will be visible only decades after their death. No one has returned from the grave to complain yet.

For merchants of fear, governments are the most lucrative target because the treasury has plenty of cash from taxes. And government can raise taxes whenever they like. It can even print money. So, you need to convince the ministers that there is a looming danger. Then you make them an offer they can't refuse. "Dear government, if you subsidize us, we will find the cure." But be careful not to solve the crisis. The atmosphere of fear must be maintained and pampered for as long as possible. Otherwise, you will be dismissed with thanks, and you will have to find another job.

In 1992, at the Earth Summit in Rio de Janeiro, governments pledged to finance the war on climate change. This funding is a source of subsidies that can never run out because climate change has been taking place nonstop since the Paleozoic and cannot be halted. So, this is a business guaranteed to thrive for a long time.

After 2000, even a climate exchange was created where climate indulgences are traded—like in the times of Martin Luther. Companies can buy a pardon for their climatic sins. We are told that unless we take part in this money-laundering scheme, the planet will burn in the hell of global warming. Even insurance companies are on board—they understand that frightened people will buy more insurance. This is why insurance companies rig statistics to make it appear as if natural disasters are getting worse.

Such fake statistics have been perfected by the World Bank economist Lord Stern in the famous Stern Report, which claimed that the longer we delay payment of the ransom, the worse we will suffer. This principle of "give me your wallet without thinking" is called the "precautionary principle." What a nice name. It is important in advertising to give crappy products at least nice-sounding names.

Merchants of fear do not actually expend much effort to solve the problem. So, they tend to underestimate the technical side. But if a sold solution doesn't work, then what? For example, if you are selling snake oil potions for hair growth and the customer finds out that you only sold him dyed plain water, grab your loot and get lost. Before they find out they have been deceived, you should already be away, drinking your Daiquiri on a beach somewhere in the Bahamas.

Biofuels not only caused famine but also have a larger carbon footprint than fossil fuels. This cure will not help the climate. There have been cases where entrepreneurs were generating solar electricity at night—or rather using diesel generators to produce fake "green energy," which has a higher feed-in tariff. Amateurs who rob trains or banks or mug people in a park are so lame. Professionals use law to steal money from people's pockets. You produce cheaply, but the law orders that customers must buy your junk product for guaranteed high prices.

So far, these "mitigation measures" have practically no observable impact on global CO_2 levels. The touted success of the Kyoto Protocol in reducing greenhouse gases generally existed only on paper. Very few people are serious about nature protection—they usually just print some advertising slogans.

Non-profit organizations like to denounce the profits of corporations, and one would expect them to criticize the climate business forcefully. But the lobby of alternative energy producers receives lots of subsidies and shares them with NGOs. You don't bite the hand that feeds you. The result: these NGOs found another target instead—they attack producers of cheap energy from traditional sources that stand in the way of the green lobby.

Another obstacle for climate policy is the existing legislation and parliamentary opposition. There are opinions that democracy is only holding back the planet-saving effort. Some say we should leave the decision to experts, for example, the climatologists. It would be like the "rule of philosophers" as the naive Plato dreamed (before his philosopher-king sold him to slavery). Democracy is no longer able to face the crises of modern times. Along with the market economy, democracy is implicated in the worst crime of the modern era—the crime of prosperity.

SUBSIDIES FROM RIO

The climate lobby did not defeat the climate skeptics by scientific evidence but with their wallet. At the Earth Summit in 1992, governments pledged to subsidize the fight against greenhouse gases.

Some important things would probably not survive without subsidies, such as the construction of motorways or basic research. At the same time, however, subsidies are a mechanism that makes it possible to build very costly stuff that nobody actually wants. Subsidies fund the climate research institutes and computer models that can "predict" the future of climate a hundred years ahead with the accuracy of a coin toss. Subsidies have also made it possible to set up institutes for risk assessment research that looks for problems where none exist.

In the field of subsidies, the year 1992 was a turning point. In that year, the Framework Convention on Climate Change (UNFCCC) was signed at the Earth Summit in Rio de Janeiro. It didn't change much in terms of climate protection, but it totally transformed the redistribution of funds. Governments around the world committed themselves in writing to finance the fight against emissions of certain harmless gases. Proponents of the hypothesis of man-made warming have literally become rich overnight. They can frankly compare the Rio summit to winning a jackpot. Their opponents, on the other hand, lost their cause with the stroke of a pen.

Luxury conferences are a representative measure of wealth. When a conference of the signatories of the Framework Convention on Climate Change was held in Copenhagen in December 2009, there were 1,200 limousines and 140 private aircraft.[714] As stated by the TaxPayers' Alliance, the Danish government's costs were around $60 million. Taken together with the costs of national delegations, the conference cost the taxpayers more than $200 million.[715]

The result of the conference was a lot of empty promises and lots of paperwork. But that is not all. These conferences are an opportunity to reward their loyal followers. If you stand on the right side of the barricade, you can have a free trip.

Naturally, climate research institutes are subject to Parkinson's laws of bureaucracy. No one wants to lose their job. No one will say, "Abolish our institute; it is unnecessary." So, the number of reported climate disasters is increasing because all the hired climatologists must show some results. The more climate researchers you employ, the more the climate 'worsens'.

Czech meteorologist R. Tolasz once wrote about these specialized climate research institutes: "The research centers were established with a simple task to deal with a small segment of a wider complex issue... By their very nature, they are not really interested in really solving the problem because it would bring about their own end. To ensure their survival, they also look for allies outside of climatology (unfortunately also in politics). The centers are generally funded from 'uncertain' research resources. They need to obtain grants no matter what... This is why we have so many studies like the Impact of Climate Change on the Nutrition of Squirrels."[716]

In early 2011, the European Commission helped establish one such institute in Brno. CzechGlobe—Global Change Research Institute—cost three-quarters of a billion Czech crowns. Of which 200 million were spent so scientists could buy their own aircraft.[717] The experts are paid by the European Commission, which also operates the climate exchange trading. It is like when a toothpaste maker hires a scientist to act in a TV commercial. The spokesperson of CzechGlobe became one of the most radical climate activists in the country. For Jan Hollan, even IPCC is too "moderate." And now, he was given a pulpit as a gift from the European Commission.

Thanks to climate hysteria, scientists receive millions of subsidies they had never dreamed of. Scientists are between two fires—politicization of science eliminates academic freedom; but on the other hand, it also brings new jobs in the field. In the years 2010-2015, Czech scientists received grants worth 135 million for "national carbon monitoring infrastructure."[718] The project was to monitor the sources of CO_2 in the Czech Republic and to find where the landscape absorbs carbon (sinks).

In 2007–2011, they were given 25 million Czech crowns (CZK) for a project "Refining the current estimates of the impacts of climate change in the water, agriculture and forestry sectors and proposing adaptation measures."[719] It was a forecast of how the Czech Republic will warm up in a hundred years. The credibility of such forecasts is low. They do not take into account the influence of natural factors such as changes in solar activity. They overestimate the impact of greenhouse gases. Regional models are not able to predict climate status in 20 years, let alone 100 years. However, the authors do not have to worry about any responsibility because no one will live long enough to see the results.

Climatologist Hans von Storch warns that if researchers run the same model or set of models several times and the results are different from each other and from the observed trend, "planners should handle them with kid gloves. Whenever possible, they'd rather wait with spending big money on adaptation projects until there is more certainty about the things to come."[720]

The study states that it was done to implement the conclusions of the European Commission's "Green Paper" called "Adapting to Climate Change in Europe—Options for EU Action" from June 2007. The subsidy was provided by the Ministry of Environment. The ministry wanted to use this study for preparation of a "climate change adaptation strategy." Scientists were hired by politicians, and nobody was concerned about politicisation of science. Already in the research design, scientists are required to accept the conclusions of the UN Intergovernmental Panel on Climate Change—a place where government representatives have the last say.

There are abundant funding programs in the European Union, as long as you have the right set of beliefs. The EU will not finance anything that is not in line with its political plans. And it's not about small money. The European Union's budget for 2014–2020 was set at EUR 960 billion. Of these, about 20% were to be invested in the war on climate.[721] The names of individual grant projects are almost poetic, for example, CLIMSAVE, REDD-ALERT, or HighNoon.[722]

The European Union has also funded scientists from the Climategate scandal. In 2007–2009 alone, the European Commission funded 28 climate change research projects worth about € 116 million, and the University of East Anglia (which includes the Climate Research Unit) participated in four of these projects. Since 1990, Phil Jones, the main character of Climategate, spent about £ 13 million on research.[723] When we focus only on project-specific funding, we see that half of it was financed by the EU. For the years 1990–2006, Jones received a total of £ 4.3 million for projects, of which £ 1.8 million were from Brussels.

Of course, scientists do not become millionaires with private mansions and jets. Grants do not go into their personal pockets; their salaries make up only a fraction of the grant. However, climate scientists are afraid of losing their jobs. They understand perfectly that if they express opinions not liked by their sponsor, they might lose funding. And their career!

Although the Framework Convention on Climate Change (UNFCCC) is a money redistribution project, one of the founding figures of this policy was a right-wing politician. Margaret Thatcher was among the first heads of states to publicly support the fight against global warming. It was at the very end of her career as Prime Minister. She had a chemistry degree and her advisor, Crispin Tickell, convinced her that carbon dioxide was a topic in which she, as a "scientist," could have greater authority than other politicians. A competitive advantage.

In her memoir, *Statecraft* (2002), Thatcher regrets her behavior at that time. "A new dogma about climate change has swept through the left-of-center governing classes... Since clearly no plan to alter climate could be considered on anything but a global scale, it provides a marvelous excuse for worldwide, supra-national socialism."[724] However, in the late 1980s, she used demonization of coal to put pressure on the striking union of miners.

She first spoke about the fight against warming in 1988 in a speech to the Royal Society and then again in 1989 at the UN. In response to the first UN climate panel report, she founded the Hadley Center for Climate Prediction and Research, a sanctuary of modern-day oracles. Instead of astrologers that used to be part of every royal court, now we have climate scientists: "With its advanced computing facilities and the superb skills of its scientists, it will help us look into the future and to predict more precisely the changes in our climate."[725]

Two years after the end of her reign, the Earth Summit was held in Rio de Janeiro, bringing together heads of states from all over the world. Even US president George Bush arrived after much hesitation. He did not have the courage to oppose everyone and added his signature to a convention he disagreed with. He committed the US to the fight against global warming, yet he did not hear a thank you. The United States was smeared in Rio as an environmental villain and Bush as a hypocrite because it was clear to everyone that he had not signed out of genuine faith.

It was the Cuban dictator Fidel Castro who was the darling of the conference. He couldn't give a five-hour monologue, as he was accustomed to at home, but his hate-speech about awful West had the greatest applause of all speakers: "With only 20% of the world's population, they consume two-thirds of all metals and three-fourths of the energy produced worldwide. They have poisoned the seas and the rivers. They have polluted the air." The dictator thundered. And he didn't hide he came to the conference to ask for cash. "Now that the supposed threat of communism has disappeared and there is no more pretext to wage cold wars or continue the arms race and military spending, what then is preventing these resources from going immediately to promote Third World development and fight the ecological destruction threatening the planet?"[726]

Going to Rio was the biggest mistake of Bush's presidency. That's what his close associate, John H. Sununu, thinks. What would Ronald Reagan have done in his place? Ed Meese, who worked with Bush's predecessor at the White House, believes that Reagan would have handled the situation better. He would have flown to Rio, but only to explain vigorously to everyone why he wouldn't sign.[727] He was a well-known opponent of using "environmental extremism" to strengthen the grip of Big Government.

KYOTO SCHEME

The Kyoto Protocol was an international treaty in which states pledged to pretend as if they were reducing greenhouse gases.

While the Earth Summit (1992) ended in general proclamations only, in Kyoto, Japan (1997), several states made specific commitments to reduce greenhouse gas emissions. However, it was only a symbolic gesture anyway since countries with the highest emissions did not join (USA) or did not have binding targets (BRIC: Brazil, India, China).

The Czech Republic did make a pledge—my country committed to get emissions 8% lower than in 1990—but that objective had already been met before the pledge was signed. Kyoto did not require us to reduce emissions anymore; it even allowed us to increase emissions a bit.

The Czech Republic reduced its emissions after 1989 but not thanks to environmentalists. It was due to the breakdown of the Soviet economic block (Comecon) and the painful restructuring of the industry. In 1985, the Czech Republic had an annual emission of 168 million tons of CO_2. In 1990, it was 155 million tons of CO_2. And in 1995, it was only 123 million tons.[728] Production faltered, and emissions just followed.

Recent reports cunningly show only the 1990 data and the latest year (such as 2013), giving the illusion that Kyoto is responsible for reducing the emissions. It is an irony, but the greenhouse gases fell the most when the prime minister was Václav Klaus, a climate skeptic. The same situation was in Germany because in East Germany, there was a large decrease in production after the fall of the Berlin Wall.[729]

In addition to declining production and falling exports, there is another way to reduce greenhouse gas emissions. Move production to other countries. When you impose climate taxes, increase energy costs, and make labor more expensive, companies will flee from Europe to overseas, of course. Along with production, they will take CO_2 emissions with them, as well as jobs and tax revenues. The euphemism is "carbon leakage."

Britain once prided itself in reducing its emissions by 18% compared to the 1990 levels. However, when Defra (Department of Environment, Food, and Rural Affairs) ordered an analysis from the Stockholm Environment Institute (SEI), it turned out it was just a statistical illusion. Britain seemingly reduced its emissions by relocating production to developing countries. In fact, emissions from British firms increased by 20%.[730]

Excluding countries whose geography makes it possible to use hydroelectric power plants (Austria, Norway) or countries with developed nuclear energy (in France nuclear power provides over 70% of its electricity), Germany has probably gone the furthest in its quest for renewable energy. There, renewable resources combined (wind, biomass, sun, water) already produce a quarter of all electricity. But is it really good news?

As a result, German electricity prices are higher than the European average.[731] In spite of the green policy, CO_2 emissions in Germany have been increasing in recent years because Germany decided to shut down their nuclear power plants after the Fukushima incident in Japan. There is no other way to compensate for lost energy than massive construction of new coal-fired power plants or importation of energy (from coal power plants abroad). So, the Germans have increased their energy prices without reducing their carbon footprint—they just shot their own foot. Maybe they wanted to lead the world by example. However, according to the International Energy Agency, in 2014, solar and wind power plants together produced less than 1% of the world's total energy consumption, i.e., including both electricity and transportation.[732]

And there is also the Chinese energy strategy. In China, they have discovered that you can show reductions in emissions even though they actually remain the same. China takes part in the profitable Clean Development Mechanism. This means that European companies can redeem their climate sins by sponsoring a project to reduce CO_2 emissions in developing countries—such as China.

However, three-quarters of the projects were frauds that deliberately increased the emissions of the HFC-23 greenhouse gas that is generated by the production of refrigeration equipment. And then the Chinese were paid by the Europeans to reduce the emissions back to where they were. An extortion racket. Half of the ransom was collected by the Chinese government through taxation.[733]

When these frauds were discovered, UN-based Bonn officials began to be afraid and demanded diplomatic immunity. They were afraid of jail because it was their responsibility to approve these fishy projects.[734]

Not surprisingly, the ill-famed company ENRON also supported this Kyoto scheme prior to going bankrupt due to accounting fraud. "If implemented, this agreement will do more to promote Enron's business than will almost any other regulatory initiative outside of restructuring of the energy and natural gas," wrote John Palmissano, who represented the company in Kyoto.[735] The company was particularly looking forward to generous state subventions.

Palmissano reported on climate talks in Kyoto: "Enron now has excellent credentials with many 'green' interests including Greenpeace, WWF [World Wildlife Fund]... This position should be increasingly cultivated and capitalized on (monetized)." Palmissano in Kyoto also received a prize from the Climate Institute for ENRON's support for clean energy.

By that time ENRON already had a turbulent history. Thanks to close relations with politicians, they managed to enforce deregulation of trade in natural gas and electricity and used the loose rules to increase prices. Similarly, they wanted to milk government subsidies for renewable resources. For example, the trick called Death Star was to create a virtual network overload in a location and then get the state to pay them a reward for stabilizing the network, i.e., to divert electricity elsewhere. The trick called Ricochet meant that they exported electricity to another state and then transferred it back because imported energy has a higher tariff. The company has become a symbol of crony capitalism, a corrupt connection between politics and business. Some of these practices heralded what we see today in green energy. For example, wind farms that receive subsidies for not generating energy so as to avoid grid overload.[736]

CLIMATE EXCHANGE

Climate change is sometimes seen as a modern religion. And what religion would it be if you couldn't purchase indulgences to redeem your sins?

The sale of indulgences was already criticized by Jan Hus and Martin Luther. Today, indulgences for sins against the climate are sold too, but with one difference. In the Middle Ages, indulgences were not traded on the stock exchange. Today, indulgences for greenhouse gas emissions are sold on commodity exchanges along with grain or soybeans. It works like this. A company that reduces its CO_2 emissions gets a tradable certificate for its laudable act. The certificate can then be sold to another company that has high emissions. It can buy the certificate at the stock exchange to relieve its conscience.

If a modern Martin Luther wanted to denounce the climate indulgence system, he would probably point out that a rich man doesn't need to worry about his sins because he has enough money to buy indulgences. A polluter buys an indulgence and continues to emit pollution. When one company increases emissions by one ton and sends money to another company that reduces emissions by one ton, the net emissions do not change, of course. Some people may feel good about it because now we are "carbon neutral." At the least, the emissions have not increased overall.

Often, however, this neutrality is merely an illusion. When an "evil" coal power plant sends money to a "divine" hydroelectric power plant under construction, it doesn't cause any extra emission reduction. The hydroelectric power plant would have been built anyway because, in that area, they have no better energy options. A full one-third of the projects receiving indulgence (offset) money from the Clean Development Mechanism (CDM) were hydroelectric power stations. For example, the Brazilian San Antonio dam was already under construction when it received this "green money."[737] But this is not the type of project that environmentalists would have praised in the past. During its construction, a large area of forest was cut down, and local natives lost their homes. The owner of the hydropower plant is certainly happy when some gullible people send him extra cash when he is half through with his project. But it does not affect the climate.

The real benefit goes to someone else: The bankers. At the stock exchange, they get some percentage fee from every transaction. They make their living on that. In Chicago, the first large commodity exchange (CBOT) was established in the 19th century. The city of Al Capone was also the place of the first climate exchange (Chicago Climate Exchange, CCX) a century later. It was launched after 2000 as a place to trade climate sin indulgences (offsets). While trading on the Chicago Climate

Exchange was only voluntary, its European subsidiary, which was established in 2005, had the advantage that the EU made it mandatory to purchase offsets. It is so easy to make money when you can order people to buy your stuff. In 2011, according to a World Bank report, global carbon trade was worth $176 billion.[738] This is more than all OECD aid to developing countries.[739] The European Climate Exchange (ECX) accounted for about 80% of this market.

Climate business also has ties to politics. The bank Goldman Sachs, one of the pillars of the Chicago Climate Exchange, was the second-largest contributor to President Barack Obama's election campaign (2008).[740] Obama was their man in the White House because he was on the board of the Joyce Foundation in Chicago at a time when the foundation funded the Chicago Climate Exchange with its grant. Glenn Beck, Fox TV journalist, uncovered the link between Obama and the climate exchange.[741] As a consequence, a campaign, stopbeck.com, was launched against Beck, and Fox News was sent threatening letters until they decided to fire Beck in 2011. He was one of the few journalists in the USA who covered the Climategate scandal.

On the technical side, the architect of the Chicago Climate Exchange was Richard Sandor, the guru of stock market speculators. Sandor is called the "father of futures." It is a kind of virtual economy where you buy things that do not exist yet for money you don't have. For example, you purchase a crop of grain from next year, and you pay just a small deposit and then sell the rights to this grain to someone else. This disproportion between the deposit and the actual price of the purchased commodity is called leverage.

Sandor promoted futures in the 1970s when he headed the famous Chicago Commodity Exchange (CBOT). Futures did exist before Sandor, but the 1970s and 1980s witnessed their boom, among other things, thanks to computers and telephones, which greatly accelerated the stock market speculations.

However, the climate offsets (indulgences) are a bit of a different commodity. The climate exchange trades a commodity that you do not need to produce. You sell people the air they breathe. This is, of course, a paradise for shenanigans. If you steal a ton of grain from someone's warehouse, they will notice and call the police. But the CO_2 indulgences are just paper statements about something you can neither see nor touch. At the beginning of 2011, all trading on the European Climate Exchange had to be suspended for some time due to fraud. In 2009, Europol found that up to 90% of the local climate market was fraudulent in some EU countries, with a total of about €5 billion being stolen.[742]

CARBON FOOTPRINT

If the carbon footprint were not expressed in tons but in fractions of degrees Celsius of avoided warming, everyone would be laughing about this tiny war on climate."

On the Internet, you will find plenty of "carbon calculators" where you can calculate your carbon footprint. You can see how many greenhouse gas emissions are generated in the production of food, energy, and the things you consume. For example, the average carbon footprint of the Czech population is about 14 tons of CO_2 a year. Various towns join the Covenant of Mayors and boast of how much their city has reduced its footprint. Even a train ticket already has propaganda printed on the back of how much CO_2 is saved when you travel by train instead of by plane.

But try asking a woke and progressive person how much warming is avoided by this smaller footprint; they will be flabbergasted. The calculators never tell you the most important number. If I reduce my carbon footprint by one ton of CO_2, how many degrees Celsius of warming are avoided? Many people follow official recommendations in good faith, and they don't even know why.

But we can find out. For example, in the 2009 Matthews study *The Proportionality of Global Warming to Cumulative Carbon Emissions*.[743] According to Matthews, every ton of carbon dioxide you emit means an increase in global temperature of about 0.0000000000015 degrees Celsius.[744] That is 1.5 trillionths of a degree Celsius.

The authors assume that since the beginning of the Industrial Revolution, we have released about 500 gigatons (billion tons) of carbon. If we do the same thing again—a total of one trillion tons of carbon (carbon, not CO_2) together, it will bring an overall warming of 1–2°C (or around 1.5°C).

You may find comfort in the idea that your 1.5 trillionth degree of Celsius is not much, but when all of Europe takes part, we can change the world. But the EU is no longer the driving force of the world economy as it was a hundred years ago. According to the European Commission data, only about 12% of annual CO_2 emissions are generated in the European Union today. So, when the EU cuts its emissions by a few percent, its effect on global climate is about as large as a burp of one little mouse.

Economist Richard Toll, who worked at the IPCC and collaborated with Bjørn Lomborg, calculated that even if the EU had been operating under this climate policy for a hundred years, it would delay warming by only 0.05°C.[745] According to the European climate plan 20-20-20, we will pay $1 to prevent environmental damage of 10 cents.[746] That doesn't sound like a good deal.

Bjørn Lomborg says that Germany, which has invested the most in renewables, is not a good role model: "When the effects are calculated in a standard climate model, the result is a reduction in average temperature of 0.00005°C (one twenty-thousandth of a degree Celsius, or one ten-thousandth of a degree Fahrenheit). To put it another way: By the end of the century, Germany's $130 billion solar panel subsidies will have postponed temperature increases by 23 hours."[747]

You may now understand why carbon calculators give your carbon footprint in tons and not in degrees Celsius. Mayors who took the climate pledge would be an object of ridicule if they boasted of delaying warming by a fraction of a second per century.

INSURANCE

Insurers love a good panic—the more people are scared, the more they buy insurance policies. It is true that natural disasters cause higher financial damage now. But it's not because the hurricanes are getting worse. It is because we have inflation, we have more people, and those people are richer.

"Nowhere in the world is the rising number of natural catastrophes more evident than in North America," wrote Munich Reinsurance Company in its October 2012 report.[748] A reinsurance company is an insurance company that insures other insurance companies. Munich Re claimed that North America has had the highest increase in weather disasters compared with other continents. Five times more since 1980. According to Peter Höppe, a chief risk researcher for Munich Re, the insurance data clearly show now that climate change was having an effect on disaster losses. The UN climate panel, in its Third Report (2001), reprinted the alarming charts of Munich Re.[749]

What a coincidence that the wealthiest part of the world is getting the worst increase in natural disasters. Actually, it is no coincidence because it is the financial damage that is increasing, not natural disasters.

Imagine how our great-grandparents lived. There was a small cottage with small windows, a dry toilet, and no electricity. Now, there is probably a four-bedroom residence with a garage, TV, and computer in every room, not to mention ten mobile phones, a PlayStation, air conditioning, dishwasher, and an electric toothbrush. If a hurricane hits the same place a century later, of course, the financial damages are higher. This is why insured damages must be "normalized" before you compare two years. Besides, we have higher population density, there is inflation, etc. I seriously doubt the insurance experts do not know this simple math. They are lying to you on purpose.

However, there is no word about this normalization in the UN Climate Panel (IPCC) reports. The IPCC blindly believes the Munich Re sales promotion materials, the purpose of which is to sell stuff to gullible people. Actually, the only person in IPCC who peer-reviewed the Munich Re materials was a student. Laurens Bouwer received his PhD only in 2010, but already in 1999, he was a leading author at the IPCC.[750] His only qualification was a summer job at Munich Re.

If you do proper data normalization, as mentioned above, you will find that normalized damage from natural disasters did not increase in the 1950–2000 period. Miller and Muir-Wood's 2008 study noted: "We find insufficient evidence to claim a statistical relationship between global temperature increase and normalized catastrophe losses."[751] However, in its 2007 report, the UN climate panel reprinted a graph that claims the exact opposite. Normalized damage is said to go up, but no one knows where this chart comes from.[752] The scandal was reported by journalist Jonathan Leake in his article *UN Wrongly Linked Global Warming to Natural Disasters.*[753] Instead of apologizing, the United Nations climate panel denounced Leake's article as a "misleading and baseless story" in a press release. However, the IPCC did not address the criticism. It only vaguely expresses hope that the said chapter is balanced anyway and contains several statements that are actually true.[754]

STERN REVIEW

The Stern Review was commissioned by the British government to assess the economic impact of global warming. Sadly, it contains errors that would make a first-grade student blush. For example, it ignores the simple fact that the dollar in 2000 had different value than a hundred years ago.

The Stern Review (2006) was written by the World Bank economist Nicholas Stern as an analysisanalysis of the cost of global warming. He concluded that the longer we postpone the solution, the more expensive it will be. The study was commissioned by the government of Gordon Brown as an internal document of the ministry. Therefore, it could be published without peer-reviewpeer reviewpeer-review, and nobody checked its correctness. It turned out to be a mistake. Actually, a double mistake because IPCC (Intergovernmental Panel on Climate Change) quoted from Stern Review extensively in its Fourth Assessment Report. And since the quotes were shoved in after the deadline, in violation of IPCC's own procedures, nobody reviewed this either.[755]

Stern was faced with a delicate problem. Most scientists expect some 1.5°C or 2°C warming by the second half of the 21st century, w. Which is estimated to cost "0.5 - –1% of world GDP per annum by the middle of the century",," as Stern acknowledges. This doesn't mean the economy would be worse than now. It only means that global GDP would not rise 3% per year like today (which is the 20th- century average), but only 2.5% or 2% a year. One way or another, mankind will bey at least 10 ten times wealthier in 100 years.[756]

However, the mitigation (war on climate) is expected to cost even more. "The costs for stabilisstabilization at 500–-550 ppm CO_2 were centredcentered on 1% of GDP by 2050, with a range of -2% to +5% of GDP",," Stern Review says in its Executive Summary. So, we might pay 5% GDP per annum to avoid damages of 0.5 %% GDP per annum? This doesn't sound like a good deal.

Therefore, Stern decided to use much scarier scenarios to justify the costs. "With 5–-6°C warming - —which is a real possibility for the next century - —existing models that include the risk of abrupt and large-scale climate change estimate an average 5–-10% loss in global GDP, with poor countries suffering costs in excess of 10% of GDP".." This sounds much like Catch XX. If climate change won't hurt us, the mitigation policies will. And Sterns urges us to open wallets to rent-seekers ASAP. "Strong and early mitigation has a key role to play in limiting the long-run costs of adaptation. Without this, the costs of adaptation will rise dramatically".."

However, this call for urgency doesn't make economic sense either. Global GDP is expected to grow even with global warming, so our grandchildren will be much wealthier than us. They will have more money to deal with climate. The technologies that are new and costly now will have become old and cheap by then.[757] And when investing, one also needs to consider things like loans and interest rates.

Stern chose a near- zero discount rate (0.1%) instead of the usual 3% discount rate used by every bank and insurance company.[758] With almost zero discount rate, one dollar today would have the same value as one dollar a hundred years ago! If that was the case, banks would not charge people any interest.

This is why William Nordhaus, a Nobel prize winner for economics, criticized Stern in 2007.[759] We are richer than people a hundred years ago and we can expect our descendants to be richer than we are. With wage growth, however, prices will rise. Nordhaus explains the stupidity of a zero discount rate on a hypothetical situation: "Suppose that scientists discover a wrinkle in the climate system that will cause damages equal to 0.1 percent % of net consumption starting in 2200 and continuing at that rate forever after. How large would a one-time investment would be justified today to remove the wrinkle that starts only after two centuries? Using the methodology of Tthe Review, the answer is that we should pay up to 56 percent % of one year's world consumption today to remove the wrinkle."

Czech economist Václav Klaus was surprised that The Stern Review was praised by many in spite of its obvious flaws. "The only reasonable explanation is that – —without having paid sufficient attention to the arguments – —they have already invested too much into global warming alarmism. Some of them are afraid that by losing this doctrine their political and professional pride would suffer. Others are earning a lot of money on it and are afraid of losing that source of income."[760]

Stern overestimates the negative impacts and says nothing about the benefits. If everybody was thinking like that, there would be no matches, no forks, and knives and no cars in the world. Experts would show us the risks, damages and deaths caused by these things. They would not mention that we need cars for transport, knives for cooking, and matches for lighting a fire. The Stern report is not a balanced cost-benefit analysisanalysis. It conceals the positive effects of a warmer climate. Data of the Northern Hemisphere for the last hundreds of years show that agricultural production declined as it cooled and increased as it warmed.[761] Actually, the Northern Hemisphere is going to have net economic benefits even from 2°C warming, according to climate models that consider 13°C annual average temperature as optimal for economy (see Pretis et al. 2018).[762]

In 2011, the World Bank also distanced itself from the Stern Review.[763] Mendelsohn and Saher studies estimate that, by 2100, climate damage should generate about 0.01% damages of world GDP annually. This is less than the usual estimate of 0.5 to 1% of world GDP per year. And much less than Stern's 5 percent % of world GDP mentioned earlier.

Nevertheless, Stern was generously rewarded for his services. The very next year, he received a peerage and a nice collection of honorary doctorates. Now, we have to call him "Sir Nicholas".." This reminds me of the satirical series *Yes Minister,* where the government often uses promises of peerage to influence conclusions of "independent" committees.

It is also very educative to learn who were the people were behind Stern. He was the chief economist of the World Bank between 2000 and 2003, and at that time, Maurice Strong also worked there. Strong is co-founder of the Chicago Climate Exchange, where the offsets (climate indulgences) were traded. They both worked at the World Bank under director James Wolfensohn (1995--2005), who was installed to at this post by US pPresident Bill Clinton and his vVice pPresident Al Gore.[764]

Maurice Strong knew Wolfensohn well because he had helped him early in his career. Wolfensohn had already proven his ideological loyalty. He was a former director of the Rockefeller Foundation and of the Malthusian Population Council Board. In his memoirs, Strong explains why it was easy for him to persuade the World Bank economists to fight climate change. He says the economists there had a life isolated from the real world. "Virtually all those in senior management positions in the World Bank joined as young professionals and moved up through the ranks, with little experience of the world outside."[765]

BIOFUELS

Biofuels are a universal cure that allows you to kill multiple birds with one stone. Starve people in developing countries to mitigate overpopulation. Reduce jungles crawling with insects and poisonous spiders. And pump up the greenhouse gas emissions.

In order to replace 7% of transport fuels with biofuels by 2020, the EU would need around 8.8 million hectares of land to grow them, equivalent to the area of Austria.[766] If the EU wanted 100% of cars to run solely on biofuels, plantations would have to cover almost half of the EU's territory. We would have to bulldoze our cities, and nothing would grow here except oilseed rape.

There is no room for this, and so biofuels are grown overseas in developing countries—we export our problems as far as possible. In 2012, cca 1.9 million tons of palm oil was imported into the EU for this purpose, while in the US, biofuels are mainly produced from maize (corn). Both commodities are food; palm oil is the cheapest cooking oil. Of course, when corn is burned as fuel, it will be missing from the food market. Its price will, therefore, rise, severely impacting poor countries where consumers spend most of their measly wages on food.

"232 kilograms of corn is needed to produce 50 liters of bioethanol. In Mexico or Zambia, a child could live on that amount of corn for a year." This makes biofuels a "crime against humanity," protested Jan Ziegler, the United Nations Special Rapporteur on the Right to Food from 2000–2008.[767] Thanks to biofuels, the global percentage of people suffering from malnutrition ceased decreasing for the first time in half a century. It was the worst humanitarian catastrophe since China's Great Leap Forward.

Finally, it also turned out that biofuels have a higher carbon footprint than fossil fuels. The calculations must take into account the cutting down of forests to make room for the plantation. And also, the gasoline used in the tractors must be considered as well. While normal gasoline or diesel has a carbon footprint of only about 85 kg per gigajoule, European oilseed rape biofuels have a total carbon footprint of 150.3 kg CO_2 per gigajoule, and European sugar beet has 100.3 kg. Biofuels from South American sugar cane and Asian palm oil have a footprint about the same as fossil fuels—around 82 kg and 73 kg, respectively. The European Commission tried to cover up this report by the Fraunhofer agency, but it leaked.[768]

The EU also contributes to the devastation of rainforests by importing biofuels. The Orangutans in Borneo today are literally surrounded by plantations of biofuels and their living space is shrinking. Companies cut down forests, sell timber, and then they get climate subsidies for plant-ing biofuels.[769] The European Union decided to deal with complaints about the decline of forests in a smart way. At the beginning of 2010, the public learned that the EU wanted to reclassify plantations as a kind of forests.[770] You can make a problem disappear by simply renaming it!

US president George W. Bush also underwent an interesting about-turn in relation to biofuels. At first, he rejected the Kyoto Protocol as too cost-ly. But then he suddenly changed his mind, which demands an expla-nation. In 2005, the Bush administration made a law about mandatory adding of biofuels into transport fuels (Renewable Fuel Standard) just like in the European Union. Two years later, Bush negotiated a strategic cooperation treaty with the world's largest exporter of biofuels, Brazil.

Big business realized that taking part in the—lavishly subsidized—war on climate may be profitable. This is why the climate policy was sudden-ly embraced by Big Oil companies like Exxon Mobil, BP, or Chevron. The main source of revenue was seen in biofuels, which became a key focus even for large agro-corporations such as Monsanto.

The United States is the largest exporter of corn (maize) in the world, but in the early 21st century, it dedicated 40% of its production to biofuels, namely ethanol.[771] As a result, there was sudden shortage of food in the world market, and food prices went up. In the summer of 2008, a World Bank report confirmed that widespread cultivation of biofuels has led to food price increases by 75%.[772] This is sad because it doesn't solve the energy problems either. Even if all corn production in the US went into biofuels, it would still only replace about 12% of US gasoline consump-tion in transportation.[773] A policy like that can hardly be regarded as sustainable.

Let us not forget that in developing countries, biofuels are often grown on land stolen by rich ranchers from poor peasants, just like in Western movies. Dozens of people were murdered in Honduras, including one journalist and his partner. In some cases, a staged accident occurred; in other instances, farmers were simply shot or "disappeared." Moreover, the killers won't be punished, as the local police, courts, and authorities are in the wealthy rancher's pocket.

"Honduras has recently gone from being one of the main basic grain producers in Central America to producing half of what it needs, which in turn forces the country to import large quantities of food (rice, corn, and beans)... On the other hand, Honduras currently produces more than 300 metric tons of African palm oil, almost 70% of which is ex-ported."[774]

The main source of terror was the Dinant company of the local tycoon Miguel Facussé Barjum. Local peasants and human rights activists wrote letters to the UN in vain. The United Nations approval committee accredited Facusse plantations anyway. This means he will receive credits as a reward for fighting climate change. Credits can then be sold under the global Clean Development Mechanism.

The CDM approval committee says that assessment of human rights violations is beyond their job description.[775] Their task is only to evaluate carbon footprint, based on data three years old. Because this is how long the approval procedure takes. But already, Amnesty International's 2000 Honduras report warned what violent land conflicts are taking place there.

In the Wikileaks scandal, diplomatic correspondence leaked to the public. In one of the letters, US diplomats suspected the Facusse family of trafficking narcotics.[776] When we import biofuels from regions that resemble the Wild West, how can we be surprised when the climate change mitigation turns into a scheme run by the bad guys? Can we really say that this is clean energy?

PROFITABLE NON-PROFIT SECTOR

A non-governmental organization (NGO) from the non-profit sector is some-times paid by the government and has such a turnover that its accounting department needs an entire office floor with full-time staff working 24/7.

In 2012, Climate Action Network Europe received 33% of its budget in subsidies from the EU. The Health and Environment Alliance received 59% of its budget from the EU. The CEE Bankwatch Network—which, despite its name, is dedicated to the environment—covered 45% of its budget from the European Union. CEE should monitor EU investment in environmental protection.[777] But how can they independently super-vise their own sponsor? Friends of Earth: Europe received half of their budget each year from EU subsidies. Their budget is available online. After 2012, the funding even increased. For example, CEE Bankwatch Network was taking 79% of its budget from the EU. The EU's LIFE+ program funded 32 NGOs with more than €20,000,000 between 2016 and 2017.[778]

The European Commission is something like a European government. If an NGO is paid by the government, it shouldn't be called NGO any lon-ger. And even though the non-profit sector does not have its sharehold-ers, it does bring income to people who are employed by it. The awkward naming is not the only problem. Separation of state and church, I mean civic society, is in jeopardy.

Bureaucrats understand that they would get no public sympathy if they demonstrated in the streets for more paperwork, longer-form templates, and more expensive paperclips. Instead, they hire activists to do it for them. And the activists are trained in finding nice words to advocate for Big Government. Such people are called "sock puppet" activists.

Christopher Snowdon's study Sock Puppets: How the Government Lob-bies Itself and Why from 2012[779] notes that in Britain, 27,000 charities receive 75% or more of their budget from the government. However, the European Commission never finances groups that express serious res-ervations about the Commission's political agenda. Groups that receive money from the Commission will not bite into the hand that feeds them. Among NGOs, this creates a caste system like in medieval India. Those that are friendly to the Commission can live in luxury and outspend their opponents.

ENERGY POVERTY

We often hear that climate change impacts will be the worst for the poor. This is actually true because green policies will make their energy prices go up.

When Barack Obama ran for US president, he said that implementing his plan to combat climate warming would mean that energy prices would surge.[780] Obama said: "If somebody wants to build a coal-fired power plant, they can. It's just that it will bankrupt them... Under my plan... electricity rates would necessarily skyrocket." In the end, the ordinary citizens will pay the bill, which can't be surprising since Obama had John Holdren as his science advisor.

Long before global warming became a thing, Holdren wrote that he does not want people to have cheap energy: "The United States is threatened far more by too much energy, too soon, than by the hazards of too little, too late."[781] Because if people live in prosperity and the economy grows, the consumption of natural resources will increase. Since the resources are running out, this course must stop. Holdren adopted these views from his guru, Paul Ehrlich, author of the well-known book *Population Bomb*. Together, they wrote the book *Ecoscience,* where they suggested forced sterilization of the population in order to prevent overpopulation.[782]

In 1978, Ehrlich said, "Giving society cheap, abundant energy would be the equivalent of giving an idiot child a machine gun."[783] What would happen if such a cheap and abundant source of energy emerged? The novel by Czech author Robert Hofman, *The Fifth Column,* assumes that environmentalists would try to sabotage this technology. In the afterword, associate professor Zbyněk Hrkal from Charles University explains that the plot of the book has a precedent. In 1989, Stanley Pons and Martin Fleischmann believed they achieved nuclear fusion at room temperature. They were wrong, and their experiment did not work.

"However, the immediate responses to the news that mankind has a clean, inexhaustible source of energy at its disposal was revealing. Leading environmentalists were truly horrified. For example, Jeremy Rifkin, founder of the Global Greenhouse Network, said that despite this being cheap and clean energy, it was the worst thing that could happen to the planet. According to him, such a source of energy will only destroy the planet faster. Which clearly revealed that limiting the CO_2 emissions is just a cover for other goals."[784] If someone wants to stop economic growth, it can be most easily achieved by increasing energy prices. Just like feudal society was based on farmland, energy is the blood of industrial civilization.

It's no longer just a theory. In 2013, German Minister of Economy Sigmar Gabriel expressed concern that Germany was in danger of de-industrialization due to its support for expensive green energy.[785] In September 2013, the European Commissioner for Industry and Trade, Antonio Tajani, feared that due to excessive costs of renewables, the European Union faces an "industrial massacre"[786] Owing to the climate legislation, electricity prices in the EU are twice as high as in the US.

British charity NEA (National Energy Action) states that in Britain, 25,700 people die each winter in relation to cold. Out of that, about 10% of deaths are attributable to "fuel poverty." These people cannot afford fuel for heating. It is a deadly combination of low income and high energy prices. In summer, poor people cannot afford air conditioning and die during heatwaves.[787] The campaign Repealtheact.org.uk, therefore, advocates repealing the 2008 Climate Change Act in the United Kingdom, which makes energy more expensive for people. "Is your father among those 25,700 citizens who will die in Britain this winter due to energy poverty?" their campaign asks.

The climate policy also impacted the transportation sector. In Autumn 2018, French drivers put on their yellow vests to protest against climate tax that made their diesel more expensive. President Macron, a Rothschild banker, was accused of not caring about the ordinary people. He imposed this tax in an attempt to honor the pledge from the 2015 Paris Climate Accord. Protests sparked months-long street riots against the high cost of living. Demonstrators torched cars, trashed cans, and the police used tear gas.

In Autumn 2019, similar street riots erupted in Santiago de Chile after a municipal contract for renewables made subway tickets more expensive. Students protested, demolished the turnstiles, and evaded payment. This sparked general protests against poverty in Chile, and the government had to send the army in the streets—for the first time since Pinochet. The UN climate conference scheduled for next month had to be canceled and relocated to Spain.

Airplanes are the next target on the list. In Sweden, it became fashionable among progressive intellectuals to express "flygskam," so people who fly are ashamed. In 2019, the government of the Netherlands proposed to the European Commission a plan to impose an extra climate tax on air transport (kerosene)[788] in an attempt to bypass the 1944 Chicago Convention on International Civil Aviation, which exempted air fuels in transit from (double) taxation. In Germany, the Green Party announced plans to ban all domestic flights by 2035.[789]

In 2013, the EU decided to increase investment in the war on climate to make 20% of the EU budget![790] When the European Commissioner for Climate, Connie Heddegaard, was asked why global climate was not warming for 17 years in spite of all the CO_2, she just dismissed the concerns. In her eyes, the EU policy on climate change is right even if science was wrong.[791]

"Let's say that science, some decades from now, said 'we were wrong, it was not about climate,' would it not, in any case, have been good to do many of things you have to do in order to combat climate change?... I think we have to realize that in the world of the 21st century, for us to have the cheapest possible energy is not the answer." In short, she admitted there are hidden motivations unrelated to climate. And that she doesn't care if it makes prices go up. Ottmar Edenhofer of the UN climate panel (2010) confirmed this: "One has to free oneself from the illusion that international climate policy is environmental policy. Instead, climate change policy is about how we redistribute de facto the world's wealth."[792]

GREEN EPIDEMIC

In 2020, the global economy was shut down due to an epidemic. The green dream of less consumption, less traffic, and fewer emissions came true.

In 1969, amidst the Hongkong Flu (H3N2) epidemic, nobody tried to shut down the US economy. The Woodstock Music Festival was not canceled, and social distancing certainly was not a thing in the "Summer of Love." "The estimated number of deaths was 1 million worldwide and about 100,000 in the United States. Most excess deaths were in people 65 years and older." writes the Centers for Disease Control and Prevention about the Hongkong Flu.[793]

In 2020, the world was struck with another virus. The coronavirus Covid-19 is estimated to kill about 1% of the infected people.[794] For instance, in the 2020 March–June wave of the COVID epidemic, some 36,000 people died in Italy. In comparison, according to Rosano et al. (2019), in winter seasons 2013/14–2016/17, there were 7,027, 20,259, 15,801, and 24,981 excess deaths attributable to normal influenza in Italy.[795]

In the United States the epidemic caused the annual death rates to return to the higher levels that used to be common in the 20th century. In 2020 there died 827.7 persons per a hundred thousand people in the USA (age adjusted).[796] This is more than the previous year (715.2 persons per a hundred thousand people). But a generation earlier such numbers used to be common. In 2000 the annual deathrate was 869 persons and in 1970 it was 1222.6 persons per a hundred thousand people. In year 1900 it was 2518 persons per one thousand people.[797] Of course, without social distancing and masks, the deathrates in 2020 would have been higher.

The worst problem was actually not in the deathrates, but in "mortality displacement". It means that people of weak health, who would have otherwise died of various causes months or years apart all suddenly ended up in a hospital with Covid. This "harvesting" effect caused overburdening of hospitals with patients who need the same kind of treatment. In demography, we know a similar phenomenon from heatwaves and other epidemics.

To prevent this breakdown of health care system, world governments enforced large scale lockdowns. They ordered closing of airports, hotels, restaurants, and factories. Tourists disappeared, people lost jobs, and companies went bankrupt. The World Bank estimated that the global economy could shrink by 5.2% in the year of Covid. "That would represent the deepest recession since the Second World War." the bank estimated.[798]

As a paradox, many people also died because of the preventive safety measures. In the United Kingdom, some 75,000 deaths were expected in the following years as a consequence of the lockdown, according to a report of the *Office for National Statistics,* because of fear-induced stress, bankruptcy suicides, delayed medical examinations, untreated cancer, etc.[799][800]

In underdeveloped countries, the impact of safety measures was even worse. After decades of improving poverty and malnutrition ratios, the lockdowns reversed the trend. Medical journal *The Lancet* warned that in the first year of the pandemic, an additional 6.7 million children would suffer from severe malnutrition ("wasting"), out of which about 120,000 would die.[801] An OXFAM report estimated that 121 million more people could be "pushed to the brink of starvation this year" as a result of unemployment and disrupted food production.[802] COVID-19-linked hunger could actually cause more deaths than the virus itself.

Whereas citizens faced unemployment, bankruptcy, and hunger, global elites rejoiced. Inflaming the global panic could be used for their needs. "You never let a serious crisis go to waste," as famously said by Rahm Emanuel, President Obama's chief of staff.

Charles, the Prince of Wales, came with an idea: "We have a unique but rapidly shrinking window of opportunity to learn lessons and reset ourselves on a more sustainable path... We have a golden opportunity to seize something good from this crisis. Its unprecedented shockwaves may well make people more receptive to big visions of change."[803] The elites hope that after the lockdowns, people will get used to losing their freedom. Curfews and closed borders, what a Brave New World!

Charles' plan for the Great Reset of the global economic system was applauded by big shots like the Managing Director of the International Monetary Fund, Kristalina Georgieva, or the General Secretary of the United Nations, Antonio Gutteres. But above all, Charles's idea was welcome by the economist Klaus Schwab, who, in 1971, established (and still runs) the World Economic Forum in Davos.

Plans to reset the global economy were to become the program of the next WEF meeting. The power elite wanted to use economic stimulus for their plans. The mechanism is not complicated. Governments borrow money to jump-start the economies, giving out subsidies like candy. However, in crony capitalism, you give aid to your pals and loyal henchmen only, thereby vanquishing your enemies, who are left to die of thirst.

For Malthusians, who hate growth on principle, the corona crisis was a dream come true. Christina Figueres, former head of the UN Framework Climate Change Convention, said this about the economic lockdown due to the quarantine: "Well, that is, ironically, of course, the other side of this, right? It may be good for climate because there is less trade; there's less travel; there's less commerce."[804] It was almost impossible to talk to an environmentalist without hearing a speech about epidemics having a silver lining.

Climatologist Michael Mann tweeted with glee: "Are pandemics Gaia's immune system fighting back? Are we the virus?" Pope Francis said that the virus may be nature's revenge for climate change: "God always forgives. We forgive sometimes, but nature never forgives. We did not respond to the partial catastrophes... Who speaks now of the floods? I don't know if these are the revenge of nature, but they are certainly nature's responses."[805]   German satirical group Browser Ballet made a video, "Corona rettet die Welt." In the short film, they thank the eco virus because it executes mostly the elderly—the greedy old generation that messed up the planet, by which they mean the post-war "boomer" generation whose hard work built a comfortable life for those who made this disrespectful video.

The coronavirus lockdown was like a rehearsal, an example of what the Green New Deal would look like. A perfect experiment under open skies. "In China, emissions dropped 25% over a four-week period beginning February 3... Traffic was down 54% in the United Kingdom... Air travel, meanwhile, was down 40% in the 12 weeks since China reported its first 500 cases of COVID-19. In Europe, nine out of every ten flights have been grounded."[806]

But the lockdown lasted only a few months. The overall annual decrease in CO_2 emissions was estimated at only 5% compared with the previous year.[807] And compared to the huge natural seasonal carbon cycle, this blip was absolutely invisible. Ralph Keeling—son of the founder of the CO_2 "Keeling Curve" measurements at Mauna Loa—estimated that "global fossil fuel use would have to decline by 10% for a full year to show up in carbon dioxide concentrations. Even then, it would be a difference of only about 0.5 parts per million."[808] That is not much.

In May 2019, the global atmospheric CO_2 concentration was 414 ppm (part per million), in May 2020, it was 417 ppm and in May 2021 it was 419 ppm.[809] Still rising. In 2020 the rate of increase of CO_2 was 2.31 ppm, which is less than in previous two years. But in 2017 it was just 1.93 ppm and in 2013 it was just 1.99 ppm. So there have been quite recent years when greenhouse gases in the atmosphere were rising slower than in the Covid year. In spite of all the lockdowns.

To impact the CO_2 levels significantly, a new Great Depression is simply not enough. To undo 200 years of fossil-fuel-powered progress, you would need to turn the whole civilization into a pile of rubble.

Conservative thinkers like Dennis Prager were worried that something like that is the plan: "Why the remedy may be worse than the disease... If the government can order society to cease functioning, from restaurants and other businesses to schools, due to a possible health disaster, it is highly likely that a Democratic president and Congress will similarly declare emergency and assert authoritarian rule in order to prevent what they consider the even greater "existential threat" to human life posed by global warming."[810]

STATE OF EMERGENCY

According to green radicals, democracy is the main obstacle to saving the planet. An environmentalist knows better than elected members of parliament what is good for the country.

Thirty years of costly climate conferences have had no impact on climate at all. Bjørn Lomborg calculated that the pledges from COP 21 in Paris (2015) could reduce the expected 3°C warming by only about 0.17°C.[811] And that's the more optimistic scenario. [812]

The year-on-year increase in CO_2 in the atmosphere depends more on ocean temperature than on international agreements. Atmospheric concentrations of CO_2 may rise even in years when human emissions decline because temperatures affect solubility of CO_2 in the ocean. Therefore, the largest increase was observed in the relatively hot year 1998 (2.81 ppm), whereas, in the relatively cold year 2008, it was only 1.78 ppm (due to inertia of processes and CO_2 transport in the oceans).[813] In the warm year of 2015, some 3 ppm of carbon dioxide were added to the atmosphere, the highest annual increase in 56 years of measurement,[814] despite the fact that global anthropogenic carbon dioxide emissions stalled in the period 2014–2017.

Frustrated climate activists started to feel "climate grief" due to the impotence of the conferences. But they refused to accept that climate change is a natural process that cannot be halted by puny humans. Instead, they believed that the parliaments are too slow in passing climate legislation, and they blamed the skeptics for the delay.

British scientist James Lovelock, author of the famous Gaia theory, wrote: "Even the best democracies agree that when a major war approaches, democracy must be put on hold for the time being. I have a feeling that climate change may be an issue as severe as a war. It may be necessary to put democracy on hold for a while."[815]

The head of American EPA (Environmental Protection Agency), Melissa Young, agreed and demanded exceptional powers: "This is World War III—this is the biggest challenge to face the globe for many, many years. We need the sorts of concerted, fast, integrated, and, above all, huge efforts that went into many actions in times of war... We need to be seeing this as a crisis and emergency."[816]

They cited the US Congress as an example of "failure of democracy." When the Climategate scandal (2009) revealed that climate scientists misinformed the public about climate change, US Congress refused to vote in favor of the cap-and-trade bill. The war on climate got stuck. In the end, President Obama and his advisor John Podesta decided to bypass Congress and deal with climate through presidential decrees.[817]

They were encouraged in this by climatologist James Hansen of NASA's Goddard Institute. In the fall of 2010, in the *South China Morning Post,* he wrote that the US should take an example from the Chinese dictatorship.[818] In the article *China and the Barbarians,* he appeared envious of the communists. "I have the impression that Chinese leadership takes a long view, perhaps because of the long history of their culture, in contrast to the West with its short election cycles. At the same time, China has the capacity to implement policy decisions rapidly." In other words, a dictatorship does not have to respect the citizens' vote and can do whatever it likes.

Harvard physicist Luboš Motl commented on Hansen's views in his blog The Reference Frame: "All of us should probably get more familiar with the constitution and other laws because it is very likely that a treacherous op-ed supporting a major totalitarian party's desire to overshadow the Western democracy is not the last act that we may expect from uncontrollably unhinged lunatics of Hansen's caliber."[819]

David Shearman, Professor of Natural Sciences at the University of Adelaide, Australia, elaborated on his opinion on the benefits of tyranny in his book *The Climate Change Challenge and the Failure of Democracy.* The cover of the book reads: "Society is verging on a philosophical choice between liberty or life." The author explains that if we are to stop the catastrophic process of climate change, we must choose between liberal democracy and an authoritarian government led by experts. Which experts does he mean? He probably speaks of himself.

Even Noam Chomsky, the famous linguist and political activist, agrees: "For example, suppose it was discovered tomorrow that the greenhouse effect has been way underestimated and that the catastrophic effects are actually going to set in ten years from now, and not 100 years from now or something. Well, given the state of the popular movements we have today, we'd probably have a fascist takeover-with everybody agreeing to it because that would be the only method for survival that anyone could think of. I'd even agree to it because there just are no other alternatives around right now."[820]

Some people actually try to put these words into action. In 2018, a group of anti-capitalism activists who call themselves Extinction Rebellion (XR) organized a rehearsal for such a coup. They blocked traffic in the streets of London and other cities to demonstrate their power to disrupt. They issued demands, including declaration of "climate emergency," some kind of martial law when civil freedoms would be suspended. And they wanted to create a "citizen assembly" to bypass the sluggish parliament. Such assemblies used to be called "Soviets" in revolutionary Russia. They chanted "system change—not climate change," making it clear they want to overthrow the existing political system.

Last but not the least, XR demands that the media should only "tell the truth" about climate. Their truth. They demonstrated in front of YouTube and Google company offices and called for ending free speech.

"YouTube, stop platforming climate denial," their banner said in November 2019.[821]

Inspired by these actions, Antifa activists intimidated a Munich NH Conference Center to disinvite an international climate skeptic conference organized by EIKE in November 2019.[822] An environmentalist organization sent the hotel hate mail claiming that EIKE spreads "dangerous propaganda dangerous to democracy." On November 9th, a mob of 15–20 people appeared inside the hotel and disturbed guests and employees, singing songs and distributing leaflets. Instead of calling the police against the bullies, NH Conference Center caved in to the pressure.

Can we learn from history? In the 1960s, student movements were radicalized like the XR of today. Even Marxist philosophers Max Adorno and his disciple Jürgen Habermas condemned their behavior as left-wing fascism. Adorno called in the police to evict students who occupied the Institute of Social Research (Frankfurt School) in 1969. They intimidated and harassed the teachers and disrupted lectures. Adorno wrote *Authoritarian Personality* (1950), a key book about the psychological roots of fascism. Habermas famously took part in Historikerstreit—a public debate about whitewashing Germany's national socialist past.

In the Czech Republic, the debate about climate soon became a debate about liberty too. Czech playwright and president Václav Havel opposed the defenders of civil freedoms in the *New York Times* article *Our Moral Footprint*. "I don't agree with those whose reaction is to warn against restricting civil freedoms. Were the forecasts of certain climatologists to come true, our freedoms would be tantamount to those of someone hanging from a 20th-story parapet."[823] Which is a surprising opinion from someone who used to be a dissident himself. Havel was in prison for criticizing the Communist Party before the Soviet Block fell apart.

Havel's political adversary, Václav Klaus, organized post-communist economic transformation as prime minister in the 1990s. As a free-market economist, he expressed his views in *Financial Times* (2007) in the article *Freedom, Not Climate, is at Risk*.[824] In his view, the fight against greenhouse gases is something that is incompatible with democracy, individual liberty, or even elementary freedom of speech. We are faced with a decision on which path to choose.

CLEXIT

The effect of the Paris Climate Accord on climate was less than symbolic. On the other hand, the outrage over Donald Trump's withdrawal from this agreement was more than real.

"The Paris Accord would undermine our economy, hamstring our workers, weaken our sovereignty, impose unacceptable legal risks, and put us at a permanent disadvantage to the other countries of the world. It is time to exit the Paris Accord," said US president Donald Trump in a speech announcing that the United States would withdraw.[825]

This international treaty was supposed to be a successor to the Kyoto Protocol of 1997. The signatories of Kyoto pledged to reduce their greenhouse gas emissions by an agreed percentage by the year 2012, at the latest. It did not lead anywhere, and global CO_2 levels are still rising. There were hopes that after Kyoto, a new agreement would come, which would be much stronger. Greenpeace said that the Paris Climate Accord heralds the "ending of the age of coal." President Obama called this agreement a "turning point," an "ambitious" step, and the set targets "bold."[826]

When Trump announced the so-called Clexit, exit from this climate accord, a storm of outrage swept through the media landscape. Al Gore condemned this move and compared climate activism to the struggle for women's suffrage and the struggle for abolition of slavery.[827] It seems as if the sum of worst fears of climate scientists materialized.

"A Trump presidency might be game over for the climate," Trump's presidency can end the climate," climatologist Michael Mann, author of the infamous hockey stick, lamented after Trump's election. "It might make it impossible to stabilize planetary warming below dangerous levels." Climatologist Kevin Trenberth added, "This is an unmitigated disaster for the planet."[828]

There were also discussions about plans to overthrow the president in order to save the planet. This process is called impeachment. It was proposed by a leading Democrat party sponsor, the billionaire Tom Steyr, founder of the NextGenClimate lobbying fund. They wanted to use the old Watergate tactic of framing an ordinary everyday political practice as if it was a bloody crime against humanity. For example, accusing Trump of collusion with Moscow—i.e., using Russian info about Trump's political opponent. In another version, Trump was accused of asking Ukrainian politicians to look into the questionable business activities of Trump's political rival.[829]

Worries over Clexit were probably an overreaction. In fact, the Paris Climate Accord had only a symbolic value like a prayer or a talisman. The analysis in *The Journal of Environment & Development* states: "The Paris Agreement is built entirely around voluntary country pledges—as different as the countries they are coming from—which are still far from adding up to achieving the objectives the agreement defines."[830] But when Trump said the same and cited an MIT scientific study as a proof, newspapers portrayed him as an analphabet who "misunderstood" science. Just because MIT scientists told the media that: "We certainly do not support the withdrawal of the US from the Paris agreement." which does not disprove Trump's statement that the Paris Climate Accord would reduce future warming just by a "tiny, tiny amount."

Trump understood the climate math quite well. The MIT climate director, John Reilly, himself admitted about the Paris Agreement: "We are making progress, but if 2°C stabilization is our goal, it's not nearly enough."[831] The MIT study cited by Trump actually reads: "Under all three variants of an extension of the Paris Agreement, an increase in the SAT relative to an 1861–1880 average exceeds 2°C in 2053, and in 2100, it reaches 3.5, 3.2 and 3.0°C, respectively."[832] So the Paris accord would not stop warming, even if it were really respected by someone.

The climate accord was also weak because of the world economic tigers such as China and India. They made only modest pledges so that they would not need to change their current GDP growth trends. China promised to start reducing its emissions, but only sometime after 2030 when the emissions should peak. India refused to set any deadline at all. Coal continues to be number one among China's primary energy sources, accounting for 66% of consumption (2012 data) followed by oil (20%), hydropower (8%), and natural gas (5%), and then nuclear (<1%). Other renewable sources such as solar and wind power plants accounted for about 1% only, despite the recent boom.[833]

America under president Donald Trump is vilified as a climate criminal, even though in the period 2007–2017, the USA and EU were the only parts of the world where emissions really went down (both at the rate of 1.5% annually).[834] [835] The United States owed this success mostly to the boom of shale gas and shale oil because natural gas has lower carbon emissions per unit of energy than coal. According to the US Energy Information Administration, after 2015, more electricity is produced from natural gas than from coal in America.[836] This also explains who the only one in Trump's government who defended the Paris Accord was. It was Secretary of State Rex Tillerson, former head of the Exxon oil corporation.[837] For Big Oil, the green subsidies in biofuels are a great path to your tax money.

Although it sounds surprising, it was actually not Mr. Trump who blocks the CO_2 emission reduction, but his opponents. The left-wing liberals enjoy talking about climate, but actions speak louder than words. In practice, they sabotage all measures to reduce emissions. Only 35% of US Democrats (left-wing) support nuclear energy. Among the Republicans (right-wing), this support is 60% (2016).[838] Support for fracking (natural gas) is similar—25% among Democrats, 66% among Republicans (2015).[839] And again, it is the environmentalists who oppose the construction of dams. Although dams help to cope with droughts or floods and produce clean electricity. For example, in California, the ten largest dams were built between 1927 and 1979.[840] But then, the environmentalists declared a green jihad on the carbon-free hydropower generating dams.

Ted Nordhaus of the Breakthrough Institute is not a climate skeptic but an award-winning environmentalist. He writes about natural gas: "It is, along with nuclear and hydroelectric power, one of the only energy sources that has ever succeeded at decarbonizing a large, modern economy at rates that even begin to approach those necessary to mitigate climate change."[841]

This whole debate is more about money than about climate. When US president Donald Trump announced cuts in the budget for politicized climate research in 2017, it was interpreted in the media as an "anti-science" or "anti-climate" attack. There was a surge of protests against the spending cuts. Nobody wants to lose money, so they organized the March for Science demonstration. When it was scheduled for Earth Day 2017, their website said: "The mischaracterization of science as a partisan issue, which has given policymakers permission to reject overwhelming evidence, is a critical and urgent matter." But if science is not politicized, then it is a mystery why scientists alongside the Democratic Party were organizing a demonstration against the Republican president.

"The impression that this will have on policymakers and the public will be to cement scientists as a politicized special interest group, just like any other lobbying group." climatologist Judith Curry said.[842] "The smartest people on the planet want to oppose Trump, and the best they can come up with is a march in support of themselves?" Curry quoted the economist Roger Pielke Jr.

Climatologist Richard Lindzen agreed with the proposed budget cuts. "They should probably cut the funding by 80 to 90% until the field cleans up... Climate science has been set back two generations, and they have destroyed its intellectual foundations." According to Lindzen, generous subsidies and grants have attracted too many money-grubbing careerists to climatology. "Remember, this was a tiny field, a backwater, and then suddenly you increased the funding to billions, and everyone got into it... Even in 1990, no one at MIT called themselves a 'climate scientist,' and then, all of a sudden, everyone was. They only entered it because of the bucks; they realized it was a gravy train. You have to get it back to the people who only care about the science."[843]

An interest group will not give up their funding without a fight. It is unlikely that the climate religion will disappear with a stroke of a pen of one American president. Former Czech president, Václav Klaus, wrote in 2017 presciently: "Trump's decision, however, did not weaken the powerful cartel of climate alarmists and will certainly not cause the change of heart of those who bet on the card of spreading alarming news (serving as motivation for attacks on people's freedom and prosperity in the developed world and on the fight against poverty in the developing world). Those people—already equally tired and worn out—have acquired new motivation and it seems that Trump's decision has pumped fresh blood into their veins. Their anti-Trump rage knows no boundaries."[844]

Indeed, this is what happened. In 2018, the climate activists orchestrated a whole lot of extensive campaigns. Students began to strike for climate on Fridays to imitate a Swedish autistic girl. Extinction Rebellion activists started to disrupt traffic in big cities. And American congresswoman Alexandria Ocasia-Cortez (AOC) proposed a Green New Deal policy. An ambitious socialist plan that would put an end to market economy and the American way of life once and for all. So, Trump's climate counter-revolution may have won a battle. And for the climate movement it was a heavy blow. But he did not win the war. The struggle for human freedom is far from over.

THE PATH AHEAD

When scared children walk on strike because they believe "we have 12 years to save the planet," it is no longer funny. These poor souls need help.

How can we rescue the environmentalist movement from the blind alley of pessimism and "environmental grief"? We need to abandon Malthusianism and its recent variants such as "limits to growth" (Club of Rome) or "population bomb" (Paul Ehrlich). The puritan program of no meat and no flying won't attract many followers either. After all, the educated, wealthy middle class who loves environmentalism the most is the one with the highest environmental footprint.[845]

Environmentalists Ted Nordhaus and Michael Schellenberger from the Breakthrough Institute wrote an interesting article *The Long Death of Environmentalism* (2011). They noted that "from virtually the moment that *An Inconvenient Truth* was released, public skepticism about global warming began to rise," with the percentage of Americans who believed global warming was exaggerated rising from 30% in March of 2006 to 35% in March of 2008. In 2019, we can see the same increase in skepticism as response to the hysteric campaign of Extinction Rebellion, Greta Thunberg, and Fridays for Future. Instinctively, people respond to such pressure with resistance.

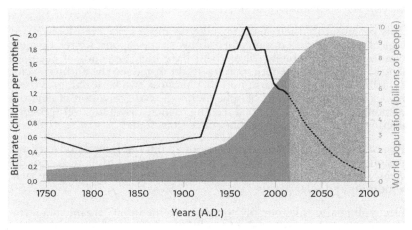

Figure 12—Global birth rates have been declining since 1970s. Global population is estimated to stop at 10 billion people around the year 2100. (Source: ourworldindata.org)

In 2015, Nordhaus and Schellenberger proposed a blueprint for a new kind of ecology. Unlike the post-modernists, they want to rehabilitate words like growth, progress, and modernization. We cannot go back to the medieval way of life. Mankind needs technical progress to ensure more intense and efficient production. That way, there will be more space left for the wilderness.

Their Ecomodernist Manifesto is from 2015, and it was even reprinted as an editorial in the science journal *Nature*. The signatories were a diverse lot, including ex-radicals (Mark Lynas), moderate environmentalists (Schellenberger and Nordhaus), and it was welcomed also by climate skeptics such as Matt Riddley (author of *The Rational Optimist*) and Roger Pielke Jr.

Mankind needs a positive vision, not environmental grief. And we do have reasons for optimism. World population growth has already begun decelerating. It is expected to stabilize by 2100 at some ten billion people. World poverty and malnutrition keeps falling. This is great news for the "Anthropocene," the age of humans. Anyone can check the facts in the project Our World in Data.

Eco-modernism was inspired by Steward Brand's book *Whole Earth Discipline* (2010), with a self-explanatory subtitle: *Why Dense Cities, Nuclear Power, Transgenic Crops, Restored Wildlands, and Geoengineering Are Necessary.*

They call this program "decoupling." It means that the growth of living standards shall no longer require more and more resources, land, and pollution. For instance, more efficient combustion engines can run further on the same amount of fuel.

This program of "thou shalt not take up more space" results in many logical consequences. It is incompatible with the support for solar panels, windmills, and biofuels. All of them have high demands of occupied land. So, what do the authors want to do to reduce the anthropogenic contribution to global warming? They propose two basic things. Firstly, nuclear power (which is a blasphemy for the old generation of environmentalists) and secondly, cloud seeding to increase cloud cover (geoengineering). Just like Bjorn Lomborg once suggested.

Renewables and energy austerity are not an option. If world poverty and malnutrition is to be eradicated, mankind will need to increase, not decrease, its energy consumption, which cannot be done with intermittent windmills and solar panels.

Decoupling also rules out any comeback to medieval "organic bio farming" requiring large stretches of land to produce very little food. Luxurious and costly eco-bio-organic food is a delicious way to spice up your diet, but it cannot feed entire mankind.

On the contrary, we need to promote GMO (genetically modified crops), which is another blasphemy for the old generation of environmentalists.

Modern agricultural production methods can do with less land and can grow more food per hectare, reducing our environmental footprint per capita. Production efficiency is so high that in the USA, only 2% of the population works in agriculture. The rest of the population has been liberated from the hard labor in the fields, and they can occupy other professions—work in tourism, write poetry, or program computer software.

As agriculture requires less manpower, people move to cities where they tend to have fewer children. In a city, you can no longer use children as cheap farmhands. Decoupling also precludes the "urban sprawl" of suburbs and satellite cities with warehouses and expensive mansions of the rich. City housing needs to get denser instead of swallowing the surrounding landscape like a slow explosion. If our fields and residential areas occupy less land, there will remain more space for wilderness and parks.

In the future, wilderness could return even to places formerly occupied by humans (rewilding). Britain now has more trees than 150 years ago because we no longer cut trees for fuel. This new wilderness will not be "pristine," so what? Even nature in Natural Reserves is seldom pristine—mostly even these protected areas are a result of thousands of years of human activity. For example, in the Krkonoše Mountains National Park in the Czech Republic, there are spruce forests that were planted only in the 19th century for logging purposes. When something is not pristine, it doesn't mean it isn't valuable or beautiful.

Since mankind is moving to cities, we need nature to follow us. Emma Marris, author of *Rambunctious Garden: Saving Nature in a Post-Wild World,* calls this "interwoven decoupling." We will no longer need nature to get our resources. But our lives will still be interwoven with nature—for spiritual and recreational purposes.

In developed countries, fewer people work in the field. Fuel is obtained by mining minerals from deep underground. We make things from plastic not wood. Many services formerly provided by ecosystems can now be replaced synthetically. However, we can integrate nature into modern urbanism, like parks, city farms, community gardens, zoos, botanical gardens, green roofs, etc. This is decoupling—nature that is here but not used for any material purposes. A green city is also more resistant to "urban heat island" effect. In hot summers, the greenery cools down the microclimate.

Let us make no mistake; most ecomodernists are not climate skeptics. Some of their climate-related views would make a skeptic cringe. Also, Schellenberger insists that we need government investments and subsidies for new technologies. This won't sound nice to free-market advocates. Yet, it is worthy of consideration.

Compared to the program of Greenpeace or Friends of the Earth, ecomodernism is more pragmatic. It sets realistic objectives. It can be carried out on a planet with 10 billion people (living mostly in cities) most of whom are poor people needing further growth in consumption instead of austerity. Fantasies about reducing global population to just half a billion people resettled to cute little eco-villages might happen someday. But only in several centuries when the demographic transition will have reached the next phase. For the nearest one hundred years, it is ecomodernism that provides realistic solutions.

Unsurprisingly, eco-modernism was met with a cold welcome from the old generation of environmentalists. They didn't like the criticism of their technophobic and doomy-gloomy position. They were outraged by the blasphemy against holy dogmas (GMO, nuclear). And they accused ecomodernists of betrayal because they engaged in dialogue with lukewarmers (moderate climate skeptics) like Matt Riddley and Owen Paterson.

The launch in Britain was an abysmal media failure. Although the whole point of ecomodernism is to depolarize tensions, the host of the first ecomodernist conference in the U.K., Mr. Paterson, appeared on TV using the offensive term "green blob." When you get two enemy camps to a peace conference, awkward moments like that are to be expected. Mark Lynas concluded: "But I do believe there has to be some way to depolarize this debate in the interests of moving forward. (Call me a hypocrite too: hell, only a few months back I was myself accusing Ridley of outright "climate change denial.") Having spent some time now with both opposing "sides," I keep being surprised by how much they actually have in common, if only they would see it."[846]

AFTERWORD

By Václav Klaus, former president of the Czech Republic

The ideology of climate alarmism, or rather scaring people with the supposedly man-made global warming phenomenon, is one of the most pressing issues of our times. A large number of individuals—mainly politicians, journalists and also inferior scientists, and also a number of institutions (especially the United Nations and the European Union) and, unfortunately, many big corporations and firms are abusing the slight increase in average global temperature (by cca 0.7°C) to radically intervene in the lives of millions or rather billions of people around the world. Every day, dozens or hundreds of protests against this ideological, not scientific, doctrine are published worldwide, but it is still not enough. So much so that some of us prefer to look the other way, unwilling to listen to any serious counterarguments.

Importantly, Vítězslav Kremlík founded the klimaskeptik.cz website and relentlessly writes and lectures in an effort to counter the prevalent current climate alarmism. Such contributions are highly significant in our rather timid times, when many people are hesitant to speak out against the dictate of political correctness. Mr. Kremlík belongs to a small group of Czech authors—Kutílek, Motl, Svoboda, Klaus—who unmask the falsehoods of this ideology, along with a large and ever-increasing number of fellow skeptics around the world.

The theme of this book, the manuscript of which I was given by the author as a birthday present (I read it carefully then, and I keep it at hand now with key sections underlined), is extremely timely. Vítězslav Kremlík understands that climate alarmism is not a fight against climate, but an attempt to shackle human freedom. Climate is just a tool or an excuse for this goal. With its quality and persuasiveness, the book makes an important contribution not only to domestic but also to the global debate. It represents an integral part of a wider protest against the assault on human liberty.

The author describes the attempts at suppressing any criticism of this dark doctrine, and he decries the efforts to muzzle dissenting voices, who refuse to bow before this new atheistic religion. In one chapter, the author sighed that "in our press today there is as much propaganda as in the Bolshevik Pravda during the Cold War." Yes, I also feel it as strongly as that! That is why it is necessary to read Kremlík's book, and, I would add, to study it with a pencil in one hand to make notes.

The author demonstrates an extraordinary range of knowledge and viewpoints, presenting an interdisciplinary analysis in the best sense of the word in order to tackle an extremely broad and poorly defined topic. Although a student of social sciences (English and History at the Faculty of Arts of Palacký University in Olomouc, Czech Republic), he demonstrates a sound command of science, which is a prerequisite for grasping this topic. He is among those who point to the implausibility of the monocausal link between CO_2 emissions and the average global temperature and draws attention to a number of other factors that influence the progression of global temperatures over time.

His great advantage is that, as a historian, he can place contemporary phenomena in the context of human history. For non-historians, the delineation of Paleolithic climate change, climate-induced wars in the Bronze Age, the disappearance of the Vikings from Greenland, the fall of the Roman Empire, etc., may be revealing. The history of climate change during the last millennium is a great lesson to all of us, as it is closely tied to what is happening today.

The author rightly criticizes the "believers of the climate change religion" and notes that climatology is a "politicized" science. The obvious political activism of climate science (and its scholars) deprived this discipline of respect. I talk about this in my book *Which Shall Destroy Us: Climate or the Climate Policy?* (Prague, Grada, 2017), in which I try to discriminate carefully the "standard sciences well defined by their scope and the starting hypotheses (physics, chemistry, biology, and also economics) from the so-called complex, multidisciplinary, or interdisciplinary studies or disciplines" (p. 52). I could add that I consider these disciplines as undisciplined, but I am not going to put this into the author's mouth.

In this context, Vítězslav Kremlík writes about the so-called post-normal science (see also my above-mentioned book, the chapter Discussion in Science, or in Climatology). Post-normal science is activist science that aims to shape politics and abandons academic objectivity.

I believe that this lively and convincing book will find its readers not only in my home country and that it will make an important contribution to our not-so-successful battle with climate alarmism.

Václav Klaus,

In Prague on June 28, 2018

REFERENCES

1   DARWALL, R., *The Age of Global Warming*, London 2013, Quartet Books Limited, p. 2.

2   WEISE, E. 'How dare you?' Read Greta Thunberg's emotional climate change speech to UN and world leaders. *USA Today*, 24.9.2019, https://eu.usatoday.com/story/news/2019/09/23/greta-thunberg-tells-un-summit-youth-not-forgive-climate-inaction/2421335001/ [cit. 13. 11. 2019].

3   BOLT, J., TIMMER, M., van ZANDEN, J. L., GDP per capita since 1820, in van ZAIDEN, J. L. et al. (eds.), *How Was Life? Global Well-being* since 1820, OECD Publishing 2014, http://dx.doi.org/10.1787/9789264214262-7-en [cit. 13. 2. 2016].

4   RAVAILLON, M Poverty in the Rich World When It Was Not Nearly So Rich, *Center for Global Development*, 28. 5. 2014, figure 1, http://www.cgdev.org/blog/poverty-rich-world-when-it-was-not-nearly-so-rich [cit. 13. 2. 2016].

5   Food Price Index, *Food and Agriculture Organization*, http://www.fao.org/worldfoodsituation/foodpricesindex/en/ [cit. 1. 2. 2017].

6   Undernourishment around the World in 2015, In: *The State of Food Insecurity in the World 2015, Food and Agriculture Organization of the United Nations*, table 1, http://www.fao.org/3/a-i4646e/i4646e01.pdf [cit. 13. 2. 2016].

7   World Day for Social Justice: UN urges action to end poverty, overcome inequality, *United Nations News*, 20. 2. 2014, http://www.un.org/apps/news/story.asp?NewsID=47180&Cr=Inequality&Cr1=#.UwoQA-uN5NIE [cit. 21. 2. 2014].

8   FIREBAUGH, G., Empirics of World Income Inequality, *American Journal of Sociology*, 1999, Vol. 104, No. 6.

9   RECTOR, R., SHEFFIELD, R., Air Conditioning, Cable TV, and an Xbox: What Is Poverty in the United States Today? *Heritage Foundation*, Backgrounder No. 2575, 18. 7. 2011, http://thf_media.s3.amazonaws.com/2011/pdf/bg2575.pdf [cit. 17.2.2014].

10   BOURGUIGNON, F., and MORRISSON, C. Inequality Among World Citizens: 1820–1992 *American Economic Review*, 2002, 92 (4): 727–744.

11   ROSER, Max. The short history of global living conditions and why it matters that we know it. https://ourworldindata.org/a-history-of-global-living-conditions-in-5-charts [cit. 21. 12. 2019].

12   In the Holocene thes oscillations are called Bond Events. In the glacial, there were comparable oscillations called DO Events (Dansgaard-Oeschger Events).

13   GLASSNER, B., *The Culture of Fear: Why Americans Are Afraid of the Wrong Things*, New York 2000, Basic Books.

14   GLASSNER, B., Narrative techniques of fear mongeringfear-mongering, *Social Research: An International Quarterly*, 2004, Vol. 71, Issue 4.

15   KING, A., SCHNEIDER, B., *The First Global Revolution: A Report by the Council of The Club of Rome*, London 1993, Orient Longman, p. 75.

16   MICHAELS, D., Manufactured Uncertainty: Protecting Public Health in the Age of Contested Science and Product Defense, *Annals of New York Academy of Sciences*, 2006, Vol, 1076,

17   *Key Word Energy Statistics 2017*. International Energy Agency, https://www.iea.org/publications/freepublications/publication/Key-World2017.pdf [cit. 18.7.2018], table World Total Energy Supply in 2015, p. 6.

18   BAWDEN, T., COP21: Hitting the climate change targets agreed in Paris will cost $16.5trn, *The Independent*, 13. 12. 2015, http://www.independent.co.uk/environment/climate-change/cop21-hitting-the-climate-change-targets-agreed-in-paris-will-cost-165trn-a6771816.html [cit. 18.12.2016]

19   LOMBORG, B., Paris climate promises will reduce temperatures by just 0.05°C in 2100 (Press release), *Lomborg.com*, 11/2015, http://www.lomborg.com/press-release-research-reveals-negligible-impact-of-paris-climate-promises [cit. 9.10.2016].

20   DELINGPOLE, J., Global warming is not our most urgent priority, *The Spectator*, 11. 6. 2008, https://www.spectator.co.uk/2008/06/global-warming-is-not-our-most-urgent-priority/ [cit. 9. 7. 2017]

21   NORDHAUS, T., SCHELLENBERGER, M., The long death of environmentalism, *Breakthrough Institute*, 25. 2. 2011, http://thebreakthrough.org/archive/the_long_death_of_environmenta [cit. 15. 5. 2016].

22   NORDHAUS, T., SCHELLENBERGER, M., The long death of environmentalism, *Breakthrough Institute*, 25. 2. 2011, http://thebreakthrough.org/archive/the_long_death_of_environmenta [cit. 15. 5. 2016].

23   PETIT, J. R. et al., Climate and atmospheric history of the past 420,000 years from the Vostok ice core, Antarctica, *Nature*, 1999, Vol. 399, Issue 6735, Figure 2 (modified).

24   KIDDER D. L., WORSLEY, T. R., Phanerozoic Large Igneous Provinces (LIPs), HEATT (Haline Euxinic Acidic Thermal Transgressions) episodes and mass extinctions, *Paleography, Paleoclimatology, Paleoecology*, 2010, Vol. 295, Issue 1–2.

25   MULKERN, A. C. Today's climate change proves much faster than change in past 65 million years, *Scientific American*, 2. 8. 2013, http://www.scientificamerican.com/article/todays-climate-change-

proves-much-faster-than-changes-in-past-65-million-years/ [cit. 15. 5. 2015].

26   MOBERG, A., Highly variable Northern Hemisphere temperatures reconstructed from low- and high-resolution proxy data, *Nature*, 2005, Vol. 433, 10. 2. 2005, p. 613-617.

27   METELKA, L., TOLASZ, R., *Změny klimatu—fakta bez mýtů*, Praha 2009, Centrum pro otázky životního prostředí, figure 2.

28   SVOBODA, J., Globální oteplování nebo globální omyl, *Neviditelnypes.cz*, 23. 2. 2007, http://neviditelnypes.lidovky.cz/veda-globalni-otepleni-nebo-globalni-omyl-f18-/p_veda.aspx?c=A070222_223307_p_veda_wag [cit. 8. 12. 2014].

29   BÖHM, R. et al., Regional temperature variability in the European Alps: 1760–1998 from homogenized instrumental series, *International Journal of Climatology*, 2001, Vol. 21, Issue 14, p. 1779–1801.

30   WENIGER, G. S., 150 years of Neanderthal research—a hopeless situation but not serious. In: *Continuity and discontinuity in the peopling of Europe*, CONDEMI S., WENIGER G.S. (eds.), Springer 2011, p. 380.

31   HEMMING, S. R., Heinrich events: Massive late Pleistocene detritus layers of the North Atlantic and their global climate imprint, *Reviews of Geophysics*, 2004, Vol. 42, Issue RG1005.

32   KUPER, R. et al., Climate-controlled Holocene occupation in the Sahara: Motor of Africa's evolution, *Science*, 2006, Vol. 313, No. 803.

33   BOND, G .et al., Persistent solar influence on North Atlantic climate during the Holocene, *Science*, Vol. 294, Issue 2130, 7. 12. 2001.

34   BOND, G. et al., A pervasive millennial-scale cycle in North Atlantic Holocene and glacial climates, *Science*, 1997, Vol. 278, Issue 5341.

35   CLAUSSEN, M. et al., Simulation of an abrupt change in Saharan vegetation in the Mid-Holocene, *Geophysical Research Letters*, 1999, Vol. 26, Issue 14.

36   CULLEN, H. M. et al., Climate change and the collapse of the Akkadian empire: Evidence from the deep sea, *Geology*, 2000, Vol. 28, No. 4.

37   BERNHARDT, C. E. et al., Nile Delta vegetation response to Holocene climate variability, *Geology*, 2012, Vol. 40, No. 7.

38   STAUBWASSER, M. et al., Climate change at the 4.2 ka BP termination of the Indus valley civilization and Holocene south Asian monsoon variability, *Geophysical Research Letters*, 2003, Vol. 30, No. 8.

39   ROHLING E. J. et al., Holocene atmosphere-ocean interactions: records from Greenland and the Aegean Sea, *Climate Dynamics*, 2002, Vol. 18, Issue 7.

40   ORLAND, I. J., Climate deterioration in the Eastern Mediterra-

nean as revealed by ion microprobe analysis of a speleothem that grew from 2.2 to 0.9 ka in Soreq Cave, Israel, *Quaternary Research,* 2009, Vol. 71, Issue 1.

41   GILL, R. B., *The great Maya droughts: Water, life, and death,* New Mexico 2001, University of New Mexico Press.

42   BOND, G. et al., Persistent solar influence on North Atlantic climate during the Holocene, *Science,* 2001, Vol. 294, No. 2130.

43   BEER, J. et al., Solar variability over the past several millenia. *Space Science Reviews,* 2006, Vol. 125, Issue 1.

44   DENTON, G. H., KARLÉN, W., Holocene climatic variations –their pattern and possible cause, *Quaternary Research,* 1973, Vol. 3, Issue 2.

45   HUMLUM, O. et al., Identifying natural contributions to late Holocene climate change, *Global and Planetary Change,* 2001, Vol. 79, Issue 1–2, p. 145–156, Figure 8. Data from: ALLEY, R. B., The Younger Dryas cold interval as viewed from central Greenland, *Quaternary Science Reviews,* 2000, Vol. 19, Issue 1–5, p. 213–226.

46   JASPERS, K., *The origin and goal of history,* Massachussetts 1965, Yale University Press, 3rd edition, from the first German edition Vom Ursprung und Ziel der Geschichte (1949) translated by Michael Bullock.

47   ARMSTRONG, K., *The great transformation: The beginning of our religious traditions,* London 2006, Random House.

48   LANDON, J. C., *World history and the eonic effect. Civilization, darwinism, and theories of evolution,* Montauk (NY) 2016, South Fork Books, 5th edition, online edition http://history-and-evolution.com [cit. 23. 2. 2017].

49   ARNEBORG, J. et al., Human diet and subsistence patterns in Norse Greenland AD c.980–AD c.1450: Archaeological Interpretations, *Journal of the North Atlantic,* 2012, Special Volume 3, p. 119–133.

50   Papal letters concerning the bishopric of Gardar in Greenland during the fifteenth century, Document No. AJ-060, *Wisconsin Historical Society Digital Library and Archives,* http://www.americanjourneys.org/pdf/AJ-060.pdf [cit. 10. 5. 2017].

51   FAGAN, B., *The Little Ice Age,* New York, 2001, Basic Books, p. 127.

52   LAMB, H. H., *Historic storms of the North Sea, British Isles and Northwest Europe,* Cambridge 1991, Cambridge University Press, p. 33. Cited from https://notalotofpeopleknowthat.wordpress.com/2014/02/06/storminess-of-the-little-ice-age/ [retrieved 7.7.2017]

53   NUSSBAUMER, S. U. et al., Fluctuations of the "Mer de Glace" (Mont Blanc area, France) AD 1500–2050, *Zeitschrift für Gletscherkunde und Glazialgeologie,* Band 40 (2005/2006), p. 58.

54   STECKEL, R. H., New light on the "Dark Ages": The remarkably

tall stature of Northern European men during the medieval era, *Social Science History,* Vol. 28, No. 2, July 2004.

55 ALLEN, R., The great divergence in European wages and prices from the Middle Ages to the First World War, *Exploitations in Economic History,* 2001, Vol. 38, Issue 2.

56 ZHANG, D. et al., The causality analysis of climate change and large-scale human crisis, *Proceedings of the National Academy of Science,* 2011, Vol. 108, No. 42.

57 NEUBERGER, H., Climate in art, *Weather,* 1970, Vol. 25, Issue 2.

58 OVERTON, M., Agricultural Revolution in England 1500–1850, *BBC,* 17. 2. 2011, http://www.bbc.co.uk/history/british/empire_sea-power/agricultural_revolution_01.shtml [cit. 19. 2. 2014].

59 TOWNSEND, M., HARRIS, P., Now the Pentagon tells Bush: climate change will destroy us, *Guardian,* 22. 2. 2004. http://www.theguardian.com/environment/2004/feb/22/usnews.theobserver [cit. 8. 8. 2014].

60 SCHWARTZ, P., RANDALL, D., An abrupt climate change scenario and its implications for United States national security, *A Report for the US Department of Defense,* October 2003

61 HUSOVÁ, K, JEŘÁBEK, J., *Klima v tísni,* Praha 2009, Člověk v tísni o.p.s., https://www.varianty.cz/publikace/67-bohous-a-dasa-klima-v-tisni [cit. 8. 8. 2016].

62 THOMPSON, A., Global warming could fuel war, *Livescience,* 9. 7. 2007, http://www.livescience.com/1660-global-warming-fuel-war.html [cit. 8. 8. 2014].

63 ZHANG, D. et al., The causality analysis of climate change and large-scale human crisis, *Proceedings of the National Academy of Science,* 2011, Vol. 108, No. 42.

64 DIAMOND, J., *Collapse—How societies choose to fail or succeed.* New York, 2005, Viking Press.

65 BAUR, E., FISCHER, E., LENZ, F., *Human heredity,* New York 1931, Macmillan, p. 697–9. Cited from: *The Nazi Germany sourcebook: an anthology of texts,* STACKELBERG, R., WINKLE S.A. (eds.), London 2002, Routledge, p. 75.

66 DAVENPORT, C. B., SCUDDER, M. T., *Naval Officers, Their Heredity and Development,* Washington 1919, Carnegie Institution of Washington. Citováno z: FARBER, S.A. US Scientists' role in the eugenics movement (1907–1939): A contemporary biologist's perspective, *Zebrafish,* 2008, Vol. 5, Issue 4.

67 MARKS, J., Racism, Eugenics, and the burdens of history, IX *International Congress of Human Genetics,* 20. 8. 1996, Rio de Janeiro. Cited from: FARBER, S.A. U.S.US Scientists' role in the eugenics movement (1907–1939): A contemporary biologist's perspective,

Zebrafish, 2008, Vol. 5, Issue 4.

68   GALTON, F., *Hereditary genius, an inquiry its laws and consequences*, Second edition, New York 1892, MacMillan and Co.

69   SMITH, J. D., WEHMEYER, M. L., Who was Deborah Kallikak? *Intellectual and Developmental Disabilities*, 2012, Vol. 20, Issue 2.

70   KARP, R. J. et al., Fetal alcohol syndrome at the turn of the 20th century. An unexpected explanation of the Kallikak family. *Archives of Pediatrics and Adolescent Medicine*, 1995, Vol. 149, Issue 1.

71   LUDMERER, K. M., American geneticists and the eugenics movement 1905–1935, *Journal of the History of Biology*, 1965, Vol. 2, No. 2.

72   MARKS, J., Historiography of eugenics, *American Journal of Human Genetics*, 1993, Vol. 52, Issue 3.

73   LUDMERER, K. M., American geneticists and the eugenics movement 1905–1935, *Journal of the History of Biology*, 1965, Vol. 2, No. 2.

74   PEARL, R., The biology of superiority, *The American Mercury*, 1927, Vol. 12, No. 47.

75   Scientific racism, history of. In: *Encyclopedia of Race and Racism*. (MOORE, J.H. ed.), New York 2007, Macmillan Reference.

76   ALLEN, G., Misuse of biological hierarchies: The American eugenics movement 1900–1940, *History and Philosophy of Life Sciences*, 1983, Vol. 5, No. p.116. Cited from: LEONARD, T. C., Eugenics and economics in the progressive era, *Journal of Economic Perspectives*, 2005, Vol. 19, Number 4.

77   The second international congress of eugenics address of welcome, Science, 1921, Vol. 54, Issue 1397.

78   GRADY, K. E., A review of Three Generations, No Imbeciles: Eugenics, the Supreme Court and Buck v. Bell, *Georgia State University Law Review*, 2010, Vol. 26, Issue 4, http://readingroom.law.gsu.edu/cgi/viewcontent.cgi?article=2422&context=gsulr [cit. 15. 2. 2017].

79   BUTLER, D., Eugenics scandal reveals silence of Swedish scientists, *Nature*, 1997, Vol. 389, Issue 6646.

80   KELLAWAY, K., How the Observer brought the WWF into being, *Guardian*, 7. 11. 2010, http://www.theguardian.com/environment/2010/nov/07/wwf-world-wildlife-fund-huxley [cit. 21. 2. 2014].

81   HUXLEY, J. S., Eugenics and society (The Galton Lecture given to the Eugenics Society 17. 2. 1936), *Eugenics Review*, 1936, Vol. 28, No. 2, p. 24.

82   NESTRUCK, J. K., Was George Bernard Shaw a monster? *The Globe And Mail*, 1. 7. 2011, http://www.theglobeandmail.com/arts/theater-and-performance/was-george-bernard-shaw-a-monster/arti-

cle585209/?page=all [cit. 21. 2. 2017].

83   PEARCE, F., *Land grabbers. The new fight over who owns the Earth,* London 2013, Eden Project Books, p. 89.

84   WATERFIELD, B., Dutch Prince Bernhard was member of Nazi party, *Telegraph.* 5. 3. 2010, http://www.telegraph.co.uk/news/world-news/europe/netherlands/7377402/Dutch-Prince-Bernhard-was-member-of-Nazi-party.html [cit. 21. 2. 2014].

85   HIND, J., Did I say that? Prince Philip, queen's consort, 88, *Guardian.* 21. 6. 2009, http://www.theguardian.com/lifeandstyle/2009/jun/21/quotes-by-prince-philip [cit. 21. 2. 2014].

86   PEARCE, F., *Land grabbers. The new fight over who owns the Earth,* London 2013, Eden Project Books.

87   PEARCE, F., *Land grabbers. The new fight over who owns the Earth,* London 2013, Eden Project Books.

88   ELLIS, S., Of elephants and men: Politics and nature conservation in South Africa, *Journal of Southern African Studies,* 1994, Vol. 20, No 1., p. 55.

89   POOLE, Robert M., Heartbreak on the Serengeti, *National Geographic,* February 2006, http://www7.nationalgeographic.com/ngm/0602/feature1/text4.html [cit. 18. 2. 2014].

90   National Research Council, *The life sciences recent progress and application to human affairs, The world of biological research requirements for the future,* Washington 1970, The National Academies Press.

91   WURSTER, F., DDT goes on trial in Madison, *BioScience,* 1969, Vol. 19, No. 9.

92   SWEENEY, E. M., *EPA hearing examiner's recommendations and findings concerning DDT hearings,* Apr 25, 1972, 40 CFR 164.32, cited from ROBERTS, D. et al., *The excellent powder: DDT's political and scientific history,* Indianapolis 2016, Dog Ear Publishing, p. 204.

93   CARSON, R., *Silent spring,* Boston, 1962, Houghton Mifflin Company.

94   WURSTER, D. H. et al., Bird mortality following DDT spray for Dutch elm disease, *Ecology,* 1965, Vol. 46, No. 4.

95   Chart and Table of Bald Eagle Breeding Pairs in Lower 48 States, *US Fish and Wildlife Service,* https://www.fws.gov/midwest/eagle/population/chtofprs.html [cit. 18. 2. 2017].

96   MORRIS, A., MEINERS, R., DESROCHES, P. (eds), *Silent spring at 50: The false crises of Rachel Carson,* Washington D.C. 2012, Cato Institute, Figure 5.1, p. 103.

97   Bald eagle soars off endangered species list, *US Department of the Interior News,* 28. 6. 2007, http://tinyurl.com/noljrk6 [cit. 7. 2. 2014].

98   VAN NAME, W. G., Threatened extinction of the bald eagle. *Ecology,* 1921, Vol. 2, Issue 1, p. 76–78.

99   SMALLWOOD, K. S., THELANDER, C. G., Bird mortality at the Altamont Pass Wind Resource Area, California, *Journal of Wildlife Management,* 2008, Vol. 72, No 1.

100   LAURA, Z., US to give 30-year wind farm permits; thousands of eagle deaths seen, Reuters.com, 14. 12. 2016.

101   JUKES, T., DDT, human health and the environment, *Boston College Environmental Affairs Law Review,* 1971, Vol 1, Issue 3.

102   CONIS, E., Debating the health effects of DDT: Thomas Jukes, Charles Wurster and the fate of an environmental pollutant, *Public Health Reports,* 2010, Vol. 125, No. 2.

103   ESKENAZI, B. et al., The Pine River statement: Human health consequences of DDT Use, *Environmental Health Perspectives,* 2009, Vol. 117, No. 9.

104   Public health statement for DDT, DDE, and DDD, *Agency for Toxic Substances and Disease Registry,* September 2002, https://www.atsdr.cdc.gov/phs/phs.asp?id=79&tid=20 [cit. 3. 2. 2017].

105   COHEN, J. M. et al., How absolute is zero? An evaluation of historical and current definitions of malaria elimination, *Malaria Journal,* 2010, Vol. 9, No. 2013.

106   COHEN, J. M. et al., Malaria resurgence: a systematic review and assessment of its causes, *Malaria Journal,* 2012, Vol. 11, No. 122.

107   MURRAY, C. J. et al., Global malaria mortality between 1980 and 2010, *Lancet,* 2012, Vol. 379, No. 9814.

108   ATTARAN, A., Where did it all go wrong? *Nature,* 2004, Vol. 430, Issue 7002.

109   MURRAY, C. J. et al., Global malaria mortality between 1980 and 2010, *Lancet,* 2012, Vol. 379, No. 9814.

110   FINKEL, M., Malaria: Stopping a global killer, *National Geographic,* July 2007, http://ngm.nationalgeographic.com/ngm/0707/feature1/text4.html [cit. 7. 2. 2016].

111   EHRLICH, P. R., *The population bomb,* New York 1968, Ballantine Books.

112   DIXON, B., In praise of prophets, *New Scientist and Science Journal,* 1971, Vol. 51, No. 769.

113   EHRLICH, P., EHRLICH, A., HOLDREN, P., E*coscience, Population, resources, environment,* New York 1977, W. H. Freeman and Co.

114   SHAIDLE, K., Science Czar John P. Holdren's disturbing beliefs about America, capitalism and humanity, *Examiner,* 16. 7. 2009, http://www.examiner.com/article/science-czar-john-p-holdren-s-disturbing-beliefs-about-america-capitalism-and-humanity [cit. 21. 2. 2014].

115   EHRLICH, P., EHRLICH, A., HOLDREN, P., *Ecoscience, Population, resources, environment,* New York 1977, W. H. Freeman and Co, p. 787–8.

116   MALTHUS, T. R., *An Essay on the principle of population as it affects the future improvement of society,* London 1798, reprint by Electronic Scholarly Publishing Project 1998, p. 33–34, http://www.esp.org/books/malthus/population/malthus.pdf [cit. 7. 2. 2017].

117   MALTHUS, T. R., *An Essay on the principle of population as it affects the future improvement of society,* Reprint, London: Reeves and Turner, (1798) 1878, p. 412 1826, John Murray, 6th edition, Book 4, Chapter 5, http://m.harunyahya.com/tr/Buku/3984/The-Social-Weapon-Darwinism/chapter/5124/The-history-of-ruthlessness-from-www.econlib.org/library/Malthus-to-Darwin/malPlong30.html#dd12 [cit. 7. 2. 201611. 3. 2017].

118   MILLER, H. I., Norman Borlaug—the genius behind the green revolution, *Forbes,* 18. 1. 2012, http://www.forbes.com/sites/henrymiller/2012/01/18/norman-borlaug-the-genius-behind-the-green-revolution/ [cit. 21. 2. 2014].

119   EHRLICH, P., EHRLICH, A., The population bomb revisited, *The Electronic Journal of Sustainable Development,* 2009, Vol. 1, No. 3.

120   Interview with Jean-Jacques Cousteau, *UNESCO Courier,* November 1991, http://unesdoc.unesco.org/images/0009/000902/090256eo.pdf [cit. 11. 5. 2016].

121   CHURCHILL, J. L., The limits to influence. The Club of Rome and Canada 1968 to 1988, PhD thesis, *University of Waterloo* (Canada) 2006, p. 38, https://uwspace.uwaterloo.ca [cit. 24. 2. 2017].

122   JANTSCH, E., Perspectives on planning. Proceedings of the OECD working symposium on long-range forecasting and planning. Bellagio, Italy, 27. 10—2. 11. 1968, http://files.eric.ed.gov/fulltext/ED044791.pdf [cit. 24. 2. 2017].

123   MEADOWS, D. H., Limits to Growth: *A Report for the Club of Rome's Project on the Predicament of Mankind,* New York 1977, New American Library.

124   BP Statistical Review of World Energy, June 2016, http://www.bp.com/en/global/corporate/energy-economics/statistical-review-of-world-energy.html#BPstats [cit. 2. 2. 2017].

125   NORDHAUS, W. D., World dynamics: measurement without data. *The Economic Journal,* 1973, Vol. 83, No. 332.

126   KRUGMAN, P., Limits to growth and other stuff, *New York Times,* 22. 4. 2008, http://krugman.blogs.nytimes.com/2008/04/22/limits-to-growth-and-related-stuff/?_php=true&_type=blogs&_r=0 [cit. 20. 3. 2014].

127   CRICHTON, M., Aliens cause global warming, *A Caltech Michelin Lecture,* 17. 1 2003, http://heartland.org/policy-documents/aliens-cause-global-warming-lecture-michael-crichton?artId=16253 [cit. 2. 2. 2014].

128   Ibidem.

129   WHITEHEAD, R. J., Chapter 13: Club of Rome. In: *Memoirs of a Boffin,* 1995, http://www.whitehead-family.ca/drrennie/memoirs.html [cit. 17. 2. 2014].

130   CHURCHILL, J. L., The limits to influence. The Club of Rome and Canada 1968 to 1988, PhD thesis, *University of Waterloo* (Canada) 2006, p. 54, https://uwspace.uwaterloo.ca/bitstream/handle/10012/747/jlchurch2006.pdf?sequence=1&isAllowed=y [cit. 24. 2. 2017].

131   HOBBES, T., *Leviathan,* Praha 2010, Oikoymenh.

132   VAN DIEREN, W. (ed.), *Taking nature into account. A report to the Club of Rome,* New York 1995, Copernicus, p. 19.

133   KING, A., SCHNEIDER, B., *The first global revolution. A report by the Council of the Club of Rome,* London 1993, Orient Longman, p. 71.

134   MIDDLETON, D., The Simon-Ehrlich wager at seven billion people, *Wattsupwiththat.com,* 25. 1. 2012, http://wattsupwiththat.com/2012/01/25/the-simon-erlich-wager-at-seven-billion-people/ [cit. 7. 7. 2014].

135   MIELE, F., Living without limits: an interview with Julian Simon, *Skeptic,* 1997, Vol. 5, No. 1. Cited from https://jasoncollins.org/2011/05/20/the-simon-ehrlich-bet/ [cit. 20. 7. 2014].

136   SIMON, J., *The ultimate resource.* Princeton, 1981, Princeton University Press.

137   HUBBERT, M. K., *Nuclear energy and the fossil fuels,* Shell Development Company, *Publication No. 95,* June 1956, p. 35, http://www.hubbertpeak.com/hubbert/1956/1956.pdf [cit. 3. 2. 2017].

138   LORENZINI, P., Chernobyl myths, *The American Spectator,* 22. 1. 2006, http://spectator.org/articles/47512/chernobyl-myths [cit. 20. 7. 2014].

139   THE CHERNOBYL FORUM 2003–2005. *Chernobyl's Legacy: Health, Environmental and Socio-economic Impacts and Recommendations to the Governments of Belarus, the Russian Federation and Ukraine.* Vídeň 2006, International Atomic Energy Agency, p. 7.

140   GLAZKO T., GLAZKO, V., Genetické důsledky Černobylu, *Vesmír,* 2006, Vol. 85, Issue. 201.(in Czech language)

141   PETERKA, M. et al., Chernobyl: Relationship between the number of missing newborn boys and the level of radiation in the Czech regions, *Environmental Health Perspectives,* 2007, Vol. 115, Issue 12.

142   NORTON, A. Higher birth-defect rate seen in Chernobyl area. *Reuters,* 24.3.2010. https://www.reuters.com/article/us-defect-chernobyl/higher-birth-defect-rate-seen-in-chernobyl-area-idUSTRE62N4L820100324 [cit. 7. 7. 2019].

143   ZAGANJOR, I. Et al. Describing the Prevalence of Neural Tube Defects Worldwide: A Systematic Literature Review. Plos ONE, 2016,

Vol. 11, Issue 4.

144 BROWNE, A., Myth of Chernobyl suffering exposed, *The Guardian*, 6. 1. 2002, http://www.theguardian.com/world/2002/jan/06/socialsciences.highereducation [cit. 7. 7. 2014].

145 BERTOLLINI, R. et al., Reduction of births in Italy after the Chernobyl accident. *Scandinavian Journal of Work, Environment and Health*, 1990, Vol. 16, No. 2.

146 Chernobyl: the true scale of the accident. *Joint news release WHO/IEA/UNDP,* 5. 9. 2005 http://www.who.int/mediacentre/news/releases/2005/pr38/en/ [cit. 20. 7. 2014].

147 Chernobyl: the true scale of the accident. https://www.who.int/mediacentre/news/releases/2005/pr38/en/index1.html [cit. 24 2. 2019].

148 AAPM Position Statement on Radiation Risks from Medical Imaging Procedures. Issued in December 2011. https://www.aapm.org/org/policies/details.asp?id=318&type=PP

149 PTranscript of Michael Crichton's lecture 15. 10. 2005 at the The Independent Institute in the debate on "States of Fear: Science or Politics?" http://www.independent.org/events/transcript.asp?id=111 [cit. 24 2. 2017].

150 Present and future environment impact of the Chernobyl accident. *International Atomic Energy Agency,* Vienna 2001, http://www-pub.iaea.org/MTCD/publications/PDF/te_1240_prn.pdf [cit. 18. 7. 2014].

151 HIGGINGBOTHAM, A., Is Chernobyl a wild kingdom or a radioactive den of decay? *Wired,* 14. 4. 2011, http://www.wired.com/2011/04/ff_chernobyl/ [cit. 17. 7. 2014].

152 POLANECKÝ, K. a kol., *Chytrá energie,* Praha 2010, Hnutí Duha.

153 BIELLO, D., What you should and shouldn't worry about after the Fukushima nuclear meltdowns, *Scientific American,* 9. 1. 2014, http://www.scientificamerican.com/article/what-to-worry-about-after-fukushima-nuclear-disaster/ [cit. 18. 8. 2014].

154 KEMM, K., There was no Fukushima nuclear disaster, *Committee for a Constructive Tomorrow,* 12. 10. 2013, http://www.cfact.org/2013/10/12/physicist-there-was-no-fukushima-nuclear-disaster/ [8. 8. 2014].

155 MADRIGAL, A. C., 25 other energy disasters from the last year, *The Atlantic,* 21. 3. 2011, http://www.theatlantic.com/technology/archive/2011/03/25-other-energy-disasters-from-the-last-year/72814/ [cit. 17. 8. 2014].

156 BROOK, B.W. et al. Why nuclear energy is sustainable and has to be part of the energy mix. *Sustainable Materials and Technologies,* 1-2 (2014), p. 8-16.

157 GORE, A., *Earth in the balance.* New York, 1992, Houghton

Mifflin.

158   PEARCE, F., Ozone hole "innocent" of Chile's ills, *New Scientist,* 12. 8. 1993, http://www.newscientist.com/article/mg13918870.900-ozone-hole-innocent-of-chiles-ills.html [cit. 20. 2. 2014].

159   SCHEIN, O.D. et al., Ocular and dermatologic health effects of ultraviolet radiation exposure from the ozone hole in southern Chile, *American Journal of Public Health,* 1995, Vol. 85, No. 4.

160   PERDUE, M., Revealed bug eyed hoax, *Reading Eagle* 7. 11. 1995, http://news.google.com/newspapers?nid=1955&-dat=19951107&id=j2wlAAAAIBAJ&sjid=baYFAAAAIBA-J&pg=2719,5157781 [cit. 10. 2. 2014].

161   LOMBORG, B., *A skeptical environmentalist.* Cambridge, 2001, Cambridge University Press.

162   SHABECOFF, P., Race for substitutes to help save ozone. *New York Times,* 31. 3. 1988, http://www.nytimes.com/1988/03/31/business/race-for-substitutes-to-help-save-ozone.html [cit. 18. 2. 2014].

163   MADURO, R., The Bronfmans, Part II: The ozone depletion hoax. *Executive Intelligence Review,* 1989, Vol. 16, No. 36, http://www.larouchepub.com/eiw/public/1989/eirv16n36-19890908/eirv16n36-19890908_009-the_bronfmans_part_ii_the_ozone.pdf [cit. 17. 2. 2014].

164   LAMBRIGHT, H., *The case of ozone depletion,* Monographs in Aerospace History (NASA History Division), No. 38, 2005, http://history.nasa.gov/monograph38.pdf [cit. 7. 2. 2014].

165   FARMAN, J. C. et al., Large losses of total ozone in Antarctica reveal seasonal ClOx/NOx interaction. *Nature,* 1985, Vol. 315, Issue 6016.

166   LAMBRIGHT, H., *The case of ozone depletion,* Monographs in Aerospace History (NASA History Division), No. 38, 2005, p. 14, http://history.nasa.gov/monograph38.pdf [cit. 7. 2. 2014].

167   *Geophysical Research Letters,* 1986, Vol. 13, Issue 12.

168   HICKMAN, L., James Lovelock on the value of skeptics and why Copenhagen was doomed, *Guardian,* 29. 3. 2010, http://www.theguardian.com/environment/blog/2010/mar/29/james-lovelock [cit. 17. 2. 2014].

169   ANDERSON, J. G. et al., Ozone destruction by chlorine radicals within the Antarctic vortex: The spatial and temporal evolution of ClO-O3 anticorrelation based on in situ ER-2 data, *Journal of Geophyscial Research,* 1989, Vol. 94, Issue D9.

170   MORAN, D. E. et al., Measuring sustainable development—nation by nation, *Ecological Economics,* 2008, Vol. 64, Issue 3.

171   BURNEY, J. A., Greenhouse gas mitigation by agricultural intensification, *Proceedings of the National Academy of Sciences,* 2010, Vol. 107, No. 26.

172   FIALA, N., Measuring sustainability: Why the ecological footprint is bad , economics and bad environmental science, *Ecological Economics,* 2008, Vol. 6, No. 7.

173   KREMLÍK, V., Opravdu ekologická stopa překračuje biokapacitu Země? *Osel.cz,* 30. 4. 2013, http://www.osel.cz/index.php?clanek=6873 [cit. 23. 2. 2014]. (in Czech language)

174   VAN DEN BERGH, J. C. J. M. et al., Spatial sustainability, trade and indicators: an evaluation of the 'ecological footprint', *Ecological Economics,* 1999, Vol 29, Issue 1.

175   EWING, B. et al. *Ecological Footprint Atlas 2010.* Oakland, Global Footprint Network, 2010, p. 90, http://www.scribd.com/doc/47405935/The-Ecological-Footprint-Atlas-2010-Global-Footprint-Network [cit. 17. 2. 2014].

176   SCHIERMEIER, Q. Eat less meat: UN climate-change report calls for change to human diet. *Nature,* 8.8.2019, https://www.nature.com/articles/d41586-019-02409-7

177   Halve meat and dairy production to protect climate, nature and health. *Greenpeace,* 5.3.2018, https://www.greenpeace.org/eu-unit/issues/nature-food/1100/halve-meat-and-dairy-production-to-protect-climate-nature-and-health/

178   HALL, M. Should there be a 'meat tax' to fight climate change? *Deutsche Welle,* 16.10.2018, https://www.dw.com/en/should-there-be-a-meat-tax-to-fight-climate-change/a-45868996 [cit. 10. 5. 2019],

179   Danish green party calls for red meat to be removed from Copenhagen school meals. *The Local,* 19.9.2019, https://www.thelocal.dk/20190919/danish-green-party-calls-for-red-meat-to-be-removed-from-copenhagen-school-meals [cit. 10. 10. 2019],

180   Ekologická stopa České republiky, *Ekologickastopa.cz,* 7. 2. 2012 [cit. 10. 5. 2013], (in Czech language) http://web.archive.org/web/20130503011049/http://www.ekologickastopa.cz:80/ekologicka-stopa/208-326-ekologicka-stopa-ceske-republiky.htm

181   ESQUIVEL, P. 15 years after Erin Brockovich, town still fearful of polluted water, *Los Angeles Times,* 12. 4. 2015, [cit. 25. 2. 2017], http://www.latimes.com/local/california/la-me-hinkley-20150413-story.html

182   http://www.rhine.org/what-we-do/journal-of-parapsychology.html [cit. 25. 2. 2017],

183   BAKER, M. 1500 scientists lift the lid on reproducibility, *Nature,* 2016, Vol. 533, Issue 7604.

184   IOANNIDIS, J. P. A. Why most published research findings are false, *PLoS Medicine,* 2005, Vol. 2, No. 8.

185   FREEDMAN, D. H. Lies, damned lies and medical science, *The Atlantic,* 4. 10. 2010, http://www.theatlantic.com/magazine/archive/2010/11/lies-damned-lies-and-medical-science/308269/ [cit. 25.

2. 2014]

186   JHA, A. Tenfold increase in scientific research papes retracted for fraud, *Guardian* 1. 10. 2012, http://www.theguardian.com/science/2012/oct/01/tenfold-increase-science-paper-retracted-fraud [cit. 25. 2. 2014].

187   FANG, F. C. et al. Misconduct accounts for the majority of retracted scientific publications, *Proceedings of the National Academy of Science*, 2013, Vol. 110, No. 3.

188   http://retractionwatch.com/ [cit. 25. 2. 2018].

189   STEEN, R. G. Retractions in the medical literature: how many patients are put at risk by flawed research? *Journal of Medical Ethics*, 2011, Vol. 37, No. 11.

190   NOVA, J. Climate money, *Science and Public Policy Institute*, 21. 7. 2009, http://scienceandpublicpolicy.org/images/stories/papers/originals/climate_money.pdf [cit. 25. 2. 2014].

191   WATTS, A. Friday funny: The newest member of the Union of Concerned Scientists, *Wattsupwiththat.com*, 11. 10. 2011, http://wattsupwiththat.com/2011/10/07/friday-funny-the-newest-member-of-the-union-of-concerned-scientists/ [cit. 25.2.2014].

192   MEHO, L. I. The rise and rise of citation analysis, *Physics World*, 2007, Vol. 20, No. 1.

193   SIMKIN, M. V., ROYCHOWDHURY, V. P. Read before you cite! *Complex Systems*, 2003, Vol. 14, No. 269, http://www.complex-systems.com/pdf/14-3-5.pdf [cit. 20.2.2017].

194   SHECKMAN, R. How journals like Nature, Cell and Science are damaging science, *Guardian*, 9. 12. 2013, http://www.theguardian.com/commentisfree/2013/dec/09/how-journals-nature-science-cell-damage-science [cit. 7. 7. 2014].

195   STRONG, M. *Where on Earth are we going?* Canada 1999, Random House.

196   STRONG, M. *Report to shareholders, Earth Inc. 1 January 2031* In: Where on Earth are we going? Canada 1999, Random House. http://www.harveymead.org/wp-content/uploads/2013/05/Strong.pdf [cit. 21. 2. 2014]

197   WARD, B., DUBOS, R. *Only one Earth*, New York 1972, W. W. Norton and Co.

198   STRONG, M. *Where on Earth are we going*, Canada 1999, Random House.

199   FROST, D. Maurice Strong interview, BBC 1972, interviewed by David Frost, http://www.youtube.com/watch?v=1YCatox0Lxo [cit. 20. 2. 2017]

200   JONES, F. O. For many a follower, sacred ground in Colorado, *New York Times*, 11. 1. 2008, http://www.nytimes.com/2008/01/11/

travel/escapes/11crestone.html?pagewanted=all&_r=0 [cit. 21. 2. 2014].

201 RAVERLY, A. T., *Refuge in Crestone: A sanctuary for interreligious dialogue*, London 2014, Lexington Books, p. 67.

202 WOOD, D. The wizard of Baca Grande, *West Magazine*, Kanada, květen 1990, http://www.scribd.com/doc/113290706/Maurice-Strong-Wizard-Baca-Grande-1990 [cit. 21. 2. 2014]

203 WOOD, D. The wizard of Baca Grande, *West Magazine*, Kanada, květen 1990, http://www.scribd.com/doc/113290706/Maurice-Strong-Wizard-Baca-Grande-1990 [cit. 21. 2. 2014]

204 Germany risks de-industrialisation, if energy shift fails, *Reuters* 21.1.2014, http://uk.reuters.com/article/2014/01/21/uk-germany-energy-gabriel-idUKBREA0K0CO$_2$0140121 [cit. 20. 2. 2014].

205 ROSETT, C., RUSSEL, G. At the United Nations: The curious career of Maurice Strong, *Fox News, 8. 2. 2008,* http://www.foxnews.com/story/2007/02/08/at-united-nations-curious-career-maurice-strong/ [cit. 17. 2. 2014].

206 Tianjin launches China's first comprehensive climate exchange, *China Daily,* 13. 10. 2016, http://www.chinadaily.com.cn/m/tianjin2012/2016-10/13/content_27049435.htm [cit. 17. 2. 2014].

207 McLEAN, J. We have been conned - an Independent review of the Intergovernmental Panel on Climate Change, *Science And Public Policy Institute,* 18. 8. 2010, http://scienceandpublicpolicy.org/images/stories/papers/originals/mclean_we_have_been_conned.pdf [cit. 17. 2. 2014]

208 Greenhouse gases and climate. UNEP / WMO / ICSU. Technical Information Circular 203. November 1985.

209 BRUNDTLAND, G. H. et al. *Our common future,* Report of the World Commission on Environment and Development, 1987.

210 IPCC, 2007, Assessment Report 4, Working Group 1, chapter 2.7.1.

211 LAFRAMBOISE, D. If IPCC meetings were televised, *Noconsensus.org,* 27. 1. 2011, http://nofrakkingconsensus.com/2011/01/27/if-ipcc-meetings-were-televised/ [cit. 7. 3. 2014].

212 Responses to IAC questionnaire, *InterAcademyCouncil.net,* 2010 http://reviewipcc.interacademycouncil.net/Comments.pdf [cit. 18. 12. 2013].

213 Ibidem, p. 344.

214 Ibidem, p. 47.

215 Ibidem, p. 278.

216 Ibidem, p. 43.

217 Ibidem, p. 578.

218 Ibidem, p. 134.

219   Summary for Policymakers. In: *First Assessment Report,* Intergovernmental Panel on Climate Change, Working Group 1, 1990, p. xii.

220   Summary for Policymakers, In: *Second Assessment Report,* Intergovernmental Panel on Climate Change, Working Group 1, 1995, p. xi.

221   SEITZ, F. Major deception on global warming, *Wall Street Journal,* 12. 6. 1996, http://www.albany.edu/~scifraud/data/sci_fraud_3771.html [cit. 2. 2. 2014].

222   RICE, D. Report: 95% odds that humans are to blame for warming, *USA Today,* 20. 8. 2013, http://www.usatoday.com/story/weather/2013/08/20/climate-change-global-warming-ipcc-report/2678683/ [cit. 2.2.2014]

223   Guidance notes for lead authors of the IPCC Fourth Assessment Report on addressing uncertainties, *Intergrovernmental Panel on Climate Change,* 2005, https://www.ipcc-wg1.unibe.ch/publications/supporting-material/uncertainty-guidance-note.pdf [cit. 2. 2. 2014]

224   PATT, A. G, SCHRAG, D. P. Using specific language to describe risk and probability, *Climatic Change,* 2003, Vol. 61, No. 1.

225   PEARCE, F. Hot warning, *NewScientist,* 22. 1. 2001, http://www.newscientist.com/article/dn345-hot-warning.html [cit. 2. 2. 2014]

226   Guidance Notes for Lead Authors of the IPCC Fourth Assessment Report on Addressing Uncertainties. https://www.ipcc.ch/report/ar4/wg1/uncertainty-guidance-note-for-the-fourth-assessment-report/ [cit. 17. 8. 2019].

227   RANDALLS, S. History of the 2°C climate target. *WIREs Climate Change,* 2010, Vol. 1, No. 4, http://www.nateko.lu.se/courses/NGEA08/doc/ann/Randalls-History_of_the_2degree_climate_target.pdf [cit. 17. 3. 2014].

228   World powers accept warming limit, *BBC* 9. 7. 2009 http://news.bbc.co.uk/2/hi/8142825.stm [cit. 7. 3. 2014].

229   EVERS, M. et al.. Climate catastrophe: a superstorm for global warming research, *Der Spiegel,* 1. 4. 2010, http://www.spiegel.de/international/world/climate-catastrophe-a-superstorm-for-global-warming-research-a-686697-8.html [cit. 7. 3. 2014].

230   CRUNDEN, E.A. Economic nightmare: By 2100, climate change could tank US GDP by 10.5%. *The National Interest,* 24.8.2019, https://nationalinterest.org/blog/buzz/economic-nightmare-2100-climate-change-could-tank-us-gdp-105-75776 [cit. 21. 11. 2019].

231   JOHANSSON, A. et al. Looking to 2060: Long-term global growth prospects. *OECD.* OECD Economic Policy Papers No. 03, November 2012.

232   DIFFENBAUGH, N.S. and Burke, M. Global warming has increased global economic inequality. *PNAS,* May 2019, Vol 116, Issue 20.

233 India no longer home to the largest number of poor. *Times of India*, 27. 6. 2018, https://timesofindia.indiatimes.com/india/india-no-longer-home-to-the-largest-no-of-poor-study/articleshow/64754988.cms [cit. 18. 3. 2019].

234 PEARCE, F. Flooded out, *New Scientist*, 5. 6. 1999.

235 WILSON, P. Glaciergate threatens a climate change, *The Australian*, 23. 1. 2010.

236 KOTLYAKOV, V. M. The future of glaciers under the expected climate warming, In: *Variations of Snow and Ice in the Past and at Present on a Global and Regional Scale*, UNESCO, Paris, 1996.

237 ROSE, D. Glacier scientist: I knew the data hadn't been verified. *Daily Mail*, 24. 1. 2010, http://www.dailymail.co.uk/news/article-1245636/Glacier-scientists-says-knew-data-verified.html#ixzz0dUo-PiTkG [cit. 18. 3. 2014].

238 BAGLA, P. No sign yet of Himalaya meltdown, Indian report finds, *Science*, 2009, Vol. 326, Issue 5955.

239 VAUGHAN, A. UN climate scientists review Himalayan glaciers claim, *The Guardian*, 19. 1. 2000, https://www.theguardian.com/environment/2010/jan/19/un-climate-scientists-himalayan-glaciers [cit. 7. 5. 2014].

240 BOOKER, Ch. Pachauri: the real story behind the Glaciergate scandal, *The Telegraph*, 23. 1. 2010, http://www.telegraph.co.uk/comment/columnists/christopherbooker/7062667/Pachauri-the-real-story-behind-the-Glaciergate-scandal.html [cit. 7. 5. 2014].

241 OWEN, L. A. Latest Pleistocene and Holocene glacier fluctuations. *Quaternary Science Reviews*, 2009, Vol. 28, Issue 21-22, figure 6.

242 NORTH, R. And now for Africagate, *EU Referendum* 7. 2. 2010 http://eureferendum.blogspot.cz/2010/02/and-now-for-africagate.html [cit. 2. 2. 2014]

243 KLIMÁNEK, O. Zpráva mezivládního klimatického panelu: 5600 nevědeckých citací, strach, katastrofy a politické motivy. Indie z panelu vystoupila, *Scinet.cz*, 30. 4. 2010. http://www.scinet.cz/zprava-mezivladniho-klimatickeho-panelu-5600-nevedeckych-citaci-strach-katastrofy-a-politicke-motivy-indie-z-panelu-vystoupila.html [cit. 2. 2. 2014] (in Czech language)

244 GOSSELIN, P. German state court orders Stefan Rahmstorf to cease and desist violating journalist's personal rights, *Notrickzone.com*, 7. 11. 2011, http://notrickszone.com/2011/11/07/german-court-orders-stefan-rahmstorf-to-cease-and-desist-violating-journalists-personal-rights/ [cit. 2.2.2014]

245 Sahel: The region is "ground zero" for climate change—Egeland, *IRINnews.org*, 2. 6. 2008, http://www.irinnews.org/report/78515/sahel-region-is-ground-zero-for-climate-change-egeland [cit. 1. 2. 2014]

246 GABBATISS, J. World's largest desert has grown even larger due

to climate change. *The Independent,* 29.3.2018. https://www.independent.co.uk/environment/sahara-worlds-largest-desert-climate-change-growth-global-warming-sahel-a8280361.html [cited 1.10.2019]

247   PEARCE, F. Africa's deserts are in spectacular retreat, *NewScientist,* 8. 9. 2002, http://www.newscientist.com/article/dn2811-africas-deserts-are-in-spectacular-retreat.html [cit. 1. 2. 2014]

248   WANG, Ch. et al. Multidecadal covariability of North Atlantic sea surface temperature, African dust, Sahel rainfall and Atlantic hurricanes, *Journal of Climate,* 2012, Vol. 25, No. 15.

249   OWEN, J. Sahara greening due to climate change? *National Geographic,* 31. 7. 2009, http://news.nationalgeographic.com/news/2009/07/090731-green-sahara.html [cit. 1. 2. 2014]

250   NORTH, R. Amazongate—the smoking gun, *EU Referendum,* 3. 7. 2010, http://eureferendum.blogspot.cz/2010/07/amazongate-smoking-gun.html [cit. 2.2.2014]

251   BOOKER, Ch. Amazongate: At last we reach the source, *Telegraph,* 10. 7. 2010, http://www.telegraph.co.uk/comment/columnists/christopherbooker/7883372/Amazongate-At-last-we-reach-the-source.html [cit. 9. 2. 2014].

252   *Outsourcing hot air,* Amsterdam 2012, Greenpeace International, http://www.greenpeace.org/international/Global/international/publications/forests/2012/REDD/OutsourcingHotAir.pdf [cit. 19. 2. 2014].

253   We reject REDD+ in all its versions—Letter from Chiapas, Mexico opposing REDD in California's Global Warming Solutions Act (AB 32), *Redd-monitor.org,* 30. 4. 2013, http://www.redd-monitor.org/2013/04/30/we-reject-redd-in-all-its-versions-letter-from-chiapas-mexico-opposing-redd-in-californias-global-warming-solutions-act-ab-32/ [cit. 19. 2. 2014].

254   IPCC, 2007, Assessment Report 4, Working Group 1, figure 3.14.

255   MARENGO, J. A. et al. The drought of 2010 in the context of historical droughts in the Amazon region, *Geophysical Research Letters,* 2011, Vol. 38, Issue 12.

256   HAFFER, J. Hypotheses to explain the origin of species in Amazonia, *Brazilian Journal of Biology,* 2008, Vol. 68, No. 4.

257   Are humans to blame for global warming? *Fora TV,* video of the debate at Commonwealth Club at San Francisco 27. 6. 2008, http://www.youtube.com/watch?v=d899rZFkIE4 [cit. 5. 5. 2016]

258   LAFRAMBOISE, D. Citizen audit, *Noconsensus.org,* 14. 4. 2010, http://noconsensus.org/CitizenAuditReport.pdf [cit. 17. 1. 2014].

259   PEARCE, F. Climate panel adopts controversial "grey" evidence. *Newscientist,* 26. 6. 2011, http://www.newscientist.com/article/dn21940-climate-panel-adopts-controversial-grey-evidence.html [cit. 3. 12. 2014].

260   WEBSTER, B., PENGAMENTA, R. UN must investigate warming 'bias', says former climate chief, *sunday Times,* 15. 2. 2010, http://www.thetimes.co.uk/tto/environment/article2144989.ece [cit. 20. 5. 2014].

261   HOUGHTON, J. Me and God, *sunday Telegraph,* 10. 6. 1995, http://john-adams.co.uk/wp-content/uploads/2010/02/houghton-and-god.pdf [cit. 17. 3. 2014].

262   IAC review of IPCC - Biographies of Review Committee. http://reviewipcc.interacademycouncil.net/IPCCbios.html [cit. 19. 2. 2014]

263   McINTYRE, S. Pachauri: No conflict of interest policy for AR5. *Climateaudit.org,* 18. 6. 2011, http://climateaudit.org/2011/06/18/pachauri-no-conflict-of-interest-policy-for-ar5/ [cit. 19. 2. 2014]

264   PEARCE, F. Climate panel adopts controversial "grey" evidence, *New Scientist,* 26. 6. 2011.

265   The science of climate change: Editorial, *Science,* 2001, Vol. 292, Issue 5520.

266   ALBERTS, B. The InterAcademy Council: Inventing a New Global Organization. *The Scientist,* March 2004, https://www.the-scientist.com/opinion-old/the-interacademy-council-inventing-a-new-global-organization-50426 [cit. 18. 08. 2019].

267   PACHAURI, R. The science is absolutely first rate, *Rediff.com,* 5. 6. 2007, http://www.rediff.com/news/2007/jun/05inter.htm [cit. 18. 12. 2013].

268   PACHAURI, R. Testimony before the US Senate Committee on Environment and Public Works, 25. 2. 2009, http://www.epw.senate.gov/public/index.cfm?FuseAction=Files.View&FileStore_id=d8c3fda8-d987-4d98-be99-c2c06395dfc4 [cit. 7. 2. 2014].

269   Responses to IAC questionnaire, *InterAcademzCouncil.net,* 2010, http://reviewipcc.interacademycouncil.net/Comments.pdf [cit. 18. 12. 2013].

270   GRAY, W. Statement of Dr. William Gray: The role of science in environmental policy-making, *US Senate Committee on Environment and Public Works,* 28. 9. 2005, http://www.epw.senate.gov/hearing_statements.cfm?id=246768 [cit. 7. 12. 2013].

271   Responses to IAC questionnaire, InterAcademyCouncil.net, 2010, p.57, http://reviewipcc.interacademycouncil.net/Comments.pdf [cit. 18. 12. 2013].

272   Ibidem, p. 31.

273   Ibidem, p. 180.

274   Ibidem, p. 96—97.

275   LAFRAMBOISE, D. *The deliquent teenager who was mistaken for the world's top climate expert,* Toronto 2011, Ivy Avenue Press, http://nofrakkingconsensus.files.wordpress.com/2011/10/delinquentteenag-

er_sample.pdf [cit. 15. 3. 2016]

276   McINTYRE, S. IPCC WG3 and the Greenpeace karaoke, *Climateaudit.org*, 14. 6. 2011, http://climateaudit.org/2011/06/14/ipcc-wg3-and-the-greenpeace-karaoke/ [cit. 2. 12. 2013]

277   RANDERSON, J. Western lifestyle unsustainable, says climate expert Rajendra Pachauri, *Guardian*, 28. 11. 2009, http://www.theguardian.com/environment/2009/nov/29/rajendra-pachauri-climate-warning-copenhagen [cit. 18. 12. 2013].

278   MAX, A. UN scientist: Fighting climate change saves costs, *USA Today*, 30. 11. 2011.

279   WELLS, K., ARI, L. How Al Gore amassed a USD 200 million fortune after presidential defeat, *Financial Post*, 6. 5. 2013.

280   Carlo Carraro biography, https://www.ipcc.ch/organization/short_bio_bureau/short-bio-Carraro.pdf [cit. 7. 5. 2017]

281   LAFRAMBOISE, D. Pachauri's latest award: Can you say conflict-of-interest? *Noconsensus.org*, 14. 7. 2014, http://nofrakkingconsensus.com/2013/07/14/pachauris-latest-award-can-you-say-conflict-of-interest/ [cit. 7. 5. 2017]

282   KLIMÁNEK, O. Šéf IPCC Rádžendra Pačaurí má z „ochrany" klimatu dojnou krávu—vítejte v klimatickém průmyslu, *Scinet.cz*, 2. 1. 2010, http://www.scinet.cz/sef-ipcc-radzendra-pacauri-ma-z-ochrany-klimatu-dojnou-kravu-vitejte-v-klimatickem-prumyslu.html [cit. 7. 5. 2014]

283   KPMG review of personal financial records of Dr. Rajendra K. Pachauri and other records of TERI for the period 1 April 2008 to 31 December 2009. *The Energy and Resources Institute*, March 2010, p. 13, https://www.scribd.com/document/36401538/KPMG-review-of-personal-financial-records-of-Dr-Rajendra-K-Pachauri-and-other-records-of-TERI-for-the-period-1-April-2008-to-31-December-2009 [cit. 7. 5. 2017]

284   PACHAURI, R.K. *Return to Almora*, Kalkata 2010, Rupa & Co.

285   In 2007 in the case Massachussetts vs EPA the Supreme Court decided that EPA must take a decision if the CO_2 emissions should be regulated under the Clean Air Act. In 2009 EPA decided they indeed must be regulated. It is called an "endangerment finding").

286   BERNER, R. A, KOTHAVALA, Z. Geocarb III: A revised model of atmospheric CO_2 over phanerosoic time, *American Journal of Science*, 2001, Vol. 301, No. 2.

287   DIPPERY, J. K. Effects of low and elevated CO_2 on C3 and C4 annuals, *Oecologia*, Vol. 101, Issue 1.

288   IDSO, C. D., IDSO, K.E. Energy, carbon dioxide and Earth's future: Pursuing the prudent path, *CO_2Science.org*, 1999, http://www.CO2science.org/about/position/energy.php [cit. 7. 2. 2014].

289   RIDDLEY, M. Getting crops ready for a warmer tomorrow, *Wall*

Street Journal, 7. 7. 2012, http://online.wsj.com/news/articles/SB20001 4240527023047086045775031909537677780 [cit. 20. 1. 2013]

290   AINSWORTH, E. A., ROGERS, A. The response of photosynthesis and stomatal conductance to rising CO_2: Mechanisms and environmental interactions, *Plant, Cell & Environment,* 2007, Vol. 30, Issue 3.

291   ZHOU, L. et al. Variations in northern vegetation activity inferred from satellite data of vegetation index during 1981 to 1999, *Journal of Geophysical Research,* 2011, Vol. 106, Issue D17.

292   TOL, R. J. S. The economic impact of climate change in the 20th and 21st centuries, Assessment Paper, *Copenhagen Consensus on Human Challenges 2011,* http://www.copenhagenconsensus.com/sites/default/files/climate_change.pdf [cit. 21. 8. 2014]

293   JONES, G. V. et al. Climate change and global wine quality, *Climatic Change,* 2008, Vol. 73, No 3.

294   LYONS, B. The backward attacks on Norman Borlaug, *Spiked,* 9. 9. 2009, http://www.spiked-online.com/newsite/article/7422#.WMkZ-Vm_hBsc [cit. 2. 2. 2017]

295   White House: Global warming out, 'global climate disruption' in, *FoxNews.com,* 16. 9. 2010, http://www.foxnews.com/politics/2010/09/16/white-house-global-warming-global-climate-disruption/ [cit. 1. 2. 2014]

296   DOUGLAS, J. H. Climate change—chilling possibilities. *Science News,* 1975, Vol. 107, 1. 3. 1975, p. 138, https://www.sciencenews.org/sites/default/files/8983 [cit. 20. 2. 2017]

297   LOTT, M. Eight botched environmental forecasts, *Foxnews. com,* 30. 12. 2010, http://www.foxnews.com/scitech/2010/12/30/botched-environmental-forecasts/ [cit. 21. 2. 2014].

298   GWYNNE, P. The cooling World, *Newsweek,* 28. 4. 1975.

299   PONTE, L. *The cooling,* New York 1976, Prentice-Hall, p. 237.

300   IPCC, Assessment Report 4, Working Group 1, Chapter 3.3.4.

301   BHATTACHARYA, A. et al. Drought in the Sahara-Sahel region: Lessons from dust records of the past 300 years, *American Geophysical Union,* Fall Meeting 2009, http://adsabs.harvard.edu/abs/2009AGUFMPP24B..02B [cit. 10. 2. 2017]

302   GUPTA, A. K et al. Abrupt changes k in Holocene Asian southwest monsoon and their links to the North Atlantic Ocean, *Nature,* Vol. 421, 23. 1. 2003, p. 354-357.

303   MARKONIS, Y. et al. Persistent multi-scale fluctuations shift European hydroclimate to its millennial boundaries. *Nature Communications,* May 2018, Vol. 9, Article No: 1767 (2018) [cit. 14. 7. 2018]

304   PIELKE, R. Brisbane floods in historical context, *Blogspot. cz,* 12. 1. 2011, http://rogerpielkejr.blogspot.cz/2011/01/bris-

bane-floods-in-historical-context.html [cit. 14. 2. 2014]

305   BRÁZDIL, R. Meteorologické extrémy a povodně v České republice—Přirozený trend nebo následek globálního oteplování? *Geografie—Sborník České geografické společnosti*, 2002, Vol 107, No. 4, p. 349–370, http://www.kar.zcu.cz/texty/Brazdil2002.htm [cit. 18. 7. 2014]. (in Czech)

306   MUDELSEE, M. et al. No upward trends in the occurrence of extreme floods in central Europe, *Nature*, 2003, Vol. 425. No. 6954.

307   BRÁZDIL, R. et al. Studium historických povodní v České republice jako příspěvek k historické hydrologii. *In: Bratislava, Hydrologické dni 2005*, Slovenský výbor pre hydrológiu a Český výbor pro hydrologii, Bratislava, p. 311-329. http://data.geogr.quonia.cz/Reznickova_Klimatologie/Clanek_Hydrologicke_dni_2005.pdf [cit. 21. 2. 2014] (in Czech)

308   VAŠKŮ, Z. Naše malé pluviály, *Vesmír*, 1997, Vol. 76, Issue 512, http://www.vesmir.cz/clanek/nase-male-pluvialy-(2) [cit. 19. 2. 2014] (in Czech)

309   KOCH, J., CLAGUE, J. J. Are insolation and sunspot activity the primary drivers Holocene glacier fluctuations? *PAGES News*, 2006, Vol. 14, No. 3.

310   ŠPIKOVÁ, Z. Největší přírodní katastrofy na území českých zemí za posledních 1,000 let, Diploma thesis, Olomouc 2009, Universita Palackého, Czech Republic. (in Czech)

311   VAŠKŮ, Z. Půda je nenahraditelná, *Ekolist*, 25. 4. 2008, http://ekolist.cz/cz/publicistika/rozhovory/zdenek-vasku-puda-je-nenahraditelna [cit. 19. 2. 2014] (in Czech)

312   KENNETT, D., KENNET J. P. Early state formation in southern Mesopotamia: Sea levels, shorelines, and climate change, *The Journal of Island and Coastal Archaeology*, 2006, Vol. 1, No. 1.

313   DOYLE, A. "Dying oceans rising faster than predicted, UN warns in stark report. *Climate Home News*, 25.9.2019. https://www.climatechangenews.com/2019/09/25/dying-oceans-rising-faster-predicted-un-warns-stark-report/ [cit. 18. 10. 2019]

314   Collapse Of Antarctic Ice Sheet Would Likely Put Washington, D.C. Largely Underwater. *Science Daily*, 6.2.2009, https://www.sciencedaily.com/releases/2009/02/090205142132.htm [cit. 18. 1. 2014]

315   HANSEN, J., SATO, M. Paleoclimate implications for human-made climate change, In: *Proceedings of the Milutin Milankovitch 130th Anniversary Symposium*, 2012, Figure 7, http://arxiv.org/ftp/arxiv/papers/1105/1105.0968.pdf [cit. 18. 1. 2014]

316   WATTS, A. The 500 year FUD about sea levels, *Wattsupwiththat.com*, 18. 10. 2011, http://wattsupwiththat.com/2011/10/18/the-500-year-fud-about-sea-levels/ [cit. 19. 1. 2014]

317   JEVREJEVA, S. et al. Recent global sea level acceleration started

over 200 years ago? *Geophysical Research Letters,* 2008, Vol. 35, Issue 8.

318   GRINSTED, A. et al.. Reconstructing sea level from paleo and projected temperatures 200 to 2100 AD, Climate Dynamics, 2010, Vol. 34, No. 4.

319   SIMMS, A. Farewell Tuvalu, *Guardian,* 29. 10. 2001, http://www.theguardian.com/comment/story/0,3604,582445,00.html [cit. 7. 1. 2014].

320   WEBB, A. P., KENCH, P. S. The dynamic response of reef islands to sea level rise: evidence from multi-decadal analysis of island change in the Central Pacific, *Global and Planetary Change,* 2010, Vol. 72, Issue 3.

321   OMIDI, M. Maldives sends climate SOS with undersea cabinet. *Reuters,* 17. 10. 2009, http://www.reuters.com/article/2009/10/17/us-maldives-environment-idUSTRE59G0P120091017 [cit. 20. 3. 2014].

322   KENCH, P. S. et al. Holocene reef growth in the Maldives: Evidence of mid-Holocene sea-level highstand in the central Indian Ocean, *Geology,* 2009, Vol. 35, No. 5.

323   MÖRNER, N. A. et al., New perspectives for the future of the Maldives, *Global Planetary Change,* 2004, Vol. 40, Issues 1-2.

324   MÖRNER, N. A. Open letter to President Mohamed Nasheed of the Maldives, Stockolm, 20. 10. 2009, http://scienceandpublicpolicy.org/images/stories/papers/originals/maldives_letter.pdf [cit. 23. 3. 2014].

325   CARMINATI, E., DOGLIONI, C. Appenines subduction-related subsidence of Venice, Italy, *Geophysical Research Letters,* 2003, Vol. 30, No. 13.

326   Venice to suffer from fewer storm surges, *ScienceDaily.com,* 10. 6. 2011, http://www.sciencedaily.com/releases/2011/06/110610094456.htm [cit. 10. 10. 2014].

327   GOKLANY, I. M. Death and death rates due to extreme weather events—Global and US trends 1900—2006, *Policy Paper for Civil Society Coalition on Climate Change,* November 2007, http://goklany.org/library/deaths%20death%20rates%20from%20extreme%20events%20 2007.pdf [cit. 21. 12. 2015]

328   BATTY, D. UK heatwave may have caused hundreds of deaths. The Guardian, 10.7.2010. https://www.theguardian.com/uk/2010/jul/10/uk-heatwave-deaths-rise-elderly [cit. 12. 2. 2014]

329   French heat toll almost 15,000, *BBC,* 25. 9. 2003, http://news.bbc.co.uk/2/hi/europe/3139694.stm [cit. 12. 2. 2014]

330   KYSELÝ, J. Mortality and displaced mortality during heatwaves in the Czech Republic, *International Journal of Biometeorology,* 2004, Vol. 49, No. 2.

331   BACCINI, M. et al. Impact of summer heat on urban popula-

tion mortality in Europe during the 1990s: An evaluation of years of life lost adjusted for harvesting, *PLoS ONE,* 2013, Vol. 8, No. 7.

332   PIRARD, P. et al. Summary of the mortality impact assessment of the 2003 heatwave in France, *Eurosurveillance.org,* 2005, Vol. 10, Issue 7, http://www.eurosurveillance.org/ViewArticle.aspx?ArticleId=554 [cit. 23. 2. 2017]

333   TIEN, J. H. et al. Herald waves of cholera in nineteenth century London, *Journal of the Royal Society—Interface,* 2011, Vol. 8, No. 58.

334   KYSELÝ J., PLAVCOVÁ, E. Declining impacts of hot spells on mortality in the Czech Republic, 1986-2009: adaptation to climate change? *Climatic Change,* 2012, Vol. 113, No. 2.

335   CHESTNUT, L. G. et al. analysis of differences in hot-weather-related mortality across 44 US metropolitan areas. *Environment Science and Policy,* 1998, Vol. 1, Issue 1.

336   FALAGAS, M. E. et al. Seasonality of mortality: the September phenomenon in Mediterranean countries, *Canadian Medical Association Journal,* 2009, Vol. 181, No. 8.

337   PELL, J. P., COBBE, S. M. Seasonal variations in coronary heart disease, *International Journal of Medicine,* 1999, Vol. 92, Issue 12.

338   KLONER, R. A. et al. When throughout the year is coronary death most likely to occur? A 12-year population-based analysis of more than 220,000 cases, *Clinical Investigation and Reports,* 1999, Vol. 100, Issue 15.

339   KUNST, A. E. et al. The decline in winter excess mortality in the Netherlands, *International Journal of Epidemiology,* 1991, Vol. 20, No. 4.

340   MARTENS, P., HUYNEN, M. Will global climate change reduce thermal stress in the Netherlands? *Epidemiology,* 2001, Vol. 12, No. 6.

341   GOKLANY, I. M. Deaths and death rates from extreme weather events: 1900-2008, *Journal of American Physicians and Surgeons,* 2009, Vol. 14, No. 4.

342   CARRINGTON, D., HILAIRE, E. The polar bear who died of climate change, *Guardian,* 6. 8. 2013, http://www.theguardian.com/environment/picture/2013/aug/06/polar-bear-climate-change-sea-ice [cit. 7. 1. 2017]

343   LIEW, J. Starving polar bears turn to cannibalism, *Telegraph,* 8. 12. 2009, http://www.telegraph.co.uk/earth/wildlife/6760103/Starving-polar-bears-turn-to-cannibalism.html [cit. 10. 1. 2014]

344   HOAG, H. Polar bears diverged from brown bears fairly recently, *Scientific American,* 10. 5. 2014, http://www.scientificamerican.com/article/polar-bears-diverged-from-brown-bears-fairly-recently/ [cit. 17. 11. 2014].

345   IFFT, G. N. The changing Arctic, *Monthly Weather Review*, November 1922, p. 589, https://docs.lib.noaa.gov/rescue/mwr/050/mwr-050-11-0589a.pdf [cit. 7. 2. 2017]

346   BENGTSON, L. The early 20th century warming in the Arctic—A possible mechanism, *Journal of Climate*, 2004, Vol. 17, No. 20.

347   IPCC, 2007, Assessment Report 4, Working Group 1, FAQ 4.1.

348   CROCKFORD, S. J. The IUCN polar bear specialist group says its global population estimate was a "qualified guess", *Polarbearscience.com*, 30. 5. 2014, http://polarbearscience.com/2014/05/30/iucn-polar-bear-specialist-group-says-its-global-population-estimate-was-a-qualified-guess/ [cit. 7. 7. 2014].

349   FEARS, D. Polar bears will continue as 'threatened,' not 'endangered', *Washington Post*, 22. 12. 2010, http://www.washingtonpost.com/wp-dyn/content/article/2010/12/22/AR2010122206411.html [cit. 27. 2. 2014]

350   CAMPBELL, C., LUNAU, K. The war over the polar bear. *Macleans.ca*, 25. 1. 2008, https://www.biologicaldiversity.org/news/media-archive/PolarBearMacleans1-23-08.pdf [cit. 20. 2. 2014]

351   MONNET, Ch. et al. Observations of mortality associated with extended open-water swimming by polar bears in the Alaskan Beaufort Sea, *Polar Biology*, 2006, Vol. 29, No. 8.

352   Transcript of Charles Monnet interview 23. 2. 2011, http://www.peer.org/assets/docs/doi/7_28_11_Monnett-IG_interview_transcript.pdf [cit. 14. 2. 2014]

353   BOOKER, Ch. Polar bear expert barred by global warmists, *Telegraph*, 27. 6. 2009, http://www.telegraph.co.uk/comment/columnists/christopherbooker/5664069/Polar-bear-expert-barred-by-global-warmists.html [cit. 3. 7. 2015]

354   HARVEY, J.A. et al. Internet Blogs, Polar Bears, and Climate-Change Denial by Proxy. *Bioscience*, Aprl 2018, Vol 68, Issue 4. https://academic.oup.com/bioscience/article/68/4/281/4644513 [cit. 3. 10. 2019]

355   LAFRAMBOISE, D. Was this zoologist punished for telling school kids politically incorrect facts about polar bears? *Financial Post*, 16.10.2019, https://business.financialpost.com/opinion/was-this-zoologist-punished-for-telling-school-kids-politically-incorrect-facts-about-polar-bears [cit. 13. 11. 2019]

356   ADAM, D. Carbon emissions creating acidic oceans not seen since dinosaurs, *Guardian*, 10. 3. 2009, http://www.theguardian.com/environment/2009/mar/10/carbon-emissions-oceans-copenhagen [cit. 13. 2. 2014]

357   TURLEY, C. et al. Reviewing the impact of increased atmospheric CO_2 on oceanic pH and the marine ecosystem. In: Schellnhuber. H.J. et al. (eds.), *Avoiding Dangerous Climate Change*, Cambridge 2006, Cambridge University Press, p. 65.

358   BERNER, R. A., KOTHAVALA, Z. Geocarb III: A revised model of atmospheric CO_2 over phanerosoic time, *American Journal of Science*, 2001, Vol. 301, No. 2.

359   JACOBSON, M. Z. Studying ocean acidification with conservative, stable numerical schemes for nonequilibrium air-ocean exchange and ocean equilibrium chemistry, *Journal of Geophysical Research*, 2005, Vol. 110, Issue D07302.

360   PELECHERO, C. et al. Pre-industrial to modern interdecadal variability in coral reef pH, *Science*, 2005, Vol. 309, No. 5744.

361   DE'ATH, G. et al. Declining coral calcification on the Great Barrier Reef, *Science*, 2009, Vol. 323, No. 5910.

362   McINTYRE, S. "Unprecedented" in the past 153 Years, *Climateaudit.org*, 3. 6. 2009, https://climateaudit.org/2009/06/03/unprecedented-in-at-least-the-past-153-years/ [cit. 11. 2. 2014]

363   BESSAT, F., BUIGUES, D. Two centuries of variation in coral growth in a massive Porites colony from Moorea (French Polynesia): a response of ocean-atmosphere variability from south central Pacic, *Paleogeography, Paleoclimatology, Paleoecology*, 2001, Vol. 175, Issues 1-4, p. 381-392.

364   McNEIL B. I. et al. Coral reef calcification and climate change: the effect of ocean warming, *Geophysical Research Letters*, 2004, Vol. 31, Issue 22.

365   LANDSEA, Ch. Chris Landsea resignation letter. *Climatechangefacts*, 17. 1. 2005 http://www.climatechangefacts.info/ClimateChange-Documents/LandseaResignationLetterFromIPCC.htm [cit. 20. 2. 2014]

366   IPCC, 2007, Assessment Report 4, Working Group 1, Chapter 10.3.6.3.

367   HOLLAND, G., WEBSTER, P. Heightened tropical cyclone activity in the North Atlantic: natural variability or climate trend? *Philosophical Transactions of the Royal Society*, 2007, Vol. 365, No. 1860.

368   PIELKE, R. Updated major hurricane drought figure, *Blogspot.cz*, 9. 9. 2013, http://rogerpielkejr.blogspot.cz/2013/09/updated-major-hurricane-drought-figure.html [cit. 20. 2. 2014]

369   PIELKE, R. The NHC Sandy report, *Blogspot.cz*, 12. 2. 2013, http://rogerpielkejr.blogspot.cz/2013/02/the-nhc-sandy-report.html [cit. 21. 2. 2014]

370   PIELKE, R. Sandy and the top 20 normalized US hurricane losses, *Blogspot.cz*, 13. 10. 2012, http://rogerpielkejr.blogspot.cz/2012/10/sandy-and-top-20-normalized-us.html [cit. 10. 2. 2014]

371   PIELKE, R. Hurricanes and human choice, *The Wall Street Journal*, 31. 10. 2012, http://online.wsj.com/news/articles/SB10001424052970204840504578089413659452702 [cit. 17. 1. 2014].

372   PIELKE, R. et al. Normalized hurricane damages in the United

States 1900—2005, *Natural Hazards Review,* 2008, Vol. 9, No. 1.

373 MUSTAIN, A. Emperor penguin numbers double previous estimates, *Livescience,* 13. 4. 2012, http://www.livescience.com/19677-emperor-penguin-numbers-double-previous-estimates-satellites-show.html [cit. 15. 12. 2013]

374 BAKER, A. J. et al. Multiple gene evidence for expansion of extant penguins out of Antarctica due to global cooling, *Proceedings of the Royal Society B: Biological Sciences,* 2006, Vol. 273, No. 1582.

375 EMSLIE, S. D. et al. A 45,000 yr record of Adélie penguins and climate change in the Ross Sea, Antarctica, *Geology,* 2007, Vol. 35, No. 1.

376 MULWANEY, R. et al. Recent Antarctic Peninsula warming relative to Holocene climate and ice shelf history, *Nature,* 2012, Vol. 489, No. 7414.

377 DORAN, P. T. et al. Antarctic climate cooling and terrestrial ecosystem response, *Nature,* 2002, Vol. 415, Issue 7380.

378 TURNER, J. et al. Absence of 21st century warming on Antarctic Peninsula consistent with natural variability, Nature, 2016, Vol. 535, Issue 7612, p. 411–415.

379 DORAN, P., Zimmerman, K. Examining the Scientific Consensus on Climate Change. EOS, 2009 Vol. 90, Issue 3.

380 MARLON, J. R. et al. Long-term perspective on wildfires in the western USA, *Proceedings of the National Academy of Sciences,* 2012, Vol. 109, No 9.

381 TOBIN, M. Timber harvest falls in national forests, *Ecowest. org,* 28. 5. 2013, http://www.ecowest.org/2013/05/28/timber-harvest-falls-in-national-forests/ [cit. 8. 7. 2014].

382 SZALAY, J. Giant Sequoias and Redwoods: The Largest and Tallest Trees, *Livescience,* 4. 5. 2017, https://www.livescience.com/39461-sequoias-redwood-trees.html [cit. 8. 7. 2017].

383 FISCHER, D. Climate change has doubled forest mortality, *Dailyclimate.org,* 22. 1. 2009, http://www.dailyclimate.org/tdc-newsroom/trees/climate-change-has-doubled-forest-mortality [cit. 18. 7. 2014].

384 CRICHTON, M. *State of fear,* New York, 2004, Harper Collins.

385 Mac CLEERY, D. Re-inventing the US Forest Service: Evolution from custodial management, to production forestry, to ecosystem management. In: *Re-inventing forestry agencies. Experiences of institutional restructuring in Asia and the Pacific.* DURST, P. et al. (eds.), Bangkok 2008, Food and Agriculture Organization of the United Nations, http://www.fao.org/docrep/010/ai412e/AI412E06.htm [cit. 20. 7. 2014]

386 MANNING, R. Spotted owl surviving 20 years after controversial decision, *Oregon Public Broadcasting,* 24. 6. 2010, http://www.opb.org/news/article/spotted-owl-surviving-20-years-after-controversial-de-

cision/ [cit. 20. 7. 2014].

387   ANTHONY, B., CLARK, D. A. Burned landscape of southwest Oregon: What's in it for Northern Spotted Owls? In: *Fire Science Brief,* 2008, Issue 15 (October), p. 3. http://www.firescience.gov/projects/ briefs/04-2-1-52_FSBrief15.pdf [cit. 10. 10. 2015]

388   COPÉE, B. *To strašné vedro,* Luxembourg, 2005, European Commission - General Directorate of Environment. (in Czech), http:// ec.europa.eu/environment/pubs/pdf/weather/cs.pdf [cit. 3. 4. 2016]

389   *Forest Fires in Europe 2010,* Joint Research Centre Scientific and Technical Reports, Report No. 11, Lucemburk 2011, European Commission. http://forest.jrc.ec.europa.eu/media/cms_page_media/9/forest-fires-in-europe-2010.pdf [cit. 7. 1. 2017]

390   WALLENIUS, T. Major decline in fires in coniferous forests—reconstructing the phenomenon and seeking for the cause. *Silva Fennica,* 2011, Vol. 45, No. 1.

391   Amazon fires increase by 84% in one year - space agency. *BBC,* 21.8.2019, https://www.bbc.com/news/world-latin-america-49415973 [cit. 17. 10. 2019].

392   Fires in Brazil. *Earth Observatory - NASA.* Updated 22.8. 2019. https://earthobservatory.nasa.gov/images/145464/fires-in-brazil [cit. 18. 10. 2019].

393   GORE, A. *Earth in the Balance,* Boston 1992, Houghton Mifflin.

394   BREZINA, I. Sebeobrana proti klimatickému lháři, *Neviditelnypes.cz,* 1. 11. 2007, http://neviditelnypes.lidovky.cz/ekologie-kurz-sebeobrany-proti-klimatickemu-lhari-f81-/p_spolecnost. aspx?c=A071031_120815_p_spolecnost_wag [cit. 18. 2. 2014].

395   PIELKE, R. et al. Normalized hurricane damages in the United States 1900—2005, *Natural Hazards Review,* 2008, Vol. 9, No. 1.

396   LOUGH, J.M., BARNES, D.J. Environmental controls on growth of the massive coral Porites, *Journal of Experimental marine Biology and Ecology,* 2000, Vol 245, Issue 2.

397   ROBERTS, D. An interview with accidental movie star, *Grist.org,* 9. 5. 2006, http://grist.org/article/roberts2/ [cit. 21. 3. 2014].

398   TAPPER, J. Al Gore's inconvenient truth—a 30,000 USD utility bill, *ABC News,* 26. 2. 2007, http://abcnews.go.com/Politics/Global-Warming/story?id=2906888 [cit. 12. 8. 2014].

399   MOSER, S. Kleinhückelkotten, S. Good Intents, but Low Impacts: Diverging Importance of Motivational and Socioeconomic Determinants Explaining Pro-Environmental Behavior, Energy Use, and Carbon Footprint. *Environment and Behavior,* 2018, Vol. 50, Issue 6.

400   BRODER, J. M. Gore's dual role: Advocate and investor, *New York Times,* 2. 11. 2009, http://www.nytimes.com/2009/11/03/business/energybn-environment/03gore.html?_r=0 [cit. 17. 2. 2014].

401   Ecological disaster feared, *The Vancouver sun,* 11. 5. 1982, http://wattsupwiththat.com/2011/01/19/same-news-different-century/ The article provides a link to the data source: online archiv https://news.google.com/ [cit. 1. 1. 2017]

402   BURN-CALLANDER, R. We're facing a mass extinction event,' claims Bob Geldof, *Telegraph,* 3. 10. 2013, http://www.telegraph.co.uk/earth/environment/globalwarming/10353206/Were-facing-a-mass-extinction-event-claims-Bob-Geldof.html [cit. 3. 1. 2014]

403   VERKAIK, R. Just 96 months to save world, says Prince Charles. *The Indepdendent,* 9. 7. 2009, http://www.independent.co.uk/environment/green-living/just-96-months-to-save-world-says-prince-charles-1738049.html [cit. 7. 7. 2014].

404   McGUIRRE, B. *Seven years to save the planet. The questions, the answers.* London 2008, Weidenfeld and Nicolson.

405   CUMMINGS, W. 'The world is going to end in 12 years if we don't address climate change,' Ocasio-Cortez says. *USA Today,* 22.1.2019. https://eu.usatoday.com/story/news/politics/onpolitics/2019/01/22/ocasio-cortez-climate-change-alarm/2642481002/

406   COUZENS, G. Baby girl survives after being shot in the chest in parents' 'global warming suicide pact', *DailyMail,* 1. 3. 2010, http://www.dailymail.co.uk/news/article-1254619/Baby-girl-survives-shot-chest-parents-global-warming-suicide-pact.html [cit. 21. 2. 2014].

407   JONES, M. K. et al. The impact of climate change on obsessive compulsive checking concerns, *Australian and New Zealand Journal of Psychiatry,* 2012, Vol. 46, No. 3.

408   WOLF, J., SALO, R. Water, water, everywhere, not qany drop to drink: climate change delusion, *New Zealand Journal of Psychiatry,* 2008, Vol. 42, No. 4.

409   School strike for climate - save the world by changing the rules | Greta Thunberg | TEDxStockholm 2018. https://youtu.be/EAmmUIEsN9A

410   You did not act in time': Greta Thunberg's full speech to MPs. *The Guardian.* 23.4.2019. https://www.theguardian.com/environment/2019/apr/23/greta-thunberg-full-speech-to-mps-you-did-not-act-in-time

411   MORNINGSTAR, C. The manufacturing of Greta Thurnberg. *The Art of Annihilation,* 17.1.2019, http://www.theartofannihilation.com/the-manufacturing-of-greta-thunberg-for-consent-the-political-economy-of-the-non-profit-industrial-complex/ [cit. 21. 9. 2019].

412   Extinction Rebellion co-founder used 'psychedelic medicine' for inspiration. *ITV,* 1.9.2019, https://www.itv.com/news/2019-09-01/extinction-rebellion-co-founder-used-psychedelic-medicine-for-inspiration

413   WONG, S. Extinction Rebellion founder calls for mass psychedelic disobedience. *New Scientist,* 19.8.2019 https://www.newscientist.

com/article/2213787-extinction-rebellion-founder-calls-for-mass-psy-chedelic-disobedience/ [cit. 21. 9. 2019].

414   BRANNEN, P. Earth is not in the midst of a sixth mass extinction. *The Atlantic,* 13.6.2017, https://www.theatlantic.com/science/archive/2017/06/the-ends-of-the-world/529545/ [cit. 21. 9. 2019].

415   In Chapter VIII "Response to Crisis" Kuhn provides a number of examples how harshly the mainstream treats those who discover "anomalies" that do not fit into the established paradigm.

416   MANN, M. et al. Northern Hemisphere temperatures during the past millennium: inferences, uncertainties, and limitations, *Geophysical Research Letters,* 1999, Vol. 26, Issue 6.

417   World Meteorological Organization, WMO statement on the status of the world climate, Report. No 913, 1999, http://nichol.as/papers/wmo913.pdf [cit. 2. 2. 2014]

418   IPCC, 2001, Third Assessment Report, Working Group 1, Summary for Policymakers.

419   JONES, P. D. et al. High-resolution paleoclimatic records for the last millennium: interpretation, integration and comparison with General Circulation Model control-run temperatures, *Holocene,* 1998, Vol. 8, Issue 4.

420   JONES, P. D., MANN, M. Climate over past millenia, *Reviews of Geophysics,* 2004, Vol. 42, Issue RG2002.

421   MANN, M. et al. Northern Hemisphere temperatures during the past millennium: inferences, uncertainties, and limitations, *Geophysical Research Letters,* 1999, Vol. 26, Issue 6.

422   JONES, P. D. et al. The evolution of climate over the last millennium, *Science,* 2001, Vol. 292, Issue 5517.

423   BRIFFA, K. R. et al. Low-frequency temperature variations from a northern tree ring density network, *Journal of Geophysical Research,* Vol. 106, Issue D3.

424   BRIFFA, K. R. et al. Unusual twentieth-century summer warmth in a 1,000 year temperature record from Siberia, *Nature,* 1995, Vol. 376, 13. 7. 1995.

425   MANN, M. E. et al. Proxy-based reconstructions of hemispheric and global surface temperature variations over the past two millennia, *Proceedings of the National Academy of Sciences,* 2008, Vol. 105, No. 36.

426   MANN, M. et al. Northern Hemisphere temperatures during the past millennium: inferences, uncertainties, and limitations, *Geophysical Research Letters,* 1999, Vol. 26, Issue 6.

427   ESPER, J. Low-frequency signals in long tree-ring chronologies

for reconstructing past temperature variability, *Science,* 2002, Vol. 295, Issue 5563.

428   MOBERG A. et al. Highly variable Northern Hemisphere temperatures reconstructed from low- and high resolution proxy data, *Nature,* 2005, Vol. 433, Issue 7026.

429   LOEHLE, C. A 2,000-year global temperature reconstruction based on non-tree ring proxies, *Energy & Environment,* 2007, Vol. 18, No. 7-8.

430   LJUNGQVIST, F. C. A new reconstruction of temperature variability in the extra-tropical Northern Hemisphere during the last two millennia, *Geografiska Annaler Series A,* 2010, Vol. 92, Issue 3.

431   Climategate email 1008619994.

432   SOON, W., BALLIUNAS, S. Proxy climatic and environmental changes of the past 1,000 years, *Climate Research,* 2003, Vol. 23, No. 2.

433   Climategate email 1047474776 of 11. 3. 2003.

434   Climategate email 1051190249 of 24. 4. 2003.

435   Climate change denier Willie Soon questioned over Koch, Exxon funding at CFACT Campus event at University of Wisconsin 3. 4. 2013, *YouTube channel Polluterwatch,* 8. 4 2013, https://www.youtube.com/watch?v=6WgTq57XQno [cit. 7. 7. 2016]

436   MOBERG A. et al. Highly variable Northern Hemisphere Temperatures reconstructed from low- and high resolution proxy data, *Nature,* 2005, Vol. 433, Issue 7026, this version of the figure includes only indirect proxy data and does not combine it with instrumental measurements, adapted from http://www.CO$_2$science.org/data/mwp/studies/l1_mobergnh.php [cit. 7. 2. 2047]

437   McINTYRE, S., McKITRICK, R. Corrections to the Mann et al. 1998 proxy data base and Northern hemispheric average temperature series, *Energy and Environment,* 2003, Vol. 14, No. 6.

438   McINTYRE, S., McKITRICK. Hockey sticks, principal components, and spurious significance, *Geophysical Research Letters,* 2005, Vol. 32, Issue 3.

439   Von STORCH, H. et al. Reconstructing past climate from noisy data, *Science,* 2004, Vol. 306, Issue 5696.

440   REGALADO, A. In climate debate the hockey stick leads to a face-off, *Wall Street Journal,* 14. 2. 2005, http://online.wsj.com/news/articles/SB110834031507653590 [cit. 2. 2. 2005]

441   BARTON, J., WHITFIELD, E. Letter from Congress to Dr. Mann, 23. 6. 2005, http://www.intellectualtakeout.org/library/primary-sources/letter-dr-michael-mann [cit. 2. 2. 2014]

442 . WEGMAN, E. J. et al. Ad hoc committee report on the hockey stick global climate reconstruction, *Science and Public Policy Institute,* 26. 4. 2006, http://scienceandpublicpolicy.org/science-papers/reprint/

ad-hoc-report [cit. 2. 2. 2014]

443   McLEAN, J. Prejudiced authors, prejudiced findings: Did the UN bias its attribution of "global warming" to humankind? *Science and Public Policy Institute,* 7/2008, http://scienceandpublicpolicy.org/images/stories/papers/originals/McLean_IPCC_bias.pdf [cit. 7.6. 2016]

444   NORTH, G. R. et al. *Surface temperature reconstructions for the last 2,000 years,* Washington 2006, The National Academies Press, https://climatechangelive.org/img/fck/file/surftemps2000yrs.pdf [cit. 7. 2. 2017]

445   BRUMFIELD, G. Academy affirms hockey stick, *Nature,* 2006, Vol. 441, No. 7097.

446   McINTYRE, S. AR4 on 1998 was the warmest year. *Climateaudit.org,* 3. 5. 2010, http://climateaudit.org/2010/05/03/ar4-on-1998-was-the-warmest-year/ [cit. 7. 2. 2014]

447   Climategate email No 1154484340.

448   Climategate email No 1177890796.

449   ORLOWSKI, A. Info commissioner finds saintly CRU crew guilty, *The Register,* 8. 7. 2010, http://www.theregister.co.uk/2010/07/08/foia_climategate/ [cit. 14. 2. 2014].

450   BRIFFA, K. et al. Annual climate variability in the Holocene: interpreting the message of ancient trees, *Quaternary Science Reviews,* 2000, Vol. 19, Issues 1–5, p. 87–105.

451   MONTFORT, A. The Yamal deception. *Bishop Hill blog,* 9.5.2012, http://www.bishop-hill.net/blog/2012/5/9/the-yamal-deception.html [cited 14. 2. 2019].

452   McINTYRE, S. The most influential tree in the world, *Climateaudit.org,* 30. 9. 2009, http://climateaudit.org/2009/09/30/yamal-the-forest-and-the-trees/ [cit. 14. 2. 2014].

453   McKITRICK, R. Defects in key climate data uncovered, *Financial Post,* 1. 10. 2009, http://climaterealizts.com/?id=4123 [cit. 14. 2. 2014].

454   HANTEMIROV, R. M, SHIYATOV, S. G. A continuous mutimillenial ring-width chronology in Yamal, northwestern Siberia, *The Holocene,* 2002, Vol. 12, Issue 6.

455   McINTYRE, S. Appeal of UEA's Yamal FOI refusal, *Climateaudit.org,* 19. 9. 2011, http://climateaudit.org/2011/09/19/appeal-of-ueas-yamal-foi-refusal/ [cit. 6. 2. 2014]

456   COSTELLA J. (ed). *Climategate emails,* The Lavoisier Group, March 2010, http://www.lavoisier.com.au/articles/greenhouse-science/climate-change/climategate-emails.pdf [cit. 5. 1. 2017]

457   WANNER, H. and RITZ, S. HOLCAT—Web based Holocene climate atlas. Oeschger Centre for Climate Research, Bern, 2011. Figure 36 on page 25 (Greenland, Vinther et al. 2006). Figure 34 on page

24 (Taylor Dome, Antarctica, Steig et al. 1998) https://www.oeschger. unibe.ch/research/projects_and_databases/web_based_holocene_climate_atlas_hoclat/index_eng.html [cit. 6. 12. 2019]

458   BELL, L. Who released the Climategate emails and why, *Forbes* 15. 3. 2013, http://www.forbes.com/sites/larrybell/2013/03/15/who-released-the-climategate-emails-and-why/ [cit. 5. 5. 2014].

459   McINTYRE, S. Appeal of UEA's Yamal FOI refusal, *Climateaudit.org,* 19. 9. 2011, http://climateaudit.org/2011/09/19/appeal-of-ueas-yamal-foi-refusal/ [cit. 6. 2. 2014]

460   Enabling science through data Access in the face of increasing protectionism. A statement by the WFS Permanent Monitoring Panel for Climatology, Erice (Italy), 19. 8. 1999, http://federationofscientists. org/PMPanels/Climate/Datastate.asp [cit. 14. 2. 2014].

461   McINTYRE, S. We have 25 years invested in this work, *Climateaudit.org,* 15. 10. 2005, http://climateaudit.org/2005/10/15/we-have-25-years-invested-in-this-work/ [cit. 7. 2. 2014].

462   Climategate email No 1107454306 of 2. 2. 2005.

463   MICHAELS, P. J. The dog ate global warming, *Nationalreview. com,* 25. 9. 2009, http://www.nationalreview.com/articles/228291/dog-ate-global-warming/patrick-j-michaels [cit. 14. 2. 2014].

464   Climategate email No 1641 of 9. 5. 2009.

465   World Meteorological Organization, *Resolution No. 40,* Ženeva 26. 10. 1995, http://www.nws.noaa.gov/im/wmocovr.htm [cit. 1. 2. 2017]

466   JONES, P. et al. High-resolution paleoclimatic records for the last millenium: interpretation, integration and comparison with General Circulation Model control run temperatures, *The Holocene,* 1998, Vol. 8, No. 4.

467   BRIFFA, K. et. al. Annual climate variability in the Holocene: interpreting the message of ancient trees, *Quaternary Science Reviews,* 2000, Vol. 19, Issue 1- 5, p. 87-105, accepted to print in 1999.

468   McINTYRE, S. IPCC and „the trick", *Climateaudit.org,* 10. 12. 2009, http://climateaudit.org/2009/12/10/ipcc-and-the-trick/ [cit. 7.2.2014]

469   Climategate email of 22.9.1999.

470   *WMO statement on the status of the world climate,* Report No. 913, World Meteorological Organization 1999, http://nichol.as/papers/wmo913.pdf [cit. 2. 2. 2016]

471   BRIFFA, K. et al. Low-frequency temperature variations from a northern tree ring density network, *Journal of Geophysical Research,* 2001, Vol. 106, No. D3, p. 2938, figure 3. Simplified version available at http://c3headlines.typepad.com/.a/6a010536b58035970c-

013488f8a8cb970c-pi [cit. 20. 2. 2017]

472 Climategate email č. 1212063122 ze dne 29. 5. 2008.

473 McINTYRE, S. Wahl Transcript Excerpt, *Climateaudit.org*, 8. 3. 2011, http://climateaudit.org/2011/03/08/wahl-transcript-excerpt/ [cit. 5. 2. 2014]

474 BROEDER, J. M. Researcher on climate is cleared in inquiry, *The New York Times*, 3. 2. 2010, [cit. 5. 2. 2014] http://www.nytimes. com/2010/02/04/science/earth/04climate.html

475 *The disclosure of climate data from the Climatic Research Unit at the University of East Anglia*, House of Commons Science and Technology Committee, March 2010, p. 46, https://www.desmogblog.com/sites/ beta.desmogblog.com/files/phil%20jones%20house%20of%20commons%20report.pdf [cit. 2. 2. 2017]

476 The CRU hack, *RealClimate.org*, 20. 11. 2009, http://www.real-climate.org/index.php/archives/2009/11/the-cru-hack/ [cit. 2. 2. 2017]

477 BRIFFA, K. et al. Trees tell of past climates, but are they speaking less clearly today? *Philosophical Transactions of the Royal Society B*, 1998, Vol. 353, Issue 1365.

478 D'ARRIGO, R. et al. On the divergence problem in northern forests: A review of the tree-ring evidence and possible causes. *Global and Planetary Change*, 2008, Vol. 60, No. 2.

479 BOX, J. E. et al. Greenland ice sheet surface temperature variability 1840-2007, *Journal of Climate*, Vol. 22, No. 14, figure 11 (upraveno).

480 BOX, J. et al. Greenland ice sheet surface air temperature variability 1840–2007, *Journal of Climate*, 2009, Vol. 22, No. 14.

481 WALSH, P. Ex-News of the World man advised UEA over 'climategate', *Eastern DailyPress*, 16. 7. 2011, http://www.edp24.co.uk/ news/crime/ex_news_of_the_world_man_advised_uea_over_climate-gate_1_965732 [cit. 15. 2. 2016]

482 WOODS, A. Public image LTD, *Music Week*, 25. 9. 2010, http://img27.imageshack.us/img27/212/musicweekseptember2010h. pdf [cit. 16. 2. 2014].

483 McINTYRE, S. Covert operations by East Anglia's CRU, *Climateaudit.org*, 14. 7. 2011, http://climateaudit.org/2011/07/14/covert-operations-by-east-anglias-cru/ [cit. 19. 2. 2014]

484 *The disclosure of climate data from the Climatic Research Unit at the University of East Anglia*. House of Commons Science and Technology Committee, 8th report of session 2009-10, March 2010, http://www. publications.parliament.uk/pa/cm200910/cmselect/cmsctech/387/387i. pdf [cit. 19. 2. 2014]

485 Scientists cleared—after one day probe, *Foxnews.com*, 31. 3. 2010, http://www.foxnews.com/scitech/2010/03/31/climate-gate-inqui-ry-largely-clears-scientists/ [cit. 19. 2. 2014]

486   FULLER, T. Oxbugh inquiry was an offer he couldn't refuse, *Wattsupwiththat.com*, 25. 4. 2010, http://wattsupwiththat.com/2010/04/25/global-warming-the-oxburgh-inquiry-was-an-offer-he-couldnt-refuse/ [cit. 19. 2. 2014]

487   Lord Oxburgh Scientific Assessment Panel, *University of East Anglia*, duben 2010, http://www.uea.ac.uk/mac/comm/media/press/crustatements/sap [cit. 19. 2. 2014]

488   SOLOMON, L. Reopen Climategate hearings, says UK parliamentarian, *National Post*, 10. 7. 2010, http://www.nationalpost.com/m/blog.html?b=fullcomment.nationalpost.com/2010/07/10/lawrence-solomon-reopen-climategate-hearings-says-uk-parliamentarian&s=Opinion [cit. 7. 2. 2016]

489   SOLOMON, L. Reopen Climategate hearings, says UK parliamentarian. *National Post* 10.7.2010. https://nationalpost.com/full-comment/lawrence-solomon-reopen-climategate-hearings-says-uk-parliamentarian [cit. 19. 2. 2019]

490   McINTYRE, S. British due diligence—Royal Society style, *Climateaudit.org*, 20. 6. 2010, http://climateaudit.org/2010/06/10/british-due-diligence-royal-society-style/ [cit. 19. 2. 2014]

491   McINTYRE, S. BP and the Climategate inquiry, *Climateaudit.org*, 21. 5. 2010, http://climateaudit.org/2010/05/21/bp-and-the-climategate-inquiry/ [cit. 19. 2. 2014]

492   RUSSEL, M. et al. The independent climate change emails review, 7. 7. 2010, http://www.cce-review.org [cit. 19. 2. 2014]

493   PEARCE, F. Montford lands some solid blows in review of 'climategate' inquiries, *Guardian*, 14. 9. 2010, http://www.theguardian.com/environment/cif-green/2010/sep/14/montford-climategate-gwpf-review [cit. 19. 2. 2014]

494   DeMELLE, B. Climategate' scientists cleared of all charges by independent review. *Grist*, 8.7.2010, https://grist.org/article/climategate-is-dead-or-long-live-climategate/ [cit. 2. 2. 2019]

495   FISCHER, D. Climategate Scientist Cleared in Inquiry, Again. Scientific American. 1.7.2010. https://www.scientificamerican.com/article/climategate-scientist-cleared-in-inquiry-again/ [cit. 2. 2. 2019]

496   RA 10 Final investigation report and decision re Professor Michael Mann, Penn State University, Pennsylvania, 1. 7. 2010, http://www.washingtonpost.com/wp-srv/politics/documents/final_report_penn.pdf [cit. 9. 2. 2014]

497   MORANO, M. Penn State investigation cited Mann's level of success... *Climatedepot*, 2. 7. 2010, http://www.climatedepot.com/2010/07/02/penn-state-investigation-cited-manns-level-of-success-in-proposing-research-and-obtaining-funding-as-some-sort-of-proof-that-he-was-meeting-the-highest-standards/ [cit. 2. 2. 2014]

498   Ken Cuccinelli's quest for climate change emails stopped. *WJLA.com*, 7. 3. 2012, http://www.wjla.com/articles/2012/03/ken-cuccinelli-

s-quest-for-climate-change-emails-stopped-73303.html [cit. 2. 2. 2014]

499   STEYN, M. Football and hockey, *National Review*, 15. 7. 2012, http://www.nationalreview.com/corner/309442/football-and-hockey-mark-steyn [cit. 5. 2. 2016]

500   MANN, M. *The hockey stick and the climate wars: Dispatches form the front lines*, New York 2013, Columbia University Press.

501 WATTS, A. Prominent climategate figure threatens lawsuit over Spoof video, *Wattsupwiththat.com*, 20. 4. 2010, http://wattsupwiththat.com/2010/04/20/prominent-climategate-figure-threatens-lawsuit-over-spoof-video-no-cap-and-trade-coalition-says-%E2%80%9Cbring-it-on%E2%80%9D/ [cit. 2. 7. 2016]

502   PEARCE, F. Strange case of moving weather posts and a scientist under siege, *Guardian*, 1. 2. 2010, http://www.theguardian.com/environment/2010/feb/01/dispute-weather-fraud [cit. 2. 7. 2016]

503   Climategate email 1189515774.

504   HEFFERNAN, O. Climategate scientist fights back, *Climate Feedback (a Nature Climate Change blog)*,15. 2. 2010, http://www.nature.com/news/2010/100215/full/news.2010.71.html [cit. 5. 6. 2016]

505   WIHBEY, J. Strange bedfellows… and fear of broad impact of Mann/UVA court ruling, *Yale Climate And Media Forum*, 20. 2. 2014, http://www.yaleclimatemediaforum.org/2014/02/strange-bedfellows-and-fear-of-broad-impacts-of-mann-uva-court-ruling/ [cit. 20. 3. 2014].

506   LIFSON, T. Michael Mann, creator of the infamous global warming 'hockey stick,' loses lawsuit against climate skeptic, ordered to pay defendant's costs. *American Thinker*, 25.8.2019. https://www.americanthinker.com/blog/2019/08/michael_mann_creator_of_the_infamous_global_warming_hockey_stick_loses_lawsuit_against_climate_skeptic_ordered_to_pay_defendants_costs.html [cit. 20. 9. 2019]

507   BRAY, D., STORCH, H. von. Climate Science: An Empirical Example of Postnormal Science, *Bulletin of the American Meteorological Society*, 1999, Vol. 80. No. 3.

508   FUNTOWICZ, S. O., RAVETZ, J.R. Science for the postnormal age, *Futures*, 1993, Vol. 25, No. 7.

509   RAVETZ, J. *Scientific Knowledge and Its Social Problems*, Oxford 1971, Clarendon Press.

510   SLUIJS, J. van der. Uncertainty as a monster in the science-policy interface: four coping strategies, *Water Science and Technology*, 2005, Vol. 52, Issue 6.

511   SCHNEIDER, S. Interview, *Discover*,October 1989, pp. 45–48, citováno z SCHNEIDER S. The double ethical bind pitfall, https://stephenschneider.stanford.edu/Mediarology/Mediarology.html [cit. 18. 12. 2017].

512   DELINGPOLE, J. 'Postnormal science' is perfect for climate

demagogues—it isn't science at all, *The Spectator,* 17. 2. 2010 https://www.spectator.co.uk/2010/02/postnormal-science-is-perfect-for-climate-demagogues-it-isnt-science-at-all/ [cit. 18. 12. 2017].

513   KØNIG, N. et al. The ethos of postnormal science, *Futures,* 2017, Vol. 91, p. 12—24.

514   RAVETZ, J. Answer and explanation to my critics, *Wattsupwith-that.com,* 22. 2. 2010, https://wattsupwiththat.com/2010/02/22/jerry-ravetz-part-2-answer-and-explanation-to-my-critics/ [cit. 18. 12. 2017].

515   RAVETZ, J. The climate crisis could be solved by courteous communication, *Guardian,* 15. 2. 2010, https://www.theguardian.com/environment/cif-green/2010/feb/15/science-conflict-resolution [cit. 18. 12. 2017].

516   RAVETZ, J. Answer and explanation to my critics, *Wattsupwith-that.com,* 22. 2. 2010, https://wattsupwiththat.com/2010/02/22/jerry-ravetz-part-2-answer-and-explanation-to-my-critics/ [cit. 18. 12. 2017].

517   PEARCE, F. Climate skeptics and scientists attempt peace deal, *NewScientist,* 2. 2. 2011, https://www.newscientist.com/blogs/short-sharpscience/2011/02/climate skeptics-scientists-at.html [cit. 18. 12. 2017].

518   ARRHENIUS, S. *Worlds in the making: The evolution of the universe.* London 2010, Kessinger Publishing LLC, p. 63.

519   BERNER, R. A, KOTHAVALA, Z. Geocarb III: A Revised model of atmospheric CO_2 over phanerosoic time, *American Journal of Science,* 2001, Vol. 301, No. 2.

520   FISCHER, H. et al. Ice core records of atmospheric CO_2 around the last three glacial terminations, *Science,* 1999, Vol. 283, No. 5408.

521   CAILLON, N. et al. Timing of atmospheric CO_2 and Antarctic temperature changes across Termination III, *Science,* 2003, Vol. 299, No. 5613.

522   PETIT, J. R. et al. Climate and atmospheric history of the past 420,000 years from the Vostok ice core, Antarctica, *Nature,* 1999, Vol. 399, Issue 6735.

523   HUMLUM, O. et al. The phase relation between atmospheric carbon dioxide and global temperature, *Global and Planetary Change,* 2013, Vol. 100, January 2013, p. 51-69.

524   KUO, C. et al. Coherence established between atmospheric carbon dioxide and global temperature, *Nature,* 1990, Vol. 343, Issue 6260.

525   KEELING, C. D. et al. Interannual extremes in the rate of rise of atmospheric carbon dioxide since 1980, *Nature,* 1995, Vol. 375, Issue 6533.

526   SOLOMON, L. *The world renowned scientists who stood up against global warming hysteria, political persecution, and fraud,* Minneapolis 2008, Richard Vigilante Books.

527   WANNING, E. Roger Revelle interview, *Omni Magazine,* 1984, Vol. 6. No. 6 (March). Cited from SOLOMON, L. The deniers, part XX: Gore's guru disagreed, *National Post,* 28. 4. 2007, https://ep.probe-international.org/2007/04/28/deniers-part-xx-gores-guru-disagreed/ [cit. 7. 8. 2016]

528   CALLENDAR, G. The artificial production of carbon dioxide and its influence on temperature, *Quarterly Journal of the Royal Meteorological Society,* 1938, Volume 64, Issue 275, http://onlinelibrary.wiley.com/doi/10.1002/qj.49706427503/pdf [cit. 7. 8. 2016]

529   BROECKER, W. Climate change: Are we on the brink of a pronounced global warming? *Science—New Series,* 1975, Vol. 189, No. 4201.

530   RASSOOL, S. I., SCHNEIDER, S.H. Atmospheric carbon dioxide and aerosols: Effects of large increases on global climate. *Science,* 1971, Vol. 173, No 3992.

531   LAMB, H. H. Climate in the 1960's changes in the world's wind circulation reflected in prevailing temperatures, rainfall patterns and the levels of the African lakes, *The Geography Journal,* 1966, Vol. 132, No. 2, http://www.jstor.org/stable/1792334 [cit. 7. 8. 2016]

532   LAMB, H. H. *Climate: Present, past and future II.* New York 1977, Barnes and Noble. Citováno z: HOMEWOOD, P. HH Lamb–"Climate: Present, past & future–Vol 2"–In review–Part I, *Notalotofpeopleknowthat.wordpress.com* 24. 6. 2012, http://notalotofpeopleknowthat.wordpress.com/2012/06/24/hh-lambclimate-present-past-futurevol-2in-reviewpart-i/ [cit. 7. 8. 2016]

533   Science and the challenges ahead. *US National Science Board,* 1974, p.24. https://archive.org/details/sciencechallenge00nati

534   A study of climatological research as it pertains to inteligence problems, *Central Inteligence Agency,* srpen 1974, http://www.climate-monitor.it/wp-content/uploads/2009/12/1974.pdf [cit. 7. 8. 2016]

535   BRYSON, R. A, MURRAY, T. J. *Climates of hunger,* Wisconsin 1979, The University of Wisconsin Press.

536   A study of climatological research as it pertains to inteligence problems, *Central Inteligence Agency,* August 1974, p. 1, http://www.climatemonitor.it/wp-content/uploads/2009/12/1974.pdf [cit. 7. 8. 2016]

537   Ibidem, p. 2 and p. 7.

538   EDWARDS, N. P. *A vast machine - Computer models, climate data, and the politics of global warming,* Cambridge (Massachussetts) 2010, MIT Press, p. 373.

539   HANSEN, J. The greenhouse effect: Impacts on current global temperaqtures and regional heatwaves. Statement of James E. Hansen, NASA Goddard Institute, presented to US Senate, Committee on Energy and Natural Resources, 23. 6. 1988.

540   HANSEN, J. *Storms of my grandchildren: The Truth About the*

Coming Climate Catastrophe and Our Last Chance to Save Humanity, London 2009, Bloomsbury Press.

541   BRANIGAN, T. Mongolia. How the winter of "white death" devatated nomad's way of life, *Guardian,* 20. 7. 2010, http://www.theguardian.com/world/2010/jul/20/mongolia-nomads-livestock-winter-poverty [cit. 7. 8. 2016]

542   FRANKLIN, M. Why Global Warming Can Mean Harsher Winter Weather. *Scientific American,* 25.2.2019, https://www.scientificamerican.com/article/earthtalks-global-warming-harsher-winter/

543   JOHNSON, P. The Nonsense of Global Warming, *Forbes,* 6. 10. 2008, http://www.forbes.com/forbes/2008/1006/025.html [cit. 2. 2. 2017]

544   SANTER, B. J. Separating signal and noise in atmospheric temperature changes: The importance of timescale, *Journal of Geophysical Research,* 2011, Vol. 116, Issue D22.

545   IDSO, C. et al. *Climate change reconsidered II: Physical science. Report of the Nongovernmental International Panel on Climate change (NIPCC),* Chicago, 2013, The Heartland Institute. Available online at: http://climatechangereconsidered.org/

546   HOMEWOOD, P. RSS confirm 2016 as tied with 1998 as warmest year. *Nataalotofpeopleknowthat,* 5. 1. 2017, https://notalotofpeopleknowthat.wordpress.com/2017/01/05/rss-confirm-2016-is-tied-with-1998-as-warmest-year/ [cit. 20. 2. 2017]. Data source from: http://www.remss.com/measurements/upper-air-temperature

547   SPENCER, R. Still epic fail: 73 climate models vs measurements—running 5-year means, *Drroyspencer.com,* 6. 6. 2013 www.drroyspencer.com/2013/06/still-epic-fail-73-climate-models-vs-measurements-running-5-year-means/ [cit. 7. 8. 2016]

548   HANSEN, J. Defusing the global warming time bomb, *Scientific American,* March 2004, Vol. 290, Issue 3.

549   RAMANATHAN,V., FENG,Y. On avoiding dangerous anthropogenic interference with the climate system: Formidable challenges ahead, *Proceedings of the National Academy of Sciences,* 2008, Vol. 105, No. 38.

550   Climategate email 125535225.

551   WATTS, A. List of excuses for the pause in global warming is now up to 52, *Wattsupwiththat.com,* 14. 9. 2014, http://wattsupwiththat.com/2014/09/11/list-of-excuses-for-the-pause-in-global-warming-is-now-up-to-52/ [cit. 7. 8. 2016]

552   FREEDMAN, A. New study blames 10-year lull in global warming on China coal use, air pollution, *Washington Post,* 5. 7. 2011, http://www.washingtonpost.com/blogs/capital-weather-gang/post/new-study-blames-10-year-lull-in-global-warming-on-china-coal-use-air-pollution/2011/07/05/gHQAwjV8yH_blog.html [cit. 7. 8. 2016]

553 FREEDMAN, A. New study blames 10-year lull in global warming on China coal use, air pollution, *Washington Post*, 5. 7. 2011, http://www.washingtonpost.com/blogs/capital-weather-gang/post/new-study-blames-10-year-lull-in-global-warming-on-china-coal-use-air-pollution/2011/07/05/gHQAwjV8yH_blog.html [cit. 7. 8. 2016]

554 McGRATH, M. Smell of forest pine can limit climate change—researchers, *BBC*, 26. 2. 2014, http://www.bbc.com/news/science-environment-26340038 [cit. 7. 8. 2016]

555 KARL, T. et al. Possible artifacts of data biases in the recent global surface warming hiatus, *Science*, 2015, Vol. 348, Issue 6242.

556 TISDALE, B. NOAA/NCDS's New pause-buster paper: A laughable attempt to create warming by adjusting past data, *Wattsupwiththat.com*, 4. 6. 2015, https://wattsupwiththat.com/2015/06/04/noaancdcs-new-pause-buster-paper-a-laughable-attempt-to-create-warming-by-adjusting-past-data/ [cit. 7. 8. 2016]

557 ROSE, D. How world leaders were duped into investing billions over manipulated global warming data, *Dailymail.co.uk*, 4. 2. 2017, http://www.dailymail.co.uk/sciencetech/article-4192182/World-leaders-duped-manipulated-global-warming-data.html [cit. 7. 8. 2016]

558 FYFE, J. C. et al. Making sense of the early-2000s warming slowdown, *Nature Climate Change*, 2016, Vol. 6, p. 224-228.

559 UPTON, J. Leading scientists say warming slowdown was real, *Climate Central*, 24. 2. 2016, http://www.climatecentral.org/news/scientists-say-warming-slowdown-was-real-20068 [cit. 20. 2. 2017]

560 SPENCER, R. Global satellites: 2016 not statistically warmer than 1998, *Drroyspencer.com*, http://www.drroyspencer.com/2017/01/global-satellites-2016-not-statistically-warmer-than-1998/ [cit. 7. 8. 2016]

561 von STORCH, H. Why is global warming stagnating? *Spiegel.de*, 20. 6. 2013, http://www.spiegel.de/international/world/interview-hans-von-storch-on-problems-with-climate-change-models-a-906721.html [cit. 7. 8. 2016]

562 MULSHINE, P. Climatologists are no Einsteins, says his successor, *Blog.nj.com*, 3. 4. 2013, http://blog.nj.com/njv_paul_mulshine/2013/04/climatologists_are_no_einstein.html [cit. 7. 8. 2016]

563 ARMSTRONG, J. S. Let's deal in science and facts, *Wall Street Journal*, 19. 11. 2010, http://online.wsj.com/news/articles/SB10001424052748703326204575616983641995488 [cit. 7. 8. 2016]

564 GREEN, K. C. et al. Validity of climate change forecasting for public policy decision making, *International Journal of Forecasting*, 2009, Vol. 25, No. 4.

565 SCHNEIDER, E. Flux correction and the simulation of changing climate, *Annales Geophysicae*, 1996, Vol. 14, Issue 3.

566 GREGORY, J. M., MITCHELL, J. F. B. The climate response

to CO_2 of the Hadley Centre coupled AOGCM with and without flux adjustment, *Geophysical Research Letters,* 1997, Vol. 24, No. 15, 1997, p. 1943.

567   KERR, R. Climate modeling's fudge factor comes under fire, *Science,* 1994, Vol. 265, No. 5178.

568   NOVA, J. How to create a crisis graph in 6 simple steps, *Joannenova.com.au,* 23. 1. 2010, http://joannenova.com.au/2010/01/how-to-create-a-crisis-graph-in-6-simple-steps/ [cit. 7. 8. 2016]

569   METELKA, L. Klimaskeptický Dunning-Kruger, *Blog.aktualne.cz,* 11. 3. 2012, http://blog.aktualne.cz/blogy/ladislav-metelka.php?itemid=15855 [cit. 7. 8. 2016] (in Czech language)

570   LONG, M. sun's shifts may cause global warming, *Discover,* 25. 6. 2007, http://discovermagazine.com/2007/jul/the-discover-interview-henrik-svensmark/ [cit. 7. 8. 2016]

571   GHOSH, P. Cloud simulator tests climate models, *BBC,* 24. 8. 2011, http://www.bbc.co.uk/news/science-environment-14637647 [cit. 7. 8. 2016]

572   CALDER, N. CERN experiment confirms cosmic ray action, *Calderup.wordpress.com,* 24. 8. 2011, http://calderup.wordpress.com/2011/08/24/cern-experiment-confirms-cosmic-ray-action/ [cit. 17. 2. 2014]

573   KLYASHTORIN, L. B. Dynamics of climatic and geophysical indices, *In: Climate change and long-term fluctuations of commercial catches: the possibility of forecasting,* FAO Fisheries Technical Paper No. 410, Rome 2001, Food and Agriculture Organization of the United Nations, p. 86, http://www.fao.org/docrep/005/y2787e/y2787e00.htm [cit. 17. 2. 2014]

574   ISKYAN, K. This is what a long economic winter feels like, *Business Insider,* 29. 10. 2016, http://www.businessinsider.com/what-a-long-economic-winter-feels-like-2016-10 [cit. 17. 2. 2017]

575   HANSEN, A. H: Schumpeter's contribution to business cycle theory, *The Review of Economics and Statistics,* Vol. 33, No. 2.

576   MODELSKI, G. Kondratieff (K-) Waves in the Modern World System. IN: *Kondratieff Waves: Dimensions and Prospects at the Dawn of the 21st Century.* Edited by: Leonid Grinin et al. Volgograd: 'Uchitel' Publishing House, 2012.—224 p. ISBN 978-5-7057-3287-6 https://www.sociostudies.org/almanac/articles/kondratieff_k_waves_in_the_modern_world_system/

577   KŘIVSKÝ, L. A, PEJML, K. Solar activity aurorae and climate in Central Europe in the last 1,000 years, *Publications of the Astronomical Institute of the Czechoslovak Academy of Sciences,* No. 75, 1988, http://www.ngdc.noaa.gov/stp/aeronomy/aurorae.html [cit. 17. 2. 2014]

578   JEVREJEVA, S. et al. Recent global sea level acceleration started over 200 years ago? *Geophysical Research Letters,* 2008, Vol. 35, Issue 8.

579   LAMBECK, K., CAZENAVE, A. Long term variations in the length of day and climate change, *Geophysical Journal of the Royal Astronomical Society,* 1976, Vol. 46, Issue 3.

580   USOSKIN, I., SOLANKI, S. Unusual activity of the sun during recent decades compared to the previous 11,000 years, *Nature,* 2004, Vol. 431, Issue 7012.

581   LAM, M. M. et al. The interplanetary magnetic field influences middle-latitude surface atmospheric pressure, *Environmenal Research Letters,* 2013, Vol. 8, No. 4.

582   GEORGIEVA K., et al. Once again about global warming and solar activity, *Memorie della Societa Astronomica Italliana,* 2005, Vol. 79, No. 969.

583   CLIVER G. et al. Solar variability and climate change' Geomagnetic aa index and global surface temperature, *Geophysical Research Letters,* 1998, Vol. 28, Issue 7.

584   LOCKWOOD, M. et al. A doubling of the sun's coronal magnetic field during the last 100 years, *Nature,* 1999, Vol. 399, Issue 6735, p. 437.

585   SOLOMON, L. The Deniers, Part XIX, Science, not politics, *National Post,* 13. 4. 2007, http://www.nationalpost.com/news/story. html?id=5b824408-9df0-4189-86fc-cf6465bf0aa8 [cit. 17. 2. 2014]

586   CHRISTENSEN, E. F., LASSEN, K. Length of the solar cycle: An indicator of solar activity closely associated with climate, *Science,* 1991, Vol. 254, Issue 5032.

587   MURSULA, K. A new method to determine a solar cycle length. *Geophysical Research Letters,* 1998,Vol. 20, No. 11.

588   Usoskin, I.G. et al. Reconstruction of solar activity for the last millennium using 10Be data. Astronomy and Astrophysics, 2004, Vol. 413, 745-751, https://www.aanda.org/articles/aa/abs/2004/02/aah4688/aah4688.html [cit. 17. 2. 2019]

589   SOLANKI, I. G. et al. Solar activity over the last 1150 years: Does it correlate with climate? In: *Proceedings of the 13th Cambridge workshop on cool stars, stellar systems and the sun of June 2004,* Cambridge 2005, http://adsabs.harvard.edu/full/2005ESASP.560...19U [cit. 17. 2. 2014]

590   METELKA, L. Lepší je být opatrný, *Ekolist.cz,* 7. 3. 2007, http://ekolist.cz/cz/publicistika/rozhovory/klimatolog-ladislav-metelka-lepsi-je-byt-opatrny [cit. 17. 2. 2014] (in Czech language)

591   Was the Little Ice Age triggered by massive volcanic eruptions? *ScienceDaily,* 30. 1. 2012, www.sciencedaily.com/releases/2012/01/120130131509.htm [cit. 17. 2. 2014]

592   BLACK, R. Volcanic origin for Little Ice Age, *BBC,* 30. 1. 2012 http://www.bbc.co.uk/news/science-environment-16797075 [cit 20. 2. 2014]

593   STOTHERS, R. B. Volcanic eruptions and solar activity, *Journal of Geophysical Research*, 1989, Vol. 94, No. B12.

594   STŘEŠTÍK, J. Possible correlation between solar and volcanic activity in a long-term scale, In: *Solar variability as an input to the Earth's environment*, WILSON A.I. (ed.), International Solar Cycle Studies (ISCS) Symposium, 23 - 28 June 2003, Tatranská Lomnica, Slovak Republic.

595   LOCKWOOD, M. et al. Open solar flux estimates from near-Earth measurements of the interplanetary magnetic field: comparison of the first two perihelion passes of the Ulysses spacecraft, *Annales Geophysicae*, 2004, Vol. 22, Issue 4, p. 1395–1405.

596   ZIELINSKI, G. Use of paleo-records in determining variability within the volcanism-climate system, *Quaternary Science Reviews*, 2000, Vol. 19, Issues 1-5, p. 417-438.

597   SHIGA, D. Lunar eclipse may shed light on climate change, *NewScientist*, 3. 3. 2008, http://www.newscientist.com/article/dn13376-lunar-eclipse-may-shed-light-on-climate-change.html [cit. 17. 2. 2014]

598   IPCC, 2007, Assessment Report 4 ,Working Group 1, Frequently Asked Questions 9.2.

599   IPCC, 2007, Assesement Report 4, Working Group 1, Summary for Policymakers, Figure 2.

600   Comment No. 2-1 by reviewer Vincent Gray to Chapter II, Working Group I, Fourth Asessment Report, IPCC, Gray's comment has reference No. 88-110, http://www.climateaudit.info/pdf/ipcc/sod/AR4WG1_Ch02_SOR_CommentResponses_EDist.pdf [cit. 7. 2. 2017]

601   IPCC, 2007, Assessment Report 4, Working Group 1, Chapter 3.4.2.1.

602   MACKEY, R. Rhodes Fairbridge and the idea that the solar system regulates the Earth's climate, In: Proceedings of the 9th International Coastal Symposium, Gold Coast, Australia, *Journal of Coastal Research*, 2007, SI 50, http://www.lavoisier.com.au/articles/greenhouse-science/solar-cycles/RichardMackeyForum2008.pdf [cit 20. 2. 2014]

603   CHARVÁTOVÁ, I., STŘEŠTÍK, J. Long-term changes of the surface air temperature in relation to solar inertial motion, *Climatic Change*, 1995, Vol. 29, Issue 3, p. 333-352.

604   Einstein's physics is considered as incomplete by the physicist Lee Smolin, author of the Loop Quantum Gravity Theoy. According to Smolin, new universes are born in black holes. Each such child-universe may have different physical laws and different number of dimensions.

605   CHARVÁTOVÁ, I. Za klimatickými změnami může být pohyb Slunce, *Osel.cz*, 21. 5. 2011, http://www.osel.cz/index.php?clanek=5708 [cit. 20. 2. 2014] (in Czech language)

606 Editorial. *Zetetic Scholar,* 1987, No. 12-13, p. 3-4,

607 TRUZZI, M. Reflections on "Project Alpha": Scientific experiment on conjuror's illusion? *Zetetic Scholar,* 1987, No. 12-13, p. 75-95. http://tricksterbook.com/truzzi/ZeteticScholars.html [cit. 2. 2. 2017]

608 KUHN, T. *The structure of scientific revolutions,* Chicago 1970, University of Chicago Press, p. 151.

609 Eisenhower's farewell address to the nation, 17. 1. 1961, http://mcadams.posc.mu.edu/ike.htm [cit. 7. 2. 2017]

610 SHERWELL, P. War of words over global warming as Nobel laureate resigns in protest, *Telegraph,* 25. 9. 2011, http://www.telegraph.co.uk/news/earth/environment/climatechange/8786565/War-of-words-over-global-warming-as-Nobel-laureate-resigns-in-protest.html [cit. 2. 2. 2017]

611 *Over 400 prominent scientists disputed man-made global warming claims in 2007,* US Senate Environment and Public Works Committee, Minority Staff Report, 20. 12. 2007, https://www.epw.senate.gov/public/_cache/files/bba2ebce-6d03-48e4-b83c-44fe321a34fa/consensusbusterscompletedocument.pdf [cit. 8. 2. 2017]

612 LAMB, H. H. *Climate: Present, past and future,* p. 46. Cited from LEWIN, B. Hubert Lamb and the transformation of climate science, *Global Warming Policy Foundation (London),* GWPF Report 17, 2014, p. 13.

613 LAMB, H. H. *Through all the changing scenes of life: A meteorologist's tale,* Climate Research Unit, 1997, cited from: LEWIN, B. Hubert Lamb and the transformation of climate science, *Global Warming Policy Foundation (London),* GWPF Report 17, 2014, p. 21.

614 LAMB, H. H. *Climate, history, and the modern world,* 2nd edn. London 1995, Routledge, p. 384. Citováno z: LEWIN, B. Hubert Lamb and the transformation of climate science, *Global Warming Policy Foundation (London),* GWPF Report 17, 2014, p. 32.

615 KELLY, M. Obituary—Hubert Horace Lamb 1913—1997, *Nature,* 1997, Vol. 388, Issue 6645.

616 SOLOMON, L. Gore's guru disagreed, *National Post,* 28. 4. 2007, https://ep.probeinternational.org/2007/04/28/deniers-part-xx-gores-guru-disagreed/ [cit. 2. 2. 2017]

617 SINGER, F., REVELLE, R., STARR, Ch. What to do about greenhouse warming. Look before you leap, *Cosmos,* 1991, Vol. 1, p. 28-33.

618 SINGER, F. The Revelle-Gore Story: Atempted political suppression of sicence, In: *Politicizing science* (Ed. M.Gough), Hoover Institution Press 2003, http://media.hoover.org/sites/default/files/documents/0817939326_283.pdf

619 GOSSELIN, P. IPCC Vice chair van Ypersele suppresses open scientific inquiry—Shuts down SEII skeptic forum, *No-*

trickszone.com, 30. 8. 2011, http://notrickszone.com/2011/08/30/ipcc-vice-chai-van-ypersele-suppresses-open-scientific-inquiry-disallows-critical-debate/ [cit. 7. 3. 2016]

620   National Research Council, *Changing climate. Report of the carbon dioxide assessment committee,* Washington D.C. 1983, The National Academies Press, p. 61, https://www.nap.edu/catalog/18714/changing-climate-report-of-the-carbon-dioxide-assessment-committee [cit. 17. 2. 2017]

621   SEITZ, R. In from the cold. Nuclear winter melts down, *The National Interest,* Autumn 1986, p. 3-17. The article that criticized Sagan was written by Fred Seitz's cousin, who was among the founders of the Marshall Institute.

622   TURCO, R. et al. Nuclear Winter: Global consequences of multiple nuclear explosions, *Science,* 1983, Vol. 222, No. 4630.

623   The eruption of Krakatoa 27. 8. 1883, Australian Government—Bureau of Meteorology, http://www.bom.gov.au/tsunami/history/1883.shtml [cit. 17. 7. 2014]

624   CRICHTON, M. Aliens cause global warming, *A Caltech Michelin lecture,* 17. 1. 2003, https://www.cfa.harvard.edu/~scranmer/SPD/crichton.html [cit. 7. 7. 2016]

625   TENNEKES, H., LUMLEY, J. L. *A first course in turbulence,* Boston 1972, MIT Press.

626   HEISER, J. Scientist's Climate Change Dissent Vindicated. 23.2.2010. *The New American.* https://www.thenewamerican.com/tech/environment/item/6813-scientists-climate-change-dissent-vindicated [cit. 3. 8. 2019]

627   TIMMER, E. Het gelijk van Henk Tennekes, *De Telegraaf,* 13. 2. 2010.

628   SOLOMON, L. The limits of predictability, *Canada.com/nationalpost,* 2. 2. 2007, http://www.canada.com/nationalpost/story.html?id=9bc9a7c6-2729-4d07-9629-807f1dee479f&k=0 [cit. 14. 7. 2014]

629   No need to panic about global warming, *The Wall Street Journal,* 27. 1. 2012.

630   DELINGPOLE, J. Climate science director forced to resign by alarmist "fatwa", *Breitbart.com,* 14. 5. 2014, http://www.breitbart.com/Breitbart-London/2014/05/14/Climate-Science-Defector-Forced-to-Resign-by-Alarmist-Fatwa [cit. 7. 7. 2014]

631   KAHAN, D. M. et al. The polarizing impact of science literacy and numeracy on perceived climate change risks, *Nature Climate Change,* 2012, Vol. 2, May 2012.

632   HOFFMAN, A. J. Talking past each other? Cultural framing of skeptical and convinced logics in the climate change debate, Organization Environment, 2011, Vol. 24, No. 1, p. 8.

633   Warning of global suicide, Ban calls for revolution to ensure

sustainable development, *UN News Centre,* 28.1.2011, http://www.un.org/apps/news/story.asp?NewsID=37405#.WM-ygpN2ExI [cit. 20. 3. 2017]

634   MIELE, F. Green New Deal is same old socialist con game. *Real Clear Politics,* 25.3.2019, https://www.realclearpolitics.com/articles/2019/03/25/green_new_deal_is_same_old_socialist_con_game__139837.html [cit. 20. 10. 2019]

635   DOUGLAS, M., Wildavsky, A. B. *Risk and culture: An essay on the selection of technical and environmental dangers,* Berkeley 1982, University of California Press.

636   TANSEY, J., O'RIORDAN, T. Cultural theory and risk—a review, *Health, Risk and Society,* 1999. Vol. 1, No. 1.

637   SMITS, M. Taming monsters: The cultural domestication of new technology, *Technology in Society,* 2006, Vol. 28, Issue 4.

638   DUNLAP, R. et al. Commitment to the Dominant Social Paradigm and concern for environmenal quality, *Social Science Quarterly,* 1984, Vol. 65, Issue 4.

639   An open letter to Pope Francis on climate change, 27.4. 2015, *The Cornwall Alliance,* https://www.heartland.org/publications-resources/publications/an-open-letter-to-pope-francis-on-climate-change [cit. 7. 11. 2017].

640   ROSSITER, C. Sacrificing Africa for climate change, *Wall Street Journal,* 4. 5. 2014, http://online.wsj.com/news/articles/SB10001424052702303380004579521791400395288 [cit. 7. 7. 2014].

641   MORANO, M. Fired for 'diverging' on climate: Progressive professor's fellowship 'terminated' after WSJ OpEd calling global warming 'unproved science', *Climatedepot.com,* 12. 6. 2014, http://www.climatedepot.com/2014/06/12/fired-for-diverging-on-climate-progressive-professors-fellowship-terminated-after-wsj-oped-calling-global-warming-unproved-science/ [cit. 7. 7. 2014].

642   GUCCIARDI, A. How just 6 corps own 90% of the media, *Storyleak.com,* 31. 7. 2013, http://www.storyleak.com/graphic-6-corporations-own-90-percent-of-media/ [cit. 20. 2. 2014]

643   LINDZEN, R. Climate of fear, *Wall Street Journal,* 12. 4. 2006 https://www.heartland.org/publications-resources/publications/climate-of-fear [cit. 20. 2. 2019]

644   McLEAN, J. D. et al. Influence of the Southern Oscillation on tropospheric temperature, *Journal of Geophysical Research,* 2009, Vol. 114, Issue D14.

645   McLEAN, J. D. et al. Censorship at AGU: Scientists denied the right of reply, *Science and Public Policy Institute,* 30. 3. 2010, http://scienceandpublicpolicy.org/originals/censorship_at_agu.html [cit. 20. 2. 2014]

646   KAY, W.W. Holtzbrinck & Bertelsmann: Agents of German Cli-

mate Imperialism. *Friends of Science,* 18.8.2019, https://blog.friendsof-science.org/2019/08/18/holtzbrinck-bertelsmann-agents-of-german-climate-imperialism/ [cit. 20. 11. 2019]

647   BATTY, D., ADAM, D. Climate emails review panellist quits after his impartiality questioned, *Guardian,* 2. 2. 2010, http://www.theguardian.com/environment/2010/feb/12/climate-change-climategate-nature-global-warming [cit. 20. 2. 2014]

648   Climatologists under pressure, *Nature,* 2009, Vol. 462, Issue 7273.

649   A vote for science, *Nature,* 2012, Vol. 490, Issue 7271.

650   KLIMÁNEK, O. Klimatický boj na Wikipedii aneb manipulace kam se podíváš, *Scinet.cz,* 8. 1. 2010, http://www.scinet.cz/klimaticky-boj-na-wikipedii-aneb-manipulace-kam-se-podivas.html [cit. 20. 2. 2014] (in Czech language)

651   JEVREJEVA, S. et al. Recent global sea level acceleration started over 200 years ago? *Geophysical Research Letters,* 2008, Vol. 35, Issue 8, Figure 3.

652   GILES, J. Internet Encyklopedias go head to head, *Nature,* 2005, Vol. 438, Issue 7070.

653   The BBC became a propaganda machine for climate change zealots, says Peter Sissons... and I was treated as a lunatic for daring to dissent, *DailyMail,* 9. 2. 2011, http://www.dailymail.co.uk/news/article-1350206/BBC-propaganda-machine-climate-change-says-Peter-Sissons.html [cit. 14. 5. 2016]

654   ROSE, D. BBC's Mr. Climate Change accepted 15,000 pounds in grants from University rocked by global warming scandal, *Daily Mail,* 19. 11. 2011, http://www.dailymail.co.uk/news/article-2063737/BBCs-Mr-Climate-Change-15-000-grants-university-rocked-global-warning-scandal.html [cit. 14. 5. 2016]

655   From seesaw to wagonwheel: Safeguarding impartiality in the 21st century, *BBC Trust,* 18. 6. 2007, http://www.bbc.co.uk/bbctrust/our_work/editorial_standards/impartiality/safeguarding_impartiality.html [cit. 14. 5. 2016]

656   ORLOWSKI, A. FOIA judges: Secret 28 who made the BBC Green will not be named, *The Register,* 9. 11. 2012, http://www.theregister.co.uk/2012/11/09/bbc_beats_blogger_/ [cit. 14. 5. 2016]

657   MORABITO, M. Full list of participants to the BBC CMEP seminar on 26 January 2006, *Omnologos.com,* 11. 12. 2012, http://omnologos.com/full-list-of-participants-to-the-bbc-cmep-seminar-on-26-january-2006/ [cit. 14. 5. 2016]

658   HUDSON, P. Climategate—CRU hacked into and its implications. *BBC,* 23. 11. 2009, http://www.bbc.co.uk/blogs/legacy/paulhudson/2009/11/climategate-cru-hacked-into-an.shtml [cit. 14. 5. 2016]

659   BELLAMY, D. Global warming? What a load of poppycock! The

Daily Mail, 9. 7. 2004, http://www.sovereignty.org.uk/features/eco/hotair.html [cit. 14. 5. 2016]

660   LEAKE, J. Wildlife groups axe Bellamy as global warming heretic, *The sunday Times,* 15. 5. 2005, http://web.archive.org/web/20080906161240/http://www.timesonline.co.uk/tol/news/uk/article522744.ece [cit. 14. 5. 2016]

661   STEELE, J. Has David Attenborough become a propaganda mouthpiece promoting climate fear? *Wattsupwiththat.com,* 29. 5. 2009, http://wattsupwiththat.com/2014/05/29/has-david-attenborough-become-a-propaganda-mouthpiece-promoting-climate-fear/ [cit. 14. 5. 2016]

662   CHONG, D. FBC Media tried to cultivate 'ambassadors' for palm oil-producing Malaysia, *The Malaysia Insider, 18.* 11. 2011, http://www.themalaysianinsider.com/print/malaysia/fbc-media-tried-to-cultivate-ambassadors-for-palm-oil-producing-malaysia [cit. 14. 5. 2016]

663   *Findings of the Editorial Standards Committee of the BBC Trust: Funding arrangements and sponsorship of documentary and feature programmes on BBC World News,* BBC Trust, listopad 2011, http://www.bbc.co.uk/bbctrust/assets/files/pdf/appeals/esc_bulletins/2011/world_news.pdf [cit. 14. 5. 2016]

664   MONTFORT, A. The propaganda machine. *Bishop-hill.net,* 20. 11. 2011, http://www.bishop-hill.net/blog/2011/11/21/the-propaganda-machine.htm [cit. 14. 5. 2016]

665   Klaus ocenil i popírače změn klimatu či sympatizanta DOST, *Deník referendum,* 29. 10. 2010, http://denikreferendum.cz/clanek/6942-klaus-ocenil-i-popirace-zmen-klimatu-ci-sympatizanta-d-o-s-t [cit. 14. 5. 2016] (in Czech language)

666   Klaus uvedl film popírače klimatických změn, *Lidové noviny, 28. 6. 2007,* http://www.lidovky.cz/klaus-uvedl-film-popirace-klimatickych-zmen-fzx-/zpravy-domov.aspx?c=A070628_194330_ln_domov_fho [cit. 1. 1. 2016] (in Czech language)

667   MACH, P. Omluví se Lidové noviny? *Neviditelný* pes, 3. 7. 2007, http://neviditelnypes.lidovky.cz/media-omluvi-se-Lidové-noviny-d2t-/p_spolecnost.aspx?c=A070702_110744_p_spolecnost_wag [cit. 14. 5. 2016] (in Czech language)

668   O'NEILL, S., BOYKOFF, M. Climate denier, skeptic, or contrarian? *Proceedings of the National Academy of Sciences,* 2010, Vol. 107, No. 39, p. 1.

669   JACQUES, P. J. A. General theory of climate denial, *Global Environmental Politics,* 2012, Vol. 12, No. 2, p. 9-17.

670   WATTS, A. The silence of the Anti Defamation League suggests they endorse defamation of climate skeptics, *Wattsupwiththat.com,* 3. 3. 2014, http://wattsupwiththat.com/2014/03/03/the-silence-of-the-anti-defamation-league-suggests-they-endorse-defamation-of-climate-skeptics/ [cit. 14. 5. 2016]

671 WATTS, A. The silence of the Anti Defamation League suggests they endorse defamation of climate skeptics, *Wattsupwiththat.com*, 3. 3. 2014, http://wattsupwiththat.com/2014/03/03/the-silence-of-the-anti-defamation-league-suggests-they-endorse-defamation-of-climate-skeptics/ [cit. 14. 5. 2016]

672 LYNAS, M. Climate denial ads to air on US national television, *Marklynas.org*, 16. 5. 2006, http://web.archive.org/web/20070616094334/http://marklynas.org/2006/5/19/climate-denial-ads-to-air-on-us-national-television [cit. 14. 5. 2016]

673 ROBERTS, D. An excerpt from a new book by George Monbiot, *Grist.org*, 20. 9. 2006, http://grist.org/article/the-denial-industry/ [cit. 14. 5. 2016]

674 JOWIT, J. British campaigner urges UN to accept 'ecocide' as international crime, *Guardian*, 9. 4. 2010, http://www.theguardian.com/environment/2010/apr/09/ecocide-crime-genocide-un-environmental-damage [cit. 14. 5. 2016]

675 ORESKES, N. Beyond the Ivory Tower—The scientific consensus on climate change, *Science*, 2004, Vol. 306, No. 5702.

676 SVENSMARK, H. Cosmoclimatology—a new theory emerges, *Astronomy and Geophysics*, 2007, Vol. 48, Issue 1.

677 Scientists agree human-induced global warming is real, survey says, *Science Daily*, 21. 1. 2009, http://www.sciencedaily.com/releases/2009/01/090119210532.htm [cit. 14. 5. 2016]

678 DORAN, P. T. , ZIMMERMAN, M. K. Examining the scientific consensus on climate change, *EOS Earth And Space Science News, American Geophysical Union*, 2009, Vol. 90, No. 3, p. 22.

679 SCHULTE, K. M. Scientific consensus on climate change? *Energy & Environment*, 2008, Vol. 19, No. 2.

680 IDSO, C., et al. *Summary for Policymakers*. In: *Climate change reconsidered II: Physical science*. Report of the Nongovernmental International Panel on Climate change (NIPCC), Chicago 2013, The Heartland Institute, http://climatechangereconsidered.org/ [cit. 14. 5. 2016]

681 NOVA, J. *The skeptic handbook*, Joannenova.com.au, 2009, p. 2, http://jonova.s3.amazonaws.com/sh1/the_skeptics_handbook_2-3_lq.pdf [cit. 2. 2. 2017]

682 BURAWOY, M. For public sociology, *American Sociological Review*, 2005, Vol. 70, Issue 1.

683 POLANYI, K. *The great transformation: The political and economic origins of our time*, Boston 1944, Beacon Press.

684 McCRIGHT, A. M., DUNLAP, R. E. Anti-reflexivity: The American conservative movement's success in undermining climate science and policy, *Theory, Culture & Society*, 2010, Vol. 27, No. 2–3, p. 100–133.

685 MICHAELS, D. *Doubt is their product: How industry's assault on*

science threatens your health, Oxford 2008, Oxford University Press.

686   PFAFFENBERGER, B. The rhetoric of dread: Fear, uncertainty and doubt (FUD) in information technology marketing, *Knowledge, Technology and Policy,* 2000, Vol. 13, No. 3.

687   ORESKES, N., CONVAY, N. *Merchants of doubt,* London 2010, Bloomsbury Press, p. 142.

688   PEARCE, F. *Land grabbers. The new fight over who owns the Earth,* London 2013, Eden Project Books, p. 223.

689   SACK, K. Gore forced to make hard choices on tobacdco, *New York Times,* 30. 8. 1996, http://www.nytimes.com/1996/08/30/us/gore-forced-to-make-hard-choices-on-tobacco.html?pagewanted=1 [cit. 18. 2. 2017]

690   Report dated 5. 2. 1981, where G. H. Long from the Corporate Technology and Sales Department recommends not launching phase II of the research because government launched its own competing research in government labs and at univesities and now all the subventions go there. http://insideclimatenews.org/sites/default/files/documents/Exxon%20Review%20of%20Climate%20Research%20Program%20%281981%29.pdf [cit. 8. 2. 2017]

691   REVKIN, A. C. Exxon-led group is giving a climate grant to Stanford, *New York Times,* 21. 11. 2002.

692   BP funds $500 million in biofuels research at Berkeley, *Greenbiz.com,* 6. 2. 2007, https://www.greenbiz.com/news/2007/02/06/bp-funds-500-million-biofuels-research-berkeley [cit. 18. 2. 2017]

693   Heartland Institute 2012 fundraising plan, http://www.desmogblog.com/sites/beta.desmogblog.com/files/(1-15-2012)%202012%20Fundraising%20Plan_0.pdf [cit. 3. 12. 2016]

694   BAST, J. Joe Bast's response to scholars feeling pressure after attacks on Heartland, *Heartland.org,* 26. 5. 2012, http://blog.heartland.org/2012/05/joe-basts-response-to-scholars-feeling-pressure-after-attacks-on-heartland/ [cit. 3. 12. 2016]

695   GLEICK, P. The origin of the Heartland documents, *Huffington Post,* 20. 2. 2012, http://www.huffingtonpost.com/peter-h-gleick/-the-origin-of-the-heartl_b_1289669.html [cit. 3. 12. 2016]

696   GLEICK, P. et al. Climate change and the integrity of science, *Science,* Vol. 328, No. 5979.

697   REVKIN, A. New shade of green: Stark shift of onetime foe of genetic engineering in crops, *New York Times,* 4. 1. 2013, http://dotearth.blogs.nytimes.com/2013/01/04/new-shade-of-green-stark-shift-for-onetime-foe-of-genetic-engineering-in-crops/?_php=true&_type=blogs&_r=0 [cit. 14. 5. 2016]

698   SCHNEIDER, B. et al. Misleading math about the Earth, *Scientific American,* 2002, Vol. 286, Issue 1.

699   LOMBORG, B. Short reply to skeptical questions, sustainable

answers, 27. 6. 2002, a brief English summary of the book *Godhedens Pris,* http://www.lomborg.com/sites/lomborg.com/files/reply_to_skeptical_questions.pdf [cit. 7. 2. 2017]

700 LOMBORG, B. A response to Howard Friel's 'The Lomborg Deception', *Lomborg.com,* 23. 2. 2010, http://lomborg.com/sites/lomborg.com/files/bl_reply_to_howard_friel_0.pdf

701 Chapter 2: Malnutrition and changing food systems, In: *The state of food and agriculture 2013,* Food and Agriculture Organization, Rom 2013, http://www.fao.org/docrep/018/i3300e/i3300e00.htm [cit. 2. 2. 2017]

702 Klaus ztrácí spojence, ekolog popírač Lomborg otáčí, *Lidovky.cz,* 9. 8. 2009, http://www.lidovky.cz/klaus-ztraci-spojence-ekolog-popirac-lomborg-otaci-fxc-/zpravy-domov.aspx?c=A090809_060844_ln_domov_ppe [cit. 14. 5. 2016] (in Czech language)

703 LAURANCE, J. Breast implants "increase cancer death risk" say scientists, *Independent,* 1. 5. 2013, http://www.independent.co.uk/lifestyle/health-and-families/health-news/breast-implants-increase-cancer-death-risk-say-scientists-8598176.html [cit. 14. 5. 2016]

704 Klaus uvedl film popírače klimatických změn, *Lidovky.cz,* 28. 6. 2007, http://www.lidovky.cz/klaus-uvedl-film-popirace-klimatickych-zmen-fzx-/zpravy-domov.aspx?c=A070628_194330_ln_domov_fho [cit. 14. 5. 2016] (in Czech)

705 Klaus představí film. Autor je podvodník, říkají vědci, *Aktualne.cz,* 27. 6. 2007, http://zpravy.aktualne.cz/domaci/klaus-predstavi-film-autor-je-podvodnik-rikaji-vedci/r~i:article:455756/ [cit. 14. 5. 2016] (in Czech)

706 FOX, F. Massacring the truth in Rwanda, *Living Marxism,* 1995, Issue 85, December 1995.

707 DURKIN, M. The global-warmers were bound to attack, but why are they so feeble? *The Telegraph,* 18. 3. 2007, http://www.telegraph.co.uk/news/uknews/1545873/The-global-warmers-were-bound-to-attack-but-why-are-they-so-feeble.html [cit. 14. 5. 2016]

708 MAIBACH, E. et al. *A National survey of television meteorologists about climate change: Education,* Fairfax (Virginia) 2011, George Mason University, Center for Climate Change Communication.

709 GRAY, B. On the hijacking of the American Meteorological Society, *Wattsupwiththat.com,* 16. 6. 2011, http://wattsupwiththat.com/2011/06/16/on-the-hijacking-of-the-american-meteorological-society-ams/ [cit. 14. 5. 2016]

710 LEWIS, M. Forecastthefacts.org—Political activists gagging our TV Meteorologists on climate issues, *Wattsupwiththat.com,* 22. 1. 2012, http://wattsupwiththat.com/2012/01/22/forecastthefacts-org-political-activists-gagging-our-tv-meteorologists-on-climate-issues/ [cit. 14. 5. 2016]

711 STRICKLAND, E. The new face of environmentalism, *East*

Bay Express, 2. 11. 2005, http://www.eastbayexpress.com/oakland/
the-new-face-of-environmentalism/Content?oid=1079539 [cit. 14. 5.
2016]

712   PIELKE, R. My unhappy life as a climate heretic, *Wattsupwith-that.com,* 4. 12. 2016, https://wattsupwiththat.com/2016/12/04/roger-pielke-jr-my-unhappy-life-as-a-climate-heretic/ [cit. 14. 5. 2016]

713   BRYCE, R. How the Center for American Progress campaigned to supress speech, *National Review,* 26. 10. 2016, http://www.nation-alreview.com/article/441438/wikileaks-john-podesta-silenced-climate-change-dissent [cit. 14. 5. 2016]

714   GILLIGAN, A. Copenhagen climate summit: 1200 limos, 140 private planes and caviar wedges, *The Telegraph,* 5. 12. 2009, http://www.telegraph.co.uk/earth/copenhagen-climate-change-con-fe/6736517/Copenhagen-climate-summit-1200-limos-140-pri-vate-planes-and-caviar-wedges.html [cit. 14. 5. 2016]

715   *The cost of Copenhagen,* London, Taxpayers Alliance, Research Note No. 51, 17. 11. 2009, http://www.taxpayersalliance.com/costofco-penhagen.pdf [cit. 14. 5. 2016]

716   TOLASZ, R. Kradené maily proti klimatické změně, *Blog.aktu-alne.cz,* 29. 11. 2009, http://blog.aktualne.centrum.cz/blogy/radim-to-lasz.php?itemid=8169 [cit. 14. 5. 2016] (in Czech)

717   RYCHLÍK, M. EU to fund CzechGlobe climate change proj-ect, *Česká pozice,* (date of publication not stated), http://ceskapozice.lidovky.cz/eu-to-fund-czechglobe-climate-change-project-fzt-/tema.aspx?c=A101216_175231_pozice_1709 [cit. 14. 5. 2017]

718   isvav.cz project No. LM2010007. Data available also at https://www.rvvi.cz

719   isvav.cz project No. SP/1a6/108/07 Data available at: https://www.rvvi.cz

720   SCHIERMEIER, Q. The real holes in climate science, *Nature,* 2010, Vol. 463, 20. 1. 2010.

721   *An EU budget for low-carbon growth. Press release of the European Commission,* Warsaw 19. 11. 2013, http://ec.europa.eu/clima/policies/finance/budget/docs/pr_2012_03_15_en.pdf [cit. 14. 5. 2016]

722   ROSENTHAL, J. *The EU connection in climate research,* Stanford University, Hoover Institution, Policy Review No. 162, 2010, http://www.hoover.org/publications/policy-review/article/43291 [cit. 14. 5. 2016]

723   MOTL, L. Hacked: Hadley CRU FOI2009 files, *Blogspot.cz,* 20. 11. 2009, http://motls.blogspot.cz/2009/11/hacked-hadley-cru-foi2009-files.html [cit. 15. 5. 2016].

724   WARD, B. Thatcher becomes latest recruit in Monckton's climate skeptic campaign, *Guardian,* 22. 6. 2010, http://www.theguardian.com/environment/2010/jun/22/thatcher-climate-skeptic-monckton [cit. 15.

5. 2016].

725   THATCHER, M. Speech opening Hadley Centre for Climate Prediction and Research, *Margaret Thatcher Foundation*, 25. 5. 1990, http://www.margaretthatcher.org/document/108102 [cit. 15. 5. 2017].

726   CASTRO, F. Tomorrow will be too late: Castro's speech from the Earth Summit in Rio de Janeiro 24. 6. 1992, http://www.climatechangenews.com/2012/05/02/countdown-to-rio20-fidel-castros-1992-speech/ [cit. 15. 5. 2016].

727   DARWALL, R. *The age of global warming*, London 2013, Quartet Books Limited, p. 153.

728   CO$_2$ emissions from fuel combustion—Highlights, 2009 Edition, *International Energy Agency 2009*, tables on p. 23 and 44.

729   ROSENTHAL, J. The EU connection in climate research, *Stanford University, Hoover Institute*, Policy review No. 162, 2010, http://www.hoover.org/research/eu-connection-climate-research [cit. 15. 5. 2016].

730   WATT, R. Carbon dioxide emissions associated with UK consumption increase, *Stockholm Environment Institute*, 2. 7. 2008, http://www.sei-international.org/asia/about-sei-asia/1276 [cit. 15. 5. 2016].

731   German energy prices 50% higher than EU average, *Euractiv.com*, 7. 2. 2014, http://www.euractiv.com/sections/energy/german-energy-prices-50-higher-eu-average-mckinsey-269844 [cit. 15. 5. 2016].

732   RIDDLEY, M. Wind turbines are neither clean nor green and they provide zero global energy, *Spectator*, 13. 5. 2017, https://www.spectator.co.uk/2017/05/wind-turbines-are-neither-clean-nor-green-and-they-provide-zero-global-energy/# [cit. 15. 5. 2017]. Riddley used the data from: *Key Renewable Trends 2016*, International Energy Agency, https://www.iea.org/publications/freepublications/publication/KeyRenewablesTrends.pdf [cit. 15. 5. 2017].

733   China's greenhouse gas vent threat in bid to extort billions, *Environment Investigation Agency*, 8. 11. 2011, http://www.eia-international.org/china-threat-to-vent-super-greenhouse-gases-in-bid-to-extort-billions [cit. 15. 5. 2016].

734   RUSSEL, G. UN climate organization wants immunities against charges of conflict of interest, exceeding mandate, among others, *Fox News*, 12. 6. 2012, http://www.foxnews.com/world/2012/06/12/un-climate-organization-wants-immunities-against-charges-conflict-interest/ [cit. 15. 5. 2016].

735   SOLOMON, L. ENRON's other secret, *Financial Post*, 30. 5. 2009, http://ep.probeinternational.org/2009/05/30/enrons-other-secret/ [cit. 15. 3. 2017]

736   PICKARD, M. Wind farms get £70m to do nothing, *Express*, 25. 8. 2014, http://www.express.co.uk/news/uk/502889/Wind-farm-owners-get-70m-to-do-nothing [cit. 2. 3. 2017]

737   FEARNSIDE, P. M. Tropical hydropower in the Clean Development Mechanism: Brazil's Santo Antônio Dam as an example of the need for change, *Climatic Change,* 2015, Vol. 131, No 4.

738   World Ban, State and trends of the carbon market in 2012, *Washington D.C.,* 2012, http://siteresources.worldbank.org/INTCAR-BONFINANCE/Resources/State_and_Trends_2012_Web_Optimized_19035_Cvr&Txt_LR.pdf [cit. 15. 5. 2016].

739   Development aid at its highest level ever in 2008, *Organization for Economic Development,* 30. 3. 2009, http://www.oecd.org/development/developmentaidatitshighestleveleverin2008.htm

740   YOON, R. Goldman Sachs was top Obama donor, *CNN,* 20. 4. 2010, [cit. 14. 2. 2017]. http://edition.cnn.com/2010/POLITICS/04/20/obama.goldman.donations/index.html

741   BECK, G. ShoreBank's tangled web, *FoxNews,* 21. 5. 2010, http://www.foxnews.com/story/2010/05/21/glenn-beck-shorebank-tangled-web/ [cit. 14. 2. 2016].

742   Carbon credit fraud causes more than 5 billion Euros damage for European taxpayer, *Europol,* 9. 12. 2009, https://www.europol.europa.eu/content/press/carbon-credit-fraud-causes-more-5-billion-euros-damage-european-taxpayer-1265 [cit. 15. 5. 2016].

743   MATTHEWS, H. D. The proportionality of global warming to cumulative carbon emissions, *Nature,* 2009, Vol. 459, Issue 7248.

744   Concordia University, Carbon emissions linked to global warming in simple linear relationship, *ScienceDaily,* 11. 6. 2009, http://www.sciencedaily.com/releases/2009/06/090610154453.htm [cit. 14. 2. 2016].

745   TOLL, R. J. S. An analysis of mitigation as a response to climate change, *Copenhagen Consensus Center,* [date of publication not stated], http://fixtheclimate.com/uploads/tx_templavoila/AP_Mitigation_Tol_v_3.0.pdf [cit. 14. 2. 2016].

746   LOMBORG, B. The climate policy trap, *Project Syndicate,* 14. 11. 2013, http://www.project-syndicate.org/commentary/bj-rn-lomborg-on-how-political-choices-make-bad-climate-change-policies-even-worse [cit. 7. 7. 2016]

747   LOMBORG, B. Germany's sunshine dream, *Mala Independent,* 21. 2. 2012, https://www.independent.com.mt/articles/2012-02-21/newspaper-opinions/Germany%E2%80%99s-sunshine-day-dream-306099 [cit. 18. 8. 2016]

748   PEARCE, M. 2012 another bad year for US disasters, and it may get worse. *Los Angeles Times.* 24. 12. 2014. https://www.latimes.com/nation/la-xpm-2012-dec-24-la-na-nn-us-billion-dollar-disasters-20121224-story.html [cit. 18. 8. 2016]

749   IPCC, 2001, Third Assessment Report, Working Group 2, Chapter 8, graf 8-1.

750 LAFRAMBOISE, D. *The deliquent teenager who was mistaken for the world's top climate expert,* Toronto 2011, Ivy Avenue Press, http://nofrakkingconsensus.files.wordpress.com/2011/10/delinquentteenager_sample.pdf [cit. 18. 8. 2016]

751 MILLER, S. et al. An exploration of trends in normalized weather-related catastrophe losses. In: *Climate Extremes and Society,* DIAZ, H.F., MURNANE, R.J. (eds.), Cambridge 2008, Cambridge University Press.

752 IPCC, 2007 Assessment Report 4, *Working Group 2, Chapter 1.3.8.4, figure SM.1.1.*

753 LEAKE, J. UN wrongly linked global warming to natural disasters, *The Times,* 24. 1. 2010, http://www.icimod.org/?q=5597 [cit. 18. 8. 2016]

754 *IPCC statement on trends in disaster losses,* Ženeva, 25. 1. 2010. http://www.ipcc.ch/pdf/presentations/statement_25_01_2010.pdf [cit. 18. 8. 2016]

755 LAFRAMBOISE, D. IPCC Stern review scandal—IPCC breaks 3 of its own rules, *Noconsensus.org,* 24. 4. 2010, http://nofrakkingconsensus.com/2010/04/24/the-stern-review-scandal-ipcc-breaks-3-of-its-own-rules/ [cit. 18. 8. 2016]

756 DOLAN, E. Will climate change destroy the global economy? *Niskanen Center,* July19, 2017 https://niskanencenter.org/blog/will-climate-change-destroy-global-economy/8108221 [cit. 18. 8. 2019]

757 LILLEY, P. What's wrong with Stern, *The Global Warming Policy Foundation,* GWPF Report No. 9, 18. 10. 2012, http://www.thegwpf.org/content/uploads/2012/09/Lilley-Stern_Rebuttal3.pdf [cit. 18. 8. 2016]

758 BECKERMAN, W., HEPBURN, C. Ethics of the discount rate in the Stern Review on the Economics of Climate Change, *World Economics,* 2007, Vol. 8, No. 1.

759 NORDHAUS, W. A review of the Stern Review on the economics of climate change, *Journal of Economic Literature,* Vol. XLV, September 2007, p. 686-702.

760 KLAUS, V. The climate change doctrine is part of environmentalism, not of science. Preface to the Czech edition of Nigel Lawson's "Appeal to Reason" ("Vraťme se k rozumu. O globálním oteplování střízlivě a bez emocí", Dokořán Publishers, Prague, 2009). https://www.klaus.cz/clanky/2694 [cit. 18. 8. 2019]

761 ZHANG, D. et al. The causality analysis of climate change and large-scale human crisis, *Proceedings of the National Academy of Sciences,* 2011, Vol. 108, No. 42.

762 PRETIS, F. et al. Uncertain Impacts on Economic Growth When Stabilizing Global Temperatures at 1.5°C or 2°C Warming. *Philosophical Transactions—Series A,* 2018, Volume 376, Issue 2119.

763   MENDELSOHN, R., SAHER, G. The global impact of climate change on extreme events, *World Bank,* Policy research working paper No. 5566, February 2011, p. 26. http://www.iadb.org/intal/intalcdi/PE/2011/07386.pdf [cit. 18. 8. 2016]

764   TRUELL, P. Man in the news: The renaissance banker James David Wolfensohn, *New York Times,* 13. 3. 1995, http://www.nytimes.com/1995/03/13/business/man-in-the-news-the-renaissance-banker-james-david-wolfensohn.html [cit. 18. 8. 2016]

765   STRONG, M. *Where on Earth are we going,* Canada 1999, Random House, p. 279.

766   VALIN, H. et al. The land use change impact of biofuels consumed in the EU, *A study commissioned and funfed by the Eropean Commission,* www.ecosfys.com, 27. 8. 2015, p. ix, https://ec.europa.eu/energy/sites/ener/files/documents/Final%20Report_GLOBIOM_publication.pdf [cit. 3. 2. 2017]

767   UN rapporteur calls for biofuel moratorium. *Swissinfo.ch* 11.10.2007. https://www.swissinfo.ch/eng/un-rapporteur-calls-for-biofuel-moratorium/6189782 [cit. 18. 8. 2016]

768   HARRISON, P. Once-hidden EU report reveals damage from biodiesel, *Reuters,* 21. 4. 2010, http://www.reuters.com/article/2010/04/21/us-eu-energy-biofuels-idUSTRE63K2CB20100421 [cit. 18. 8. 2016]

769   Another inconvenient truth, *Oxfam,* 25. 6. 2008, http://www.oxfam.org/en/grow/policy/another-inconvenient-truth [cit. 18. 8. 2016]

770   Palm oil plantations could be classified as forests, *The Ecologist,* 8. 2. 2010, http://www.theecologist.org/News/news_round_up/412394/palm_oil_plantations_could_be_classified_as_forests.html [cit. 18. 8. 2016]

771   WISE, T. The cost to developing countries of US corn ethanol expansion, *Global Development and Environment Institute,* Working Paper No. 12 - 02, October 2012, http://www.ase.tufts.edu/gdae/Pubs/wp/12-02WiseGlobalBiofuels.pdf [cit. 18. 8. 2016]

772   CHAKRABORTTY, A. Secret report: biofuel caused food crisis, *Guardian,* 3. 7. 2008, http://www.theguardian.com/environment/2008/jul/03/biofuels.renewableenergy [cit. 18. 8. 2016]

773   HILL, J. et al. Environmental, economic, and energetic costs and benefits of biodiesel and ethanol biofuels, *Proceedings of the National Academy of Sciences,* 2006, Vol. 103, No. 30.

774   Honduras: Human rights violations in Bajo Aguan, *FIDH—International Federation for Human Rights,* July 2011, p. 8, http://www.fidh.org/IMG/pdf/honduras573ang.pdf [cit. 18. 8. 2016]

775   AIRLIE, C., CARR, M. U.K. climate envoy Martin Hession vies to head UN carbon market's board, *Bloomberg.com,* 10. 1. 2011, http://www.bloomberg.com/news/2011-01-10/u-k-climate-envoy-martin-hession-vies-to-head-un-carbon-market.html [cit. 18. 8. 2016]

776   FRANK, D. Wikileaks Honduras: US linked to brutal businessman, *The Nation,* 21. 10. 2011, http://www.thenation.com/article/164120/wikileaks-honduras-us-linked-brutal-businessman# [cit. 18. 8. 2016]

777   SNOWDON, Ch. Euro puppets—The European Commission's remaking of civil society, *Institute of Economic Affairs,* Discussion paper No. 45, February 2013. http://www.iea.org.uk/sites/default/files/publications/files/DP_Euro%20Puppets_redesigned.pdf [cit. 18. 8. 2016]

778   SNOWDON, Ch. Still hand in glove? *Institute of Economic Affairs,* IEA Discussion Paper No. 96, February 2019, p. 27, https://velvetgloveironfist.blogspot.com/2019/02/sock-puppets-revisited.html

779   SNOWDON, Ch. Sock puppets: How the government lobbies itself and why, *Institute of Economic Affairs,* IEA Discussion Paper No. 39, 11. 6. 2012, http://www.iea.org.uk/publications/research/sock-puppets-how-the-government-lobbies-itself-and-why [cit. 18. 8. 2016]

780   MARTINSON, E. Uttered in 2008, still haunting Obama in 2012, *Politico.com,* 5. 4. 2012, http://www.politico.com/news/stories/0412/74892.html [cit. 18. 8. 2016]

781   HOLDREN, J. P. Too much energy, too soon, a hazard, *The Windsor Star,* 11. 8. 1975, http://news.google.com/newspapers?id=I-jU_AAAAIBAJ&sjid=jFEMAAAAIBAJ&pg=3972,2528093&dq=john+holdren&hl=en [cit. 18. 8. 2016]

782   EHRLICH, P., HOLDREN, J., EHRLICH, A. *Ecoscience: Population, resources, environment.* New York 1978, W. H. Freeman.

783   EHRLICH, P. An Ecologist's Perspective on Nuclear Power, *Federation of American Scientists Public Issue* Report, May/June 1978. Citováno z: DRIESEN, P. *Eco-imperialism, green power, black death,* Washington 2003, Free Enterprise Press, p.143.

784   HOFFMAN, R. *Pátá kolona,* Praha 2011, Brána. (in Czech)

785   Germany risks de-industrialisation, if energy shift fails, *Reuters,* 21. 1. 2014, http://uk.reuters.com/article/2014/01/21/uk-germany-energy-gabriel-idUKBREA0K0CO20140121 [cit. 18. 8. 2016]

786   EVANS-PRITCHARD, A. Brussels fears European industrial massacre sparked by energy costs, *Telegraph,* 8. 9. 2013, http://www.telegraph.co.uk/finance/financialcrisis/10295045/Brussels-fears-European-industrial-massacre-sparked-by-energy-costs.html [cit. 18. 8. 2016]

787   Winter deaths rise with extreme cold, *National Energy Action,* 24. 11. 2011, http://www.nea.org.uk/media/media-releases/media-releases-2011/media-211111-01 [cit. 18. 8. 2016]

788   BANNON, E. Growing support for taxing the climate impact of flying. *Transport Environment,* 26.2.2019, https://www.transportenvironment.org/news/growing-support-taxing-climate-impact-flying [cit. 7. 6. 2019]

789   SCHULTZ, F. German Greens want to ban domestic flights by

2035. *Euractiv,* 24.7.2019, https://www.euractiv.com/section/aviation/news/german-greens-want-to-ban-domestic-flights-by-2035/ [cit. 18. 9. 2019]

790   One-fifth of total EU budget to be spent on climate action (Press Release), *European Commission,* 19. 11. 2013, http://ec.europa.eu/clima/news/articles/news_2013111901_en.htm [cit. 18. 8. 2016]

791   WATERFIELD, B. EU policy on climate is right even if science was wrong, says commissioner, *Telegraph,* 16. 9. 2013, http://www.telegraph.co.uk/earth/environment/climatechange/10313261/EU-policy-on-climate-change-is-right-even-if-science-was-wrong-says-commissioner.html [cit. 18. 8. 2016]

792   BELL, L. In their own words: Climate alarmists debunk their 'science', *Forbes,* 5. 2. 2013, http://www.forbes.com/fdc/welcome_mjx.shtml [cit. 18. 8. 2016]

793   1968 Pandemic (H3N2 virus). CDC.gov [cit. 20 June 2020] https://www.cdc.gov/flu/pandemic-resources/1968-pandemic.html

794   IOANNIDIS, J.P.A. A fiasco in the making? As the coronavirus pandemic takes hold, we are making decisions without reliable data. *Statnews.com,* 17.3.2020. https://www.statnews.com/2020/03/17/a-fiasco-in-the-making-as-the-coronavirus-pandemic-takes-hold-we-are-making-decisions-without-reliable-data/ [cit. 18. 8. 2020]

795   ROSANO, A. et al. Investigating the impact of influenza on excess mortality in all ages in Italy during recent seasons (2013/14-2016/17 seasons). *International Journal of Infectious Diseases,* 2019, Vol 88, Pages 127-134. https://www.sciencedirect.com/science/article/pii/S1201971219303285

796   AHMAD F.B. et al. Provisional Mortality Data — United States, 2020. Morbidity and Mortal Weekly Report, 9 April 2021;70:519–522. DOI: http://dx.doi.org/10.15585/mmwr.mm7014e1 (age adjusted data)

797   National Center for Health Statistics - Death rates and life expectancy at birth. In: Centers for Disease Control and Prevention. (data.cdc.gov). Available at: https://data.cdc.gov/widgets/w9j2-ggv5?-mobile_redirect=true [cit. 18. 6. 2021] (data until 2018, age adjusted, both sees).

798   COVID-19 to Plunge Global Economy into Worst Recession since World War II. *World Bank,* June 8 2020 https://www.worldbank.org/en/news/press-release/2020/06/08/covid-19-to-plunge-global-economy-into-worst-recession-since-world-war-ii

799   BRAZELL, E. Lockdown 'could kill 75,000' due to canceled treatments and missed diagnoses. *Metro.co.uk* 26.9.2020 https://metro.co.uk/2020/09/26/lockdown-could-kill-75000-due-to-canceled-treatments-and-missed-diagnoses-13328942/?ito=cbshare

800   Direct and Indirect Impacts of COVID-19 on Excess Deaths and Morbidity:Executive Summary. Department of Health and Social Care,

Office for National Statistics, Government Actuary's Department and Home Office. 15 July 2020.

801   FORE, H. H. et al. Child malnutrition and COVID-19: the time to act is now. *The Lancet,* Volume 396, Issue, August 22, 2020.

802   The hunger virus: how COVID-19 is fueling hunger in a hungry world. *OXFAM,* 9.7.2020, https://www.oxfam.org/en/research/hunger-virus-how-covid-19-fueling-hunger-hungry-world

803   WEF, Prince of Wales launch Great Reset initiative to drive global change. *YouTube* 4.6.2020 https://www.youtube.com/watch?v=B3QwmnvYyGk&feature=youtu.be

804   Finding false virtue in the virus. *Washington Times,* 9.3.2020. https://www.washingtontimes.com/news/2020/mar/9/editorial-some-environmentalists-say-whats-bad-for/

805   IVEREIGH, A. Pope Francis says pandemic can be a 'place of conversion'. The *Tablet - International Catholic News Weekly,* 8.4.2020, https://www.thetablet.co.uk/features/2/17845/pope-francis-says-pandemic-can-be-a-place-of-conversion-

806   STORROW, B. Why CO_2 Isn't Falling More During a Global Lockdown. *Scientific American,* 24.4.2020. https://www.scientificamerican.com/article/why-CO_2-isnt-falling-more-during-a-global-lockdown/

807   AMBROSE, J. Carbon emissions from fossil fuels could fall by 2.5bn tons in 2020. *The Guardian,* 12.4.2020 https://www.theguardian.com/environment/2020/apr/12/global-carbon-emisions-could-fall-by-record-25bn-tons-in-2020

808   DOYLE, A. Coronavirus: in Hawaii's air, scientists seek signs of economic shock on CO_2 levels. *Climate Home News,* 26.3.2020 https://www.climatechangenews.com/2020/03/26/coronavirus-hawaii-scientists-seek-signs-economic-slowdown-air/

809   May 2020 Had the Highest Monthly Atmospheric CO_2 Reading Ever Recorded. *Scitechdaily.com* 5.6.52020 https://scitechdaily.com/may-2020-had-the-highest-monthly-atmospheric-CO_2-reading-ever-recorded/

810   PRAGER, D. Why the remedy may be worse than the disease. *American Greatness,* 17.3.2020. https://amgreatness.com/2020/03/17/why-the-remedy-may-be-worse-than-the-disease/

811   LOMBORG, B. Paris climate promises will reduce temperatures by just 0.05°C in 2100 (Press release), *Lomborg.com,* November 2015, http://www.lomborg.com/press-release-research-reveals-negligible-impact-of-paris-climate-promises [cit. 18. 8. 2016]

812   LOMBORG, B. Impact of current climate proposals, *Global Policy Journal,* 2016, Vol. 7, Issue 1.

813   Data available at the website of National Oceans and Atmosphere Administration (esrl.noaa.gov).

814   Record annual increase of carbon dioxide observed at Mauna Loa

for 2015, *National Oceanic and Atmospheric Administration,* 9. 3. 2016, http://www.noaa.gov/news/record-annual-increase-of-carbon-dioxide-observed-at-mauna-loa-for-2015 [cit. 18. 7. 2017]

815   HICKMAN, L. James Lovelock: Humans are too stupid to prevent climate change, *Guardian,* 29. 3. 2010, http://www.theguardian.com/science/2010/mar/29/james-lovelock-climate-change [cit. 18. 8. 2016]

816   CLOVER, Ch. Climate change is like World War Three, *The Telegraph,* 5. 11. 2004, http://www.telegraph.co.uk/earth/earthnews/3313024/Climate-change-is-like-World-War-Three.html [cit. 18. 8. 2016]

817   PLUMER, B. John Podesta's plan to bypass Congress on climate change, *The Washington Post,* 19. 12. 2013, http://www.washingtonpost.com/blogs/wonkblog/wp/2013/12/19/john-podestas-plan-to-bypass-congress-on-climate-change/ [cit. 18. 8. 2016]

818   HANSEN, J. The price of change, *South China Morning Post,* 3. 11. 2010, http://www.columbia.edu/~jeh1/mailings/2010/20101122_ChinaOpEd.pdf [cit. 18. 8. 2016]

819   MOTL, L. Hansen: Chinese communists have to lead us and save humanity, beat the US *Blogspot.cz,* 12. 1. 2011, http://motls.blogspot.cz/2011/01/hansen-chinese-communists-have-to-lead.html [cit. 18. 8. 2016]

820   CHOMSKY, N. *Understanding power,* 9th Edition, New York 2002, The New Press, p. 388.

821   Extinction Rebellion defies protest ban and targets Google. *The Guardian,* 16.10.2019, https://www.theguardian.com/environment/2019/oct/16/extinction-rebellion-judicial-review-protest-ban [cit. 25. 10. 2019]

822   GOSSELIN, P. Radicals Bully NH Munich Conference Center... Force Cancelation Of 13th Skeptic Climate Conference! *No TricksZone,* 19.11.2019, https://notrickszone.com/2019/11/19/radicals-bully-nh-munich-conference-center-force-cancelation-of-13th-skeptic-climate-conference/

823   HAVEL, V. Our moral footprint, *New York Times,* 27. 9. 2007.

824   KLAUS, V. Freedom, not climate, is at risk, *Financial Times,* 14. 6. 2007.

825   Statement by President Trump on the Paris Climate Accord, *White House Press Office,* 1. 6. 2017, https://www.whitehouse.gov/the-press-office/2017/06/01/statement-president-trump-paris-climate-accord [cit. 18. 7. 2017]

826   Statement by the President on the Paris Climate Agreement, 20. 12 .2015, https://obamawhitehouse.archives.gov/the-press-office/2015/12/12/statement-president-paris-climate-agreement [cit. 18. 7. 2017]

827   HICKEY, J. G. Gore claims climate battle just like fight against slavery, apartheid, *Fox News,* 13. 7. 2017, http://www.foxnews.com/politics/2017/07/13/gore-claims-climate-battle-just-like-fight-against-slavery-apartheid.html [cit. 18. 7. 2017]

828   MILMAN, O. Donald Trump presidency a 'disaster for the planet', warn climate scientists, *The Guardian,* 11. 11. 2016, https://www.theguardian.com/environment/2016/nov/11/trump-presidency-a-disaster-for-the-planet-climate-change [cit. 18. 7. 2017]

829   DELK, J. Top Democrat donor pushes for Trump impeachment, *The Hill,* 10. 6. 2017, http://thehill.com/homenews/news/337235-top-democrat-donor-pushes-for-trump-impeachment [cit. 18. 7. 2017]

830   CLÉMENCON, R. The two sides of the Paris Climate Agreement: Dismal failure or historic breakthrough, *Journal of Environment and Development,* 2016, Vol. 25, No. 1.

831   DWORTZAN, M. Expected Paris commitments insufficient to stabilize climate by century's end, *MIT News,* 22. 10. 2015, http://news.mit.edu/2015/paris-commitments-insufficient-to-stabilize-climate-by-2100-1022 [cit. 18. 7. 2017]

832   SOKOLOV, A. et al. Climate impacts of the Paris agreement, *Geophysical Research Abstracts,* 2016, Vol. 18, EGU General Assembly 2016.

833   China—International energy data and analysis, *US Energy Information Administration,* 14. 5. 2015., p. 3, https://www.eia.gov/beta/international/analysis_includes/countries_long/China/china.pdf [cit. 18. 7. 2017]

834   LACK, S. Guess Who's Most Effective At Combating Global Warming. *Forbes,* 23.8.2018. https://www.forbes.com/sites/simonlack/2018/08/23/guess-whos-most-effective-at-combating-global-warming/#4943e06d5cdb [cit. 18. 7. 2019]

835   BP Statistical Review of world energy 2019, *BP,* 68th edition, June 2019, https://www.bp.com/en/global/corporate/energy-economics/statistical-review-of-world-energy.html [cit. 18. 9. 2019]

836   EIA: Gas-fired combined cycle overtakes coal in US generating capacity. *Power Engineering,* 4.11.2019. https://www.power-eng.com/2019/04/11/eia-gas-fired-combined-cycle-now-generates-more-u-s-power-than-coal/ [cit. 18. 11. 2019]

837   USHER, B. P. Trump's climate Brexit blow to Tillerson, *BBC,* 2. 6. 2017, http://www.bbc.com/news/world-us-canada-40138740 [cit. 18. 7. 2017]

838   PORTER, E. Liberal biases, too, may block progress on climate change, *New York Times,* 19. 4. 2016, https://www.nytimes.com/2016/04/20/business/economy/liberal-biases-too-may-block-progress-on-climate-change.html?_r=1 [cit. 23. 2. 2017]

839   SWIFT, A. Americans split on support for fracking in oil, natural gas, *Gallup,* 23. 3. 2015, http://www.gallup.com/poll/182075/ameri-

cans-split-support-fracking-oil-natural-gas.aspx [cit. 23. 2. 2017]

840   ROGERS, P. California drought: Why doesn't California build big dams any more? *Mercury News,* 31. 8. 2014, https://www.mercury-news.com/2014/08/31/california-drought-why-doesnt-california-build-big-dams-any-more/ [cit. 2. 2. 2018]

841   NORDHAUS, T. Bill McKibben's misleading new chemistry, *Breakthrough Institute,* 25. 3. 2016, https://thebreakthrough.org/index.php/voices/ted-nordhaus/bill-mckibbens-misleading-new-chemistry [cit. 2. 2. 2017]

842   CURRY, J. Exactly what are scientists marching for, *Judith-curry.com,* 5. 3. 2017, https://judithcurry.com/2017/03/05/exactly-what-are-scientists-marching-for/ [cit. 18. 7. 2017]

843   VARNEY, J. Skeptical climate scientists coming in from the cold, *Real Clear Investigations,* 31. 12. 2016, http://www.realclearinvestigations.com/articles/2016/12/31/skeptical_climate_scientists_coming_in_from_the_cold.html [cit. 18. 7. 2017]

844   KLAUS, V. Will Trumps's withdrawal from the Paris Climate Accords weaken climate alarmism? *Institut Václava Klause,* 16. 6. 2017, http://institutvk.cz/clanky/915.html [cit. 18. 7. 2018]

845   MOSER, S. et al. Good intents, low impacts. *Environment and Behaviour,* 2018, Vol. 50, Issue 6.

846   LYNAS, M. Ecomodernism launch was a screw-up of impressive proportions. *The Guardian,* 30.9.2015, https://www.theguardian.com/environment/2015/sep/30/ecomodernism-launch-was-a-screw-up-of-impressive-proportions